The Man Who Wa

TALES FROM THE SIXTH DISCIPLE

Terry Shepherd Friedmann, M.D.

Manufactured in the United States of America
This edition published by Harvest Publishing
P.O. Box 33270 Denver, CO 80233-3270

Edited by Diane Cummings
Word Processing by Jennifer L. Holstad
Cover design by Janessa Marsh and Jessica Tamsett
Interior Design by Janessa Marsh

ISBN 0-9638366-7-6

Dedication

This book is dedicated to the I AM consciousness of all of humanity.

Table Of Contents

FOREWORD

There are certain writings that call us to greater insights, clearer understandings and more profound awakenings. We are now in the presence of such writing.

The dialogues taking place between Jeshua and Mattai could well be heart messages being communicated to various aspects of one's life. There is a depth within us that necessitates clarity; therefore, these messages for the heart and soul are invaluable. In these messages, the author clearly illustrates the beauty of simplicity and the power of clarity.

One's introduction to the Spiritual Laws awakens a sense of responsibility and ownership of those attributes or qualities that ignite the soul for action. Our hearts want to know, and it desires to feel connected to an infinite Source. In this reading I was elevated to the revelation that this manuscript is a *gateway to God.* As the depth of the stories unfolds, my soul stands erect in the presence of the Divine. The nurturing qualities of the dialogues warrant the soul's attention. Thus, one finds the self in the midst of intense illumination, and yet the applicability of the work is clear. The five-step process of manifestation is an example of the practicality.

This work promotes inner explorations and "heart probing;" provoking questions were evoked within me:

What if the light that one sees by is the Light of Pure Spirit?

What if the beauty felt during these readings represents the beauty that nurtures and strengthens the soul always?

In my enthusiasm to encourage readers for *The Man Who Walked with Jesus: Tales From the Sixth Disciple,* my initial desire was to direct readers to specific pages. My realization is that such direction would be sabotaging the individual discovery of inner treasures. It is wise to remember: "Once the soul has started on the soul's journey, it can never turn back."

This is a *heart directed* work. In his manuscript, Terry was not limited to historical data. He listened consistently to the magnificence of Divine Intelligence, and to him was revealed simple elegance of Pure Spirit. Here are insights to the above:

A common pitfall one encounters in this consciousness is the need to figure it all out. It is simply to be. In the beingness state, the doing comes naturally without any effort at all.

Can you be in joy when you make mistakes?

It has been said, "As we grow, we glow." Growing, glowing, and knowing takes place in this reading. Eyes of Truth see deeply within, and one realizes, "There is nothing hidden that shalt not be revealed."

While reading, let the heart be nurtured, let the mind be awake, and the soul will sing in the beauty of it all. Terry brought dynamic figures into the arena of effective daily living. This might well be regarded as a roadmap for the heart and soul!

ENJOY YOUR DIVINE ADVENTURE. READ!

Reverend Lloyd Barrett
Associate Minister, Mile Hi Church

Introduction

In 1995 an event occurred that I knew immediately would change the course of my life. As distinctive and clear as the bells ringing from a church tower, I heard a voice from I knew not where say:

> *My Beloved Terry, Hear me clearly. The ancient Biblical stories, as they have been translated and transcribed, are timeless, ageless accounts, and they have served humanity well. But now, mankind has greater knowledge, along with a greater need, and it is time to add to these stories, to clarify my message and broaden human understanding. I desire for people to explore more deeply what I say and know the Light that I give. I assign you this task, to be my scribe, to write now as my disciple Matthew wrote then, to shed new light and reveal the whole truth about my life, times and teachings.*

I could not doubt that this was Jesus speaking to me, nor could I begin to know the depths to which this assignment would take me. But I did recognize that a monumental spiritual task had been set before me. I was to chronicle the whole story of Jesus, to expand on the disciple Matthew's Biblical writings and, perhaps, set the record straight.

I am a medical doctor who long ago stepped out of mainstream philosophy and practice into what I considered to be a more complete form of healing—Holism. As a pioneer participating headlong into a new paradigm shift, I have been a leading spokesman, advocating a departure from treatment that would "patch up" body parts to truly healing the entire human being: the body, mind and spirit. I challenged people to look at their own health and come to terms with the cause and effect process that comes into play surrounding wellness. As I practiced and taught, so did I myself heal, and my inner knowing was expanding into higher consciousness. Over this time I came to know that the true gift we can give ourselves is complete knowing of our inner nature. But little did I know then that this period would be a precursor to a very challenging new phase in my life.

When I received that initial message from Jesus, I wondered *how could I possibly tell this story? Where would the information come from?* For a time all was stillness within me. And then at a point, Jesus began speaking to me again. I heard His words in my mind, and I became inspired by them. At about the same time I met a wonderful teacher who counseled me unselfishly, sharing her viewpoints on Jesus, the disciples and their wisdom. I wrote all of these words down, organized them, and they began to take shape into this book.

My ability to receive intuitive messages is not exclusive with me: anyone can receive these gifts if they choose. And so, what I have done does not make me special. It simply makes me expanded in my relationship with Jesus. It makes me expanded with the Father-Mother God. It makes me expanded in my relationship with myself and with everyone else in my life. Through this love that I have found, I have become aware of my own spiritual essence.

I have drawn a narrative that I hope will excite readers about what is possible for them. Through these stories and teachings, I hope to awaken readers' personal memories about who and what they are and to inspire a connection with God and humankind. For some, this book will be a chance for personal forgiveness, for others a confirmation of their inner knowing. Many, I hope, will view His words and realize that what Jesus did was only a shadow of their own potential. For me, writing this book has changed my life. I can make clear distinctions between what it was before this adventure and what it is now: my love and compassion have expanded in my personal relationships and even beyond to a more global point. My judgment of others has been greatly moderated. I hope that I have portrayed the events about which you'll read with wisdom, passion and humility.

Although most of the world knows this incredible God-man by the name *Jesus*, I know Him as Jeshua, which is how He was known during His lifetime.

The language spoken two thousand years ago in that Biblical land of Israel was Aramaic: Jesus and His contemporaries primarily spoke in this tongue, even though they also knew Hebrew and communicated in that language as well.

The first recordings of Jesus' story were written in Aramaic and Hebrew. The next translation according to scholars was into Greek. Later, it was translated into Latin. As Christ's message spread east, the gospel's primary spoken language continued to be Aramaic. When the teachings moved beyond the confines of the Roman Empire, reaching Syria and Mesopotamia and other nearby lands, they were translated into Syriac. Additional translations were conducted in India and China when the teachings reached those lands. And in all of these translations, problems were born: the writings were altered, and some misperceptions formed. This occurred even though I believe the basic message was protected and kept intact by God Himself.

It was not only in the translations where difficulties arose. Cultural context dictated other alterations. While none of the words in the Bible is actually false, the storytelling became subject to a certain editing that left out some very important pieces. Indeed, how could one write about an entire spiritual journey in one book? All that one can do is to draw upon one's memory and write about one's own journey; therefore, the interpretation of events lies in one's own individual understanding, which may differ from the perception of another.

The Councils of Nicaea, whose responsibility it was in the year three hundred twenty-five, to settle the dispute concerning the nature of Jesus, changed some details in the Bible. In their attempt to bring consensus to the material where there was conflict, they streamlined the writings. Their intent was to simplify the message so that it would be consistent and easily understood by the masses. Additional editing was done in the seventh century, and many of the changes had to do with references to reincarnation. Further changes were made to each of the first four gospels so that they would be more homogenous. The book of Matthew, inspired and directed by God, while more accurate and thorough than most of the other writings, was rewritten by man and altered. Many of the books of the Bible were taken from the original writings of Matthew, including the books of Mark and John the Beloved. A student of Matthew initiated the first changes, and the third pope altered it still more. Documentation of some changes exists.

What resulted was that some of Jesus' message became distorted, some of it omitted altogether. One piece that was lost at that time was, ironically enough, Jesus' key teaching: that the "kingdom of God is within oneself." He did not, as has been put forth, come to make Christians of people, but rather, He came to teach a different way to have a relationship with God and with one another.

My intent in telling Matthew's story anew is not to indict the "storychangers" or take away the joy and connection from those who love this sacred book as it has been, but to write from a point of new consciousness. More information is available, and we are more ready to accept it. I have endeavored to show Jesus as a human being, with an extraordinary sense of humor, as well as a spiritual master who was able to transmute and heal all emotional blocks. I have also strived to point out that Jesus' message was unique but very simple. But then so is every soul's message who blesses this earth.

You may ask whether I could get the story wrong or whether I might unknowingly distort things in this retelling. The answer is "no" to the first, because there is never wrongness. But could I unknowingly allow my ego to interfere and turn the story away from truth? However much I have tried to avoid this, it is possible. Yet, is it important? No, for it is always the reader's job to read between the lines, to find himself or herself within the story and realize the truth. However this story is told it cannot break apart the love that is inherent within it.

Along with the stories and revelations about Jesus and Matthew, I have inspirationally received twelve new spiritual laws, each applicable to the chapter where it is present, that are said to have come from the angelic realms. During this time of our planetary evolution, as we enter a new age of enlightenment, the souls now embodied here are more receptive and able to fully comprehend these guidelines from the Mother-Father God.

The laws, which are certainly not a repetition of the Ten Commandments, are profound principles for the development of human consciousness. They speak of creation, cause and effect, Oneness, unification and Love. The laws are not meant to be dictatorial, that if you don't follow them you will suffer or be punished. These laws exist simply as truth. We all need to be reminded of them, because we have forgotten.

Sometimes we feel burdened by recognizing that all people of the world are one family, burdened that we must accept and embrace all races and creeds as one. That burden lies in the fact that somehow we feel we must be responsible for others, to provide what they need. But that is not so. In truth, we do not owe our biological or spiritual families anything but love. Even with love, there are often misunderstandings. In our culture we sometimes expect love to look and feel a particular way and to be demonstrated in specific ways. But just as people form a kaleidoscope of different expressions, so too does love. It has a variety of flavors and can be expressed in many different ways.

In remembering again the new spiritual laws, we know that as we give them forth, so do we receive back. These laws exist to remind us that we are family, we are ONE amongst ourselves and with our Creator, and that our only responsibility is to love one another.

While the process of writing the book took me seven years, the research and experience took a lifetime.

Personally, coming from my heart, I would like to express my gratitude for being given the assignment to write this book. Also, for receiving the inspiration of the message as well as for being given the wisdom to write down the words in a simple concise and descriptive manner. I am grateful that I have had the ability and the time set aside to write the book and that I was given a mountain retreat where I could isolate myself in serenity and grandeur in order to receive inspiration. I am thankful for having the capacity to access the memory of Matthew in his life with Jesus and for the support of all the disciples for their role in the greatest story ever told. This could only have happened through persistent prayer and meditation while allowing myself to be open to Spirit. And certainly, I am thankful that I possessed the faith and commitment to see this project through to its completion.

Additionally, my gratitude goes to the peoples of Mexico for their stories of Quctzacoatl; to the peoples of Hawaii who had their own intriguing stories of Captain Cook, ones I had not heard before; to our guide in Glastonbury, England, who demonstrated that Jesus had once visited there; to the guru who guided me to the ashrams of Rishikesh, India, where I was told of Jesus' presence long ago, and to the Lakota Sioux shaman who told me of the White Buffalo.

I am also grateful to the people of Israel who still hold the energy of faith lo these many years; to the people who reconstructed the village of

Nazareth as it was two thousand years ago, and to the rabbi in Jerusalem who eloquently challenged my beliefs. I thank my dear friend, Jim Strange, for his knowledge and wisdom and also my friends who came forward when I was in need to fill in the missing words. And it should be emphasized that much is owed to the many people who have shared with me their excitement and enthusiasm for the book, for that encouragement has supported me in my perseverance in its ongoing development.

I have appreciation for all the agents and publishers who, feeling not aligned with this subject matter, decided that they could not accept this book.

And especially to the one without whose sacrifice it wouldn't have happened at all, Jesus, I pledge my eternal gratitude.

I have invited my wife, Jean-Marie, to make an addition to my Introduction, for without her none of this would have been possible. Through the writing and development of the book she has been a great support and inspiration to me. As a final note to you, the reader, as I was nearing completion of the book, an unexpected opportunity arose: a chance to visit the land I was writing about. Jean-Marie accompanied me on this trip to Israel. I am ever grateful.

Terry Shepherd Friedmann, M.D.

What a wondrous journey my beloved husband takes us on. Through my early childhood and young adult years, I lived, learned and taught the teachings of Jesus, his travels, trials and tribulations. I yearned to know more of the personal conversations and expressions that were a reality that His followers experienced. This book brings us that and so much more as we live through the expressed joys and perils of each cast member, including Pontius Pilate, and the high priest, Caiaphas. I enjoyed reading about the devotion and loyalty that Lazarus and his sisters Martha and Mary had with Master Jesus and His disciples. I felt myself having a personal relationship with each of the disciples as they journeyed with my much-loved teacher, Jesus. It is with humble gratefulness that I chose to accompany my husband on his spiritual journey and watch him embrace this masterful writing.

Jean-Marie Hepworth Friedmann

The author and his wife, Jean-Marie, at the Wailing Wall in Jerusalem.

The author in Nazareth with a local resident standing before a recreated temple as it was two thousand years ago.

A group of nomads in the desert of Israel who still speak the language of Aramaic and practice their age-old traditions.

ACKNOWLEDGEMENTS

I would like to express a special thanks to Kathleen Schoenstadt for her counseling. Additionally, I would like to thank Dr. Jim Strange for his persistent and untiring dedication to the search for truth about the man Jesus. Also, this book would not have been complete without the input of Heiderose Spang-Martindell, Betty Podesta and my editor, Diane Cummings.

Finally, above all, a big thanks goes to my supporting partner in life, my dear wife, Jean-Marie.

CHAPTER 1

The Meeting

I looked up suddenly. And stopped in my tracks. Squinting hard, I struggled to make out movement in the far distance. A throng of people, dozens perhaps, were heading my way. What in the...?

And then I saw Him, the Man in front, a stately Man dressed in simple, white garb, coming closer. The Man now surrounded by a joyous, almost frivolous, crowd. It seemed they were in celebration of some fine occasion. I was quite transfixed by the scene and, as he approached, spellbound by the Man.

Now I remembered. *Could it be?* I thought. *Is this the One I've been hearing so many rumors about? They say He performs miracles. Some say He is a prophet; others believe that He is the Christ, pure God in Man, who is here to save our people, set them free from the oppression of the Romans ... it could only be He, the One they all speak about, the one they call Jeshua*[1].

Remaining riveted, I jumped up from my seat in the tollbooth and stepped outside to get a better look. As I continued to stare open-mouthed, I realized that I was losing the dignity that my position mandated.

In order to pull myself together, I quickly shifted attention to my immediate surroundings. Close by my booth at the edge of town, I noticed the soldiers, those who came with me each day, slowly, cautiously stand up, alert to the scene ahead. And behind me, the town itself, Capernaum, a cluster of small, low-roofed houses and shops set amidst an evergreen, slightly hilly terrain.

In spite of myself, my eyes returned to the sight farther out. I was further besieged by His powerful, majestic presence. As He and the group approached, I thought He might simply pass me by, but He astonished me by advancing straight ahead and stopping right in front of me.

---

1 Jeshua was the Master's given name. The name "Jesus" is of Roman origin.

Though I wasn't thinking straight, I did figure out that this was no ordinary occasion and no common man. *How handsome He is*, I thought. Indeed, He was nearly nine hands — much taller than most, with fine, chiseled features. His hair was shoulder-length and wavy, parted, as was the custom, in the middle and colored like the sands on a beach at Galilee. His beard was full, trimmed and unparted, unlike the beards worn by those in some particular Jewish sects. But it was the piercing intensity of His hazel eyes that caught my breath. I had been impressed with the Roman hierarchy and had met heads of state and foreign dignitaries, but none inspired the wonder that I felt in this presence.

The noisy crowd gathered round, then stilled. And then He spoke. In a resonant, yet strong, determined voice, He greeted me: "Shalom, Levi, follow me."

I was rendered speechless, but thoughts began to spin. *How could He know who I am? Yet He does! His eyes reach into my very soul.*

Again He spoke, "Tax collector, all that you have and all that you are doing, you must give up!"

What can He mean? I wondered. My mind lurched on. Certainly he's not referring to my job. No, not that! My profession is everything to me. I have planned and worked hard my whole life for my position and for the riches I have. Now that I'm at the height of my career, He wants me to quit? It's not reasonable, not possible, certainly!

After a long pause I replied hesitantly, "If you're asking that I give up my work, you're asking a lot."

The Man spoke no more but simply stared at me with both purpose and compassion.

All of a sudden and almost against my will, certainly without understanding what in the world I was doing, the words tumbled out, "Yes, Rabbi, I *will* give it all up. I will follow you."

He then responded, "I want you to sell everything you have. I want you to give back all that you are able of the taxes you have collected."

With a flood of tears on my cheeks that I could not understand, I agreed, "I will do it."

Then He smiled and said in a soft, loving voice, "From this day on, I will call you Mattai.[2] The name means 'a gift from God'!"

Happy shouts of support and thunderous applause poured out from

---

2 Mattai was an Aramaic name later translated into English as Matthew.

around us, startling me. I had been so transfixed that I had forgotten we were surrounded by all of these people. Then Jeshua said, "If you wish I will have dinner at your house tonight."

Surprised, I faltered a bit, "Ah, well ... yes. Of course, of course!"

As Jeshua and the joyous group walked on, I just stood there, riveted, trying to make sense of what had just happened, this collision with such a powerhouse.

Ignoring the soldiers who had seen the exchange, who were unimpressed and now simply shrugged and walked away, advancing toward their garrison, I turned and headed for home. Consumed by bewildering, confused thoughts, I was unable to respond to my abdey[3] (servant), Jesse's, quizzical stare at my overwhelmed countenance and simply ordered him to prepare for dinner guests.

It was a great gathering that night, one with some significant overtones. I invited my many friends, those who were accustomed to gala occasions at my house, and also my fellow publicans, the dozen or so who worked for Rome as did I. A raucous celebration was underway when Jeshua arrived later with five other men, the same men I remembered seeing with Him earlier in the afternoon.

I bade them all come in, and as they entered a hush fell throughout the room as my friends and colleagues stared in puzzlement at the newcomers. Dressed in my own accustomed finery, this group seemed a bit tattered to me: their simple clothes certainly needed some mending.

After entering Jeshua gestured to the five and said to me, "Behold, these are your new brothers. They are called Peter, Andrew, John, James and Thomas."

Not only tattered, I thought. *These men are downright rough-edged. They resemble a bunch of hooligans.* However, I grasped the outstretched hands they somewhat rcluctantly offered.

One held back completely. A burly-looking fellow grumbled, "I am Peter and I remember you. You are the tax collector who came to the shoreline while I was bringing in my catch. You demanded coins for Rome. You took too much from me." I felt a stab of guilt.

Jeshua gently squeezed Peter's shoulder and said, "That is past. That was Mattai's old life. We must all forgive each other and move on." With these simple words Jeshua in one moment transformed the tension

3 Some words in this text will be introduced first with the Aramaic translation.

that had built between us.

These men, the disciples, as they would come to be known, I later learned were much concerned that Jeshua would deign to associate with those openly aligned with Rome. How will it look, they wondered, for a great teacher to be seen with those who would show disloyalty to their own people?

As we all sat down in circular fashion, as was the custom for our people, and as my servants served a delicious supper, Jeshua didn't waste any time joining in the festivities. He obviously relished the food and the companionship and regaled us with His light-hearted banter and laughter. I was congratulating myself on assembling a most congenial get-together. *What a fun-loving group Jeshua has brought along*, I thought. But hidden under the surface was the fact that each guest present was having his own experience of this Master. Some were fascinated, enthralled by His manner, but for others a cloud of suspicion and mistrust hung heavy in the air.

My first glimpse at the enigmatic nature of this man, Jeshua, came that very evening as he poked some fun at Himself. While we were relaxing with generous portions of wine, Jeshua was reminded of another occasion, of His recent "coming out," where, finding a shortage of the red nectar at a friend's wedding in Cana, He had approached a large vessel of water and miraculously turned the contents into wine. Jeshua confided to us that He hadn't wanted to call attention to Himself by performing this miracle. But His mother had prodded him into it. Then, roaring with laughter, He recounted how after the event He'd danced so vigorously that He knocked a goblet of this transformed fruit of the vine from the hands of an innocent bystander. "Oh well," He had mused, "I can always make more."

While all the disciples were doubled up with laughter, myself included, I silently marveled at the miracle. I hadn't heard this story; my impressions of Jeshua were growing, more and more favorably.

After dinner the subject turned solemn. Jeshua turned to me with a personal message, but it was meant for all to hear. He reiterated His earlier words, touching my pervading thoughts, "What you do in life, Mattai, is never a wrong thing; your collection of the taxes from the people is not wrong. However, now it is time for you to change and grow in the way that your soul desires. As a demonstration and show of faith, it is necessary for you to let go of your taxation activities and give this money back to the people. And I will tell you this: as you follow me, you will find that you have all that you need."

It seemed to me that Jeshua was setting the stage for the others that my life would be changing; at the same time he was delivering to my guests an ideal of truth in order to awaken them. I was shaken but at the same time impressed.

That evening passed quickly. It seemed almost a dream. When all of the guests finally left I went to my private chambers and tried to sleep, but thoughts of the day's events and what they might mean to my future swirled in my mind.

I sometimes dreamed of a life different from the one I had. I lived in Capernaum, a seaside village located on the northern shore of the Sea of Galilee. My job was to raise money for Rome from people who traveled along the Via Maris. The Via Maris was a major route through Israel from Egypt to Damascus, Syria. It hugged the Mediterranean Sea coast, then veered inland to Capernaum. Nearby it connected to an ancient road traversing the central part of Israel. Via Maris was built by the Romans who placed tollbooths along the way. I sat at the edge of my town in a tollbooth, collecting the taxes that would finance the repairs on this very important thoroughfare that the Romans used to move their troops around in the occupied territories.

I was greatly rewarded in my job. But my good fortune and vast wealth had come at a price, at the expense of my own people, the Jews. I saw that the Jews were persecuted and that they suffered, and at times it caused me immense guilt.

I didn't fully commit to Jeshua's summons immediately. I needed time to think it through and work it out, and I spent several days mulling over His words, sometimes feeling the truth of them and moving forward easily into the idea but at other times retreating in confusion and fear. *Growing in the way my soul desires? What does He mean?*

But what continued to fascinate me was the feeling I had that this "Jeshua" could see the real me. He could see into the depths of my soul and know me. In the end when I decided to throw in my lot with Him it was an act of faith, not without an inner struggle. I had no idea where I was going or what I would be doing, and as with many who embark upon life changing journeys, I was metaphorically dragged, kicking and screaming, toward my destiny.

During the days following my momentous meeting, my thoughts continued to return to all that had happened during the previous days. The events were constantly on my mind. I was restless and sleepless. My understanding of life and my place in it were altering completely. I was indeed experiencing a mental shift, yet this would prove only the beginning. There would be a wild ride ahead.

• • •

I was now twenty-four, well educated and with an ideal job for the goals I had set. My father, Alpheus, was an elected official, an intermediary, who traversed between Rome and Israel negotiating political differences between the two. He was also an authority on Jewish mores. As was Jewish custom, each family held a specific responsibility: mine, the Levi family, was assigned to be the "priests." This was a bit of a misnomer because most of my family members were priests in name only: they had no real authority as such. While they were allowed to teach in some of the lowly synagogues, they were in no way allowed to enter the richest temples where the rarely seen high priests held sway. The Levis were forced to look elsewhere for their survival, and they did anything they could to make ends meet. There existed in my family a bitter resentment over their fate.

I was conditioned in my family's resentment. While I grew up, I watched the priests hold themselves more and more separate from and above the people: they had their own sacred prayer room within the temple, called Holy of Holies, which no one else was allowed to enter. They accessed these sanctuaries by a covered ramp, whereby they would not have to mingle with other worshippers. There was, in fact, much other forced separation within the confines of the holy temple: the rich and politically connected were afforded "second level" seats a step away from the priests; the average people worshiped farther away in a large room and the neer-do-wells, in the most lowly places. The women were segregated entirely, forced to enter their separate room through a temple side door. Occasionally when the children were being consecrated or when the blessing was being administered during a wedding celebration, the women were allowed into the inner rooms of the temple, but they were never allowed into the Holy of Holies. Because of this separation of peoples by wealth, political class and sex, my own antipathy built.

My mother, Esther, preoccupied with my father and her household tasks, seemed to have little time for me as I was growing up. I considered her cold and remote.

From an early time I resolved to excel in school and succeed in life. I had a clear vision of being able to travel freely, extensively and always first class. My vision for success also included a large comfortable home with servants to see to my needs. I believed that the only way to achieve these lofty ideals was to align myself with Rome.

Determined to carve out my successful future and with the help of my father, I landed the job as tax collector. While this position would certainly not make me very popular with the local citizens, it would seal my alignment with Rome and secure my place in its political structure and societal life.

From my tollbooth, with soldiers checking on those going from town to town, I collected the toll fees. I received a percentage of the money I garnered for Rome. So the more I collected for them, the more I made for myself.

The idea of making a lot of money and also making a name for myself intrigued me to no end. It didn't take long for me to figure out how to add to my pay. Unfortunately, my methods would land me in a pot of trouble that would take some time for me to extricate myself from. Thinking that I could get away with just about anything, as the young often do, and eager to throw my weight around, I began leaving my toll booth and walking shop-to-shop asking business owners to hand over money for their taxes. I had no right to do this, as others were responsible for these collections. I was fairly soon found out and ordered back to my tollbooth. But meantime, I had made enemies of the shopkeepers, and they were not soon to forgive. I even had the gall to venture into Bethsaides, a neighboring seaside village, and collect from the fishermen, many of whom got away with paying no taxes. I remembered that that was precisely how Peter knew me.

While I might have felt concern for my safety because of the resentment among Jews over Roman taxation policies, I never had any real troubles because the soldiers were always visible in the background. Where travelers seemed hostile and protested their levy, they usually backed off when they saw that the soldiers wouldn't hesitate to step forward and use force against them. I was able to take their coins with little trouble.

On the rare occasions when a belligerent victim angrily refused to hand over his share and was prepared to raise a fist, I would call for reinforcements. The soldiers would rush forth to subdue the aggressor and in no time haul him off to prison. No one was ever permitted to physically resist the Romans.

During these episodes, a personal conflict brewed within me. I coveted my job, but I also empathized with my countrymen and in my heart felt compassion for them. Most of these episodes were so rare, however, that I was able to push them from my mind.

I was instructed to be gentlemanly but stern while representing the powerful arm of Rome. The Roman authorities wanted at all costs to avoid stirring up passion among the Jews, one that could lead to overt rebellion against their conquerors. I myself made sure I was polite in order to keep the peace.

Off-duty in my hometown I did not go as unnoticed as I might have preferred. Occasionally, in some public place, a citizen of Capernaum would confront me and voice his contempt over my line of business. But others, having known my family for years, were forgiving. They perceived simply that a local boy had gone wrong because these were distressing times. They knew the pressures of being under the influence of Rome.

Because I was gaining affluence and becoming a big spender, many of the merchants were only too glad to see me coming into their shops to buy expensive ornaments for my lavish home and gifts for the many ladies I entertained. My little shopping sprees served not only the shopkeepers but me as well. While they could reclaim a few of their tax dollars, I could assuage my guilt over what I had collected from them.

I liked to get away from my hometown from time to time and bask in the grandeur of Rome. I was always fascinated with the cleanliness of the neat cobblestone streets, the grand marble buildings and pristine white houses. Rome was a vital marketplace that boasted splendid selections of jewelry and gemstones, exotic décor, pottery and fine linen from as far away as Persia, the Indian States, Nubia and Britannia. I was always eager to look and to buy.

Not only did I shop while in Rome, but also, because of my political position, there were occasions when I was invited to elaborate parties given by government officials. Music filled the air, wine flowed, and gaiety reigned around long trestle tables laden with an abundance of tempting foods. Wild boar was the usual fare, but there also was an array of exotic fruits from round the world and vegetables that I had never seen before. The Romans were a particularly gluttonous people, with an unsightly habit of eating until stuffed, then forcing themselves to vomit in preparation for eating still more! I was always physically repulsed by this custom, but also incensed because some of our citizens had to go without enough to eat. When I witnessed this behavior, I had renewed doubts about my position as tax collector and emissary of Rome. But usually after much inner reflection, I would decide to journey on. I truly believed down deep inside that I could make a difference. I felt that I might eventually be able to change things and help create a better life for my people. I knew in my heart that some day the Jewish people would be free. I just didn't know when and hadn't figured out how it could happen.

In the meantime in addition to achieving my lofty goals of wealth and desirable status, I was in the enviable position of being exposed to new cultures and learning other languages. At the parties I attended I met important people from many other lands; it gave me great joy and a feeling of accomplishment to communicate and hold my own with these celebrities.

There was, however, one flaw in my seemingly bright lifestyle. While I was devoted to my Jewish religious faith, I was not enchanted with my fellow citizens' lifestyle. I felt that Jewish family and social traditions were restrictive; the binding rules and regulations inhibited my sense of adventure. So I sought acceptance by the Romans who were, simply put, more fun. The Romans were open and robust; they lived life to the fullest and certainly enjoyed material pleasures. But I was, in the eyes of Rome, a citizen of a conquered country and therefore inferior, not quite accepted as an equal.

I did have an ace-in-the-hole though.

I looked very much like a Roman, more Roman than Jewish, actually, with thin lips, a small but well-defined nose, thick eyebrows, and fine facial features. My eyes were almond-hued. I most deliberately groomed myself in Roman style by neatly trimming my fashionable beard and closely cropping my dark hair. I had another typical Roman characteristic, this one of dubious distinction: even though I was a young man and fairly tall at eight and a half hands, I was developing a waistline of some measure as a result too much rich food and drink and a sedentary pace.

I had acquired a certain charm and was self-possessed of the appropriate social graces. And so in many Roman circles I was easily able to pass myself off as one of them. While I was never totally accepted by the Roman hierarchy, I did find acceptance among some of the citizens of Rome, who were very hospitable and, when the opportunity presented itself, freely opened their homes to me. The Roman people were friendly and warm and to some extent I was able to find the camaraderie that I felt was missing in my life. I later would discover that I was attempting to fill a very empty void, one that had plagued me from childhood. It was a feeling of not belonging, of not being loved.

• • •

After that first meeting with Jeshua and the following dinner that I would later refer to as "The First Supper," the climate of my relationship with all of my friends changed. They didn't frequent my house anymore, because they didn't understand my obvious conversion. But also, I no longer needed to entertain them or even to be accepted by them. I no longer desired to be a social climber. I didn't see myself as a social dropout; the social world simply no longer had significance.

Some of my friends, enticed by Jeshua's presence that night, became quite interested in what I was doing. Others, while curious, even supportive, stayed detached and distanced themselves. By and large, all too many, intimidated by Jeshua's grandeur, decided I had been taken in and deceived, and they turned their backs on me completely.

Also, in the days that followed, I began to hear of disgruntled rumblings among the townspeople, who couldn't understand and greatly resented Jeshua's presence in my home. How could this man who is said to be so holy, this rabbi, cavort with a non-conforming Jew, who would take from his own people, they wondered. It seemed that everyone — from the disciples to the guests to the townspeople — had come up with some reason to find fault with that First Supper, an occasion I had so relished. Perhaps it was just as well I was contemplating this departure from my hometown.

At home during the next two weeks I accomplished many things. I gave farewell bonuses to my disappointed, tearful servants, most of whom had faithfully been in my employ. I undertook to dispose of most of my worldly possessions. Because of the urgency of my situation, I sold off at a much-reduced rate and incurred heavy losses, but, to be sure, my things were going fast, more quickly even than the doves that were sold each week on the temple steps. I put my house up for sale, while secretly hoping no one would buy it. I assumed that I would be away with this man, Jeshua, only for a short time. I believed that I would be back soon to reclaim my house. By the time I was ready to leave, my hidden desires seemed to have manifested: my house indeed had not sold. I hoped that in the future I could reclaim it, even if under far different circumstances. Whatever the circumstances, I never imagined that these two brief meetings with the man called Jeshua would turn out to be a lifetime commitment for me.

I next turned my attention to the monies I had received from the most recent collection of taxes, which had not yet been sent to the Roman treasury. These fees added up to quite a bit. In fact, when the money I had received from the sale of my possessions was anted into my own personal secret stash, I had in hand what seemed to me, a man on the rise, a small fortune. I took all of it and visited each taxpayer, then without explanation, handed money back. When I finished this task, I wrote my resignation letter and sent it by courier to Rome. I wondered how they would receive this news.

Next I said good-bye to my brothers and sisters and then to my mother and father, who readily decided I had taken leave of my senses. To my friends I said that I was leaving on a trip and didn't know when I would return. While they were puzzled that I had given up my job, they didn't question my traveling, because I was often away. In my mind I knew that I was severing these close relationships, and I was convinced that I must in order to meet Jeshua's challenge.

While I had come to my decision with resistance, now that it was made I leaped in completely and didn't look back. My familiar lifestyle was a part of my past; I had indeed closed the door on my old life. How strange this felt as I packed my few remaining personal belongings and prepared for my trek. I learned that Jeshua had left Capernaum and was en route to a nearby town. After walking well into the afternoon, I finally reached Him as he addressed a crowd at the town square. As I approached my first thoughts were *have I been too capricious? What have I done giving up my security?* Other thoughts followed, particularly one that begged the question, *why am I here?*

As I began to listen more intently to Him, I was suddenly jolted when I heard Him say, "Follow me. I AM the Way, the Truth, and the Light."

Is it possible? With these magnificent words is He offering what I have been searching for through these long years? And then I understood. In an instant. I was captured by a knowing that I needed to follow not only Jeshua but also His teachings of unconditional love and divine truth and to know that He was the Way to Truth.

After Jeshua stopped speaking and the crowd dispersed, I approached Him and His group of five — the same disciples who had dined at my home. Expecting them to be surprised that I had actually shown up, I blurted out, "Well, here I am."

But Jeshua wasn't surprised at all. He laughed and then said, "It was time, Mattai. We've been expecting you." *Was I ever going to get used to being called 'Mattai?'* It certainly felt strange.

I was now part of this group, yet I was still not completely accepted. Since the disciples were suspicious of *everything* Roman, and not only did I look and act Roman but was the reviled tax collector as well, they were more than wary about my presence. Jeshua was smoothing the way with words that there was a divine purpose with our particular collection of souls. But matters weren't being helped when the disciples took a look at the mass of possessions I had brought along (which I considered to be meager indeed!). As they nudged each other, frowning and pointing at this display of excess, an amused Jeshua picked through my things: several coats, three pairs of shoes, four changes of clothing—including a Roman toga for dress up! I muttered a few explanations, then sheepishly acceded to His request that I give most of it away to the needy.

Over time I began to consider these men my spiritual brothers; eventually we all came to truly accept and love each other. In the meantime I was getting to know them.

The first to open up to me was Shimun Kepa[4] (Simon Peter). He had been called Shimun the fisherman, and had lived in nearby Bethsaides. He confessed to a similar experience as mine when first meeting Jeshua. Jeshua had beckoned to Shimun, "Follow me," adding, "I want to make you a fisher of men." Then He told Shimun, "Because your life is going to change, so too will your name. I will now refer to you as Peter, because this is the name that belongs to you."

Peter said that this first encounter had been precipitated by his brother, Andreaos (Andrew). Andrew, ever seeking counsel, had set out for the Jordan River along with his good friend, Yokhannan (John), to get some advice about his future. He was looking for John the Baptist, a recognized prophet. When the two arrived, John the Baptist was baptizing a man and saying to those gathered around, "Here is One whose sandals I am not fit to tie."

The Man had responded, "Cousin, I am honored for you to baptize me."

Andrew and John then saw a ray of light surround the man's body and glow, spreading like a fire slowly outward. They were amazed, yet they immediately understood the significance and instantly forgetting their original purpose, raced home excitedly to shout the news to their respective brothers: "We have a true Meshikhah (Messiah)!"

Andrew's brother, Peter, was skeptical and returned to the shallow waters to cast his nets. But it was not long before Jeshua sought him out on the seashore and called out. Peter answered the call and Andrew enlisted as well.

Peter was a happy man and a hard worker. To him, fishing was everything. All he really wanted was to be left alone to see to his nets. But he felt the power and truth that stood behind Jeshua and decided to let go of his life as he had known it.

Peter and I had recovered from the friction of our first encounter, and we quickly developed a bond of friendship, which only deepened as time went on. Our personalities complemented. Peter was a driving force,

4 The twelve disciples are introduced by their ancient Aramaic names. After this first reference, with the exception of Mattai (Matthew), they will be referred to by their modern English names.

physically big, very strong and boisterous. He always grabbed the spotlight, and since he was so well respected, when he took action, others paid attention and usually tried to emulate him. Against this powerful presence, it is perhaps difficult—and comical too—to envision Peter henpecked by a nagging, shrewish wife. But he was, and it was the only area of his life where he never managed to gain the upper hand. I never liked Peter's wife, Beatrix. Whenever I saw her she had a big wooden spoon in her hand, waving it in the direction of poor Peter. She held forth always from the kitchen where she prided herself on preparing some of the finest meals in town.

Peter had a great sense of humor, a voracious appetite ... and a quick temper. He gently teased and joked with his children while fully appreciating the tempting, mouth-watering meals his wife presented. When Peter was verbally challenged or physically threatened, his temper flared. When he found himself in hot water, I was there to help him out of trouble.

Andrew, a slender man, not as tall as his brother but almost as strong, was a dreamer, a fervent seeker, always with an eye on the future. With his warm humility, he always played second fiddle to his brother, but it seemed not to matter to him. He was happiest in the second seat, encouraging others into the spotlight. Andrew continually sought guidance from his big brother but began to transfer his many questions to Jeshua after we all got together.

When John gave his brother news that a messiah had arrived, he also pleaded with Yacob (James) to visit Peter's home where the new holy man would be stopping in. James and John were friends of Peter, as well as of Andrew and, like him, were fisherman. As did many others in this small, close-knit village, these brothers looked up to Peter. It didn't take much then for John to persuade James to go, and the very next day James and John met the Master and enthusiastically joined the team.

These two were brothers, but one would never know it. They neither looked nor acted alike. While James had a rugged appearance and was a bit coarse of character, John, on the other hand was fine-featured and exuded effeminate mannerisms, the same affectations I had discerned among certain men in Rome who undertook discreet, or indiscreet, liaisons with other men.

Tooma (Thomas), the fifth disciple, came to things a bit differently. He had heard rumors of Jeshua turning water into khamra (wine) — an indisputable miracle, if true. But he wanted to find out for himself whether or not it was so. Thus Thomas sought out Jeshua and finally spotted Him in the street. Jeshua approached Thomas and gave His by now accustomed proposal, "You must follow me."

Thomas, a short, married man with rust-colored hair quickly growing thin, had a quick, inquiring intellect and a strong desire to know truth, but he had quite something else on his mind this day. His father had just died.

He said to Jeshua, "Rabbi, I must first bury my father."

To this Jeshua replied, "It is not important for you to bury your father. Come with me instead. Your family, who is asleep to the truths I offer, can bury your father."

Now that I was getting comfortable with all the personalities and gaining confidence, I was eager to advance myself.

"I could be a great help to you," I said to Jeshua. I explained to Him my familiarity with the inner workings of Roman politics and my fluency in other languages. To Hebrew and Aramaic, which most of our people spoke, I could add Roman, Greek and Egyptian. I also knew the best inns for sleeping and where to get good food. I strived to impress Jeshua with my sharp acuity with numbers and budgeting. During my rambling self-promotion, Jeshua simply smiled.

When I had sufficiently completed my proud presentation, Jeshua turned to me, "Mattai, you must know that I am already aware of your gifts."

Now, my face flushed; I said awkwardly, "Of course, Master. I certainly do."

But my words and my thoughts were at odds. I didn't know how He could know me. And so well. He seemed to know me at limitless depths, depths I wasn't even aware of within myself. How embarrassed and ashamed I felt!

Seeing my discomfort, Jeshua patted me on the shoulder and declared, "Mattai, I have a special assignment for you. Because of your talents, you will be responsible for taking care of our monies. You will be in charge of finances. But that is not all. You will have another important task." I looked up, timidly, expectantly.

Jeshua said, "I want you to be a liaison between our group and those we encounter as we travel, whether they be politicians, religious leaders, or business men. Those are your duties, Mattai. You are to act as our representative, our political diplomat."

Feeling my own demeanor changing — I was now standing straight and tall — I deemed myself ready to accept the challenge. I thanked Jeshua for His trust and for the opportunity to serve.

The die was cast. I had my responsibilities. Little did I know then what they would involve or to what extent I would have to tap into both my past experiences and the depths of my inner strength in order to carry out my assignment. Nor did I have any idea how these duties as treasurer and PR man would evolve prophetically and catapult me into the limelight of the most extraordinary story ever told.

We traveled throughout Israel. The crowds grew. And the disciples finally numbered twelve.

Pilipus (Phillip), also from Bethsaides, would prove an important figure in my life in later days. We would, in fact, eventually team up and travel together as Jeshua would ask us to do. Phillip was a careful man, deeply religious, who would reason out the issues, then act with gusto. I admired these traits; they would prove to blend well with my own.

Phillip took Jeshua to meet Bartolmi (Bartholomew), who joined the group. But why Bartholomew was asked, I could not say at first. I thought him an odd-looking sort, with his ruddy complexion and wrinkled skin. But it was his furrowed brow and serious demeanor that caused me particular consternation. I had trouble figuring out why he could happily agree with me in one moment, while railing in disagreement the next — over the same issue! Bartholomew had a brother, Nathaniel, who met Jeshua and listened to what He planned, but Nathaniel had doubts and also fears about what might be ahead for him and decided not to join our group.

Taddai (Thaddeus) was the organizer. Seven years older than I and fair of skin, this former shopkeeper was well qualified to manage our daily tasks and see to it that they were carried out forthrightly and in a timely manner. He treasured the words of Jeshua.

Yacob Bar-Khalpai (James), son of Alphaeus, was the youngest among us, very young, with long, shiny, black hair. Mostly he was a quiet figure, with not much to contribute. However, like most other very young men James certainly had an opinion on most topics but when challenged would back down quickly.

Shirnun Kananaya (Simon) the zealot. What a fiery personality, this man from Canaan. He spoke passionately of overthrowing "those tyrants," the Romans. Before meeting us he belonged to a loosely organized rebel group, which encouraged Jews to take the Romans by force. "Kick them out of our country," he would say. Simon underwent a profound change once under the influence of Jeshua. While still passionately desiring the freedom of our people, he was able to moderate his intent: instead of taking up arms, he saw the wisdom of using reason and will power to overcome them. As I grew to know him better, I saw that he had the ability to rally people to action; however, that was as far as it went. Before he got them moving, he would surge ahead and take action all by himself.

Ehodah Scariota (Judas Iscariot) was the last disciple to join our band of spiritual brothers. He did not come from Galilee as had the rest of us but was from Judea, a region that included the city of Jerusalem. Judas had heard of the works of Jeshua and had sought Him out. He felt that Jeshua's teachings would be a perfect vehicle to political power.

Judas quested for power for two reasons: first, he thought that a high position would bring a personal sense of freedom. Second, he truly wanted to help his people and felt that the only way to do so was to fight from within government ranks rather than from without. If he gained notoriety inside the Roman hierarchy, then perhaps he could find ways to convince Rome to loosen its grip on the Jews. Secretly, Judas fancied himself another Moses.

But Judas was misguided in these ideas and was soon taken to task by Jeshua, whose intent was to spawn personal growth, not political advancement. Jeshua would teach that it is illusion to believe that personal freedom lay anywhere other than within one's own being.

From the beginning Judas was an outsider among us and not only because he hailed from a different region. He was uncomfortable around the other disciples, and we all were a bit discomfited in his presence. Judas was quarrelsome and stubborn. While espousing good works, he harbored covetousness and greed. With his obvious hidden agenda, we all had no doubt that Judas, in order to get what he wanted, would never hesitate to lie and cheat.

When I first met Judas, I was disgusted by his behavior. I had known plenty of connivers, who, behind the scenes, manipulated for their own gains. So I was surprised and a bit disappointed when Jeshua invited him to join us, especially when Jeshua had seemed so discerning and selective in His choices, and so many others who wanted to join us were turned away. But by now I could deduce that Jeshua surely had His reasons for including Judas. As I was now beginning to look within myself, I could look back in amusement and see why, with my high Roman style — toga in tow — the other disciples had been so suspicious of my presence at first.

The core group was now complete. We each came from a different background and walk of life. We had our individual stories. We were fishermen, shopkeepers, a farmer and would-be politician, and I, tax collector. We were diverse in personality: fiery or calm, short-tempered or peace-loving, self-centered or compassionate, silent or outgoing, introspective, conniving, reflective, manipulating, accepting. Ultimately, every personality type was present among us.

And the makeup was perfectly constructed.

With Jeshua at the helm, this unique force would prove to be in perfect harmony with God's divine plan.

It seemed we had an enormous task at hand. But what was it exactly? And who were the people most immediately affected by our current events and those that would come?

The Romans had occupied Israel for a much-too-long ninety years. The Jews suffered mightily under their oppression. Many of them felt forsaken by God, that He would allow such tyranny, and they touted our commonly used expression: God "doesn't give a fig about us."

Jeshua set the foundation for His teachings by addressing the political climate, and He did so immediately. He counseled that no one ought to hate or fear the Romans, particularly us disciples. He taught that no healing could occur through hate or fear, that forgiveness is the only pathway to healing and ultimate peace.

And then He astonished me once again. While I had aligned myself with Rome in order to attain wealth and truly believed that it was derived from and dependent upon the Romans, He stated that all abundance comes only from the one source: God.

These words caused a change in me that would carry me forward during some grueling days ahead. My feelings of lack and need began to shift toward a vision of available unlimited abundance. I now deeply felt and understood His phrase, "Through God, all things are possible." I felt a new passion and a heightened state of determination concerning the teachings of Jeshua.

Jeshua obviously was key to these new ideas. But *who* was He, really, and what was His role? I had a general understanding about this Master, as did most others who had listened to the stories circulating throughout the country.

My new friend, Jeshua, was a Jew, trained in the tradition of Torah, the holy book of spiritual law and ethical behavior that formed the basis for Israel's cultural and national identity. Jeshua also was raised in the Essene[5] school, a newer version of Judaism. His family took a strong part in the Essene doctrine, particularly so His mother, Mary, who was quite skilled in this more evolved tradition. These teachings formed His solid foundation for truth, knowledge, and wisdom, which He above all others possessed.

Even though we knew this much about this Master, we disciples were mystified by His very presence. We hungered for answers about His background and training and continually pleaded with Him to reveal more.

5 The meaning of Essene is the *pious ones*.

First Spiritual Law

Be then knowing of God in man, beast and all that is before you. In the fish, in fowl, in the rocks and stones, put thought through heart to anything and be at one in it. For here we see and know the beauty of the diverse and endless creator. Know that nothing and no expression is an outcast; nor is it discarded from the Father as waste. All serves to celebrate the Creator.

Explanation:

God's plan for us is perfect. He is the vision through which everything flows in divine rhythm. Everyone and everything has been created by Him and is part of His essence. All pieces fit together as in a cosmic mandala, with each participant contributing in His perfect place in the perfect time in God's plan.

CHAPTER 2

Jeshua's Story

Finally, the moment had come. Breathless with anticipation and not wanting to miss a single word, we brothers, gathered around a campfire, were stillness itself, as Jeshua began the story of the events that led to this moment of mastery.

Just before I was born, King Herod ordered the people of Israel to travel to the birthplace of their father to be counted in a census, for the purpose of taxation. My father, Joseph, could have seen to this matter by himself, but my mother, Mary, insisted on going with him, even though she was nearing term with me in her womb. God had spoken to Mary, instructing her to travel to Bethlehem of Judea[6]*, telling her that I was to be born there. It was important for my father to attend my birth as well, because my father and mother would find themselves alone at this propitious moment, and he was needed to assist.*

When Joseph and Mary set out for Bethlehem, from Nazareth, knowing that I would be born while they were there, they left prepared, even if not in usual ways. Although they planned their travel wisely, because they stopped many times along the way to allow Mary some rest, they arrived late in the day, and there were no rooms available in any of the inns. Joseph worried about the impending event and anxiously questioned several innkeepers about where they could stay. He was directed to a stable. Going in, they found the usual array of goats, sheep, and donkeys milling about. But they were able to find a clean, quiet spot away from the animals, where they could lie down on a thick bed of hay.

My mother and father were in Bethlehem for several days prior to my birth, and the town was bustling from the influx of all

6 There was also a town named Bethlehem in Galilee, which was closer to Nazareth where Mary and Joseph lived. However, Joseph's birthplace was in Bethlehem of Judea.

those arriving for the census. From time to time they ran into residents they knew. They hoped that someone would take them in and help them. But in the end, I would be born with only the two of them present.

Mary went into labor early that evening but didn't perceive it immediately; she thought that the discomfort she felt was merely indigestion from her supper. When the impending birth was obviously close at hand, Joseph did not hesitate to step in and help, but when he gave a hand, it was with much trepidation and nervousness. He need not have worried, however, because God would be providing them all the help they needed. Remember now, most other prospective fathers had very little to do with birthing in any circumstances. Rather than assist their wives, they would have left them alone, to birth or to die.

I made my entrance into this world in the deep dark of a chilly springtime night. My parents named me Jeshua ben Joseph[7]*. I was placed in a trough that was filled with extra hay. And no makeshift garments for me! Mary covered me in fine, luxurious linens, which were gifted to her for me, her firstborn child. They would be discarded after being soiled. I was kept immaculately clean and dry and was wrapped in comforting swaddling blankets.*

I was nestled in my mother's arms and nurtured at her breast. My father fashioned a harness-like support for me, so that while walking my mother could always maintain physical contact with me. My mother rarely put me down. From the first moment of my birth, all of my needs were met. I truly had abundance and could want for nothing.

The three of us remained in the stable for a day. The morning after my birth found several local people arriving to tend the animals. They were most surprised at what they found. Others came later to help take care of Mary and me.

Soon we moved to a home and were given a room, where we stayed a week, while Mary and I gained strength for travel. It was during this time that we received news from a remarkable source.

Three wise men had followed a light in the sky in a search for me. This light was given to them, as a sign that a special event was

7 The name Jeshua was given to Mary by the Archangel Gabriel.

about to occur. What shone was an alignment of planets, all glowing like one giant bright star. The wise men believed that this special child would be the King of Jews and would change the history of mankind. They wanted to behold, welcome and honor this child with gifts and good will. Their first stop was Jerusalem, where they were presented to the king. They told the king, Herod, of the prophecy and asked whether he knew the whereabouts of this exalted one.

And then a distressing thing happened. King Herod misinterpreted the wise men's words about the purpose of this birth. He fearfully decided that his own days were now numbered, that this savior, as he interpreted the child's role, would come to overthrow him. In order to save himself, he ordered the slaughter of all male children under the age of two born in Bethlehem.

When the wise men arrived in Bethlehem and found the room where Mary, Joseph and I were staying, they honored us with a ceremonial presentation of gold and the mishkha (oils) of frankincense and myrrh. They also delivered the king's dire pronouncement.

That night, Joseph had a dream, a warning dream, that he must flee to Egypt with Mary and me, in order to keep them safe. Joseph had trusted the message from the wise men, and now he had confirmation of its truth through his dream. In the middle of the night, he roused Mary who bundled me up, and the three of us left for Egypt, where the Pharaoh ruled and the king in Jerusalem could hold no sway.

We traveled for a week to reach Egypt. My mother told me later that my father got lost a couple of times — we went in wrong directions and had to retrace our steps, and in amusement she added that Joseph would never admit that he had erred.

We settled in a small town on the Egyptian border amidst friends who opened their hearts and their homes to us after hearing about our recent trials. These were nomadic people who had come long ago from Judea.

Shortly after arriving in Egypt, the wise men's message was proven true. My parents received word that the king's decree had been carried out. This devastating news sparked extreme emotions in our household. My parents grieved for the loss of those many innocent children and for the anguish of their families, yet they were profoundly grateful to God for sending his three messengers and sparing our family. They knew that they had been truly blessed by His hand. I always remained profoundly grateful to my father for having the wisdom to correctly interpret the signs of trouble.

The framework around this time of my birth was complex. It might have been a time of unparalleled joy that the Son of God, King of the Jews, would be born and come forward to serve His people. And it was a time of joy, and there was great gratitude. Yet there was also misery and grief, because of the inhumane slaughter of so many babies. That Herod so feared losing his power that he believed he must kill hundreds in order to prevent the King of the Jews from being recognized could not be grasped. And the question, why? could never be answered. Ironically, one-thousand years before this devastating incident, in Moses' time, a similar event took place, when the Pharaoh of Egypt, afraid of losing his power, ordered the killing of newborn male children. In the years that followed I was able to see that all throughout history certain events repeat themselves, and in the repetition comes a new concept, an expansion of thought, to assist mankind.

> So now I bring a blessing to all of those mothers and to all of those children, who were sacrificed. Also, we bless all the lives that have come since those times, that there now be healing and forgiveness.

When I was two-and-a-half years old, my brother James was born. Soon I would have someone to play with.

After we had stayed four years in Egypt, Herod the Great died, and his three children, Herod Antipas, Herod Phillipus and Herod Archelaus, took over ruling the country. That is when my parents decided to return to their homeland. We went to Jerusalem but stayed only a short time, because my mother and father were still harboring apprehension about my safety. They decided to move into the upper region of Galilee. My parents chose the city of Nazareth because it was their home town, and they had friends living there. My mother also would have her own beloved parents nearby. There was a suitable school on the outskirts of town as well that they felt would be perfect for my education and social growth. It was adjacent to where my mother was educated.

Along the way while we were only temporarily relocated, my father had picked up some odd jobs in order to support the four of us. But now he was finally able to resume his trade full time, and our lives soon settled into a pattern. My father purchased a large piece of property and, with neighbors' help, he built a house and in back a shed, which would serve as a workshop for his carpentry and also as a stable for the animals. While our new home was being built we stayed in the neighboring community of Sepphoris (also called Cippori), with my grandparents, Anna and Joachin. They were my mother's parents.

Sepphoris was a small town that mirrored Rome in some ways. Public baths, protected from view, were used for ritual bathing, and a large amphitheater served as a gathering place. We spoke a special dialect of Aramaic; it differed somewhat from the Aramaic spoken by the people living around Jerusalem.

Most men labored at menial, manual work. But my father's profession was a step above. He was a highly skilled furniture maker and mason. He had learned his craft from his father, and his father before him. I was next in line and would learn this timeless trade in due time.

Smart and talented, my father could fashion almost anything if he had the proper kind of wood. But wood was scarce, hence, precious, and not everyone could afford beautiful wooden furniture. This scarcity actually assured our financial stability because it was in great demand, and the wealthy in our community would call upon my father to craft the furniture to furnish their homes. He also built many of the temple fixtures. We lived well, not ostentatiously, but most comfortably.

Several months after we moved to our house in Nazareth, my second baby brother was born. My parents named him Joses.

Initially, I was educated at home because I was too young to enter the school. My mother took on this responsibility, as my father was usually very busy in his shop.

Mother had developed a wise and patient way, which she applied devotedly to me. Unlike other women in our culture who typically were denied education because women were deemed to be second-class citizens, Mother had been well educated in the progressive Essene schools. Even so, her education lagged behind my father's because of the Essene philosophy, which was that women didn't need to know all things. But my father, like some of the other enlightened men, wanted his wife to be given the depth of our religious teachings, and so quietly at home, he tutored her in the knowledge she lacked.

In the evenings after supper, we would have our sharing. I would sit on my father's lap while he related great stories to me about our brave ancestors. I was intrigued by the perils and triumphs he spoke of.

I was born a Jew, into a family descended from the tribe of Oraḥam (Abraham). I was taught and understood well that to be a Jew meant great challenges. We Jews were grateful that we no longer lived in bondage to the Egyptians but now occupied the land that was promised to us and which we could celebrate at Passover. However, now, the Romans controlled our land. Truly, though, one could not compare these hardships. While burdened by the Romans, it was by no means as great a struggle as it had been to become free from the slavery imposed by the Egyptians.

In my youth I was childlike and childish, both necessary conditions for growing up, for indeed how could I gain wisdom without experience? I was a trial to my parents when I rebelled, especially when I broke a commandment. Indeed, there were squabbles and disappointments in my family along with passion and learning, humor and great love, all of these necessary components for fully living the human life. And still, today, with all I have learned and experienced, I embrace my humanity, understanding the richness that lies therein.

I remember a particularly vexing day for my father. My brother James and I were told time and time again not to play with our father's tools. But, for children the temptation is sometimes too great, and on a day that he was out, we scurried into his shop to check things out. When Father got home and went to work, he found some of his tools misplaced and turned his wrath toward his very deserving children.

To this day, there remains that element of temptation and the consciousness that "when the cat's away, the mice will play." We have moments of pretending that we don't have to pay attention to the laws and rules. We all test our parents; in my humanness, I certainly did. But we all need to embrace the part of our human ego that would break these laws.

When I was five years of age two significant events took place. My heart was gladdened with the arrival of a third brother, Simon. And it was greatly saddened when my beloved grandfather, Joachin, passed away. As most youngsters do, I adored my grand-parents, whom I saw often and who gave me constant affection and the kind of special attention that grandparents are known for, even spoiling me some. I noted how with such little fanfare one could arrive into this world and another depart. While God giveth, so does He taketh away.

While my parents were wonderful educators, I had a true mentor in my great-uncle, Joseph of Arimathea, my grandmother, Anna's, brother. He was an advanced elder in the temple and a wealthy supporter of his community. That support included many generous bequests to my family members, even though we were already financially secure.

Joseph of Arimathea was a powerful merchant, an investor and traveler, who owned many ships and traded goods in the far corners of the world. He also had certain spiritual gifts and recognized early my closeness with God. Uncle Joseph, as I called him, had a partial understanding of my future role in history and, in addition to supporting us financially, was committed to advancing my education and spiritual development. He became a major influence in my life.

When I was nearly six, I started my formal training at the nearby Essene school. This school had living quarters for the students, and many stayed there, to go home only once a week and during the holidays. The Essene school focused on intellectual pursuits, such as learning Sanskrit and other languages, as well as studying the nature of the Kabala. Spirituality was a serious subject as well, and we undertook teachings on the thrones of God, the Elohim and the angelic realm. We learned about body, mind, spirit purification and studied about how balanced thinking creates harmony within oneself and then extends out to positively affect the outer world. Beyond this, we were taught tolerance and allowance for the world to be as it is.

In some of the teachings by the temple, there was an attitude that the human body was secondary to the mind and spirit in spiritual undertakings. However, we in the Essene culture understood that the body was the temple of the living spirit, and we focused on how we should honor our bodies and keep them whole and healthy until our time of transition from the earthly plane. We studied, too, about how we could overcome physical discomforts to become a symbol of painless at-one-ment with God.

The Essenes advanced the old religious dietary rules by pointing out that while Moses' laws about cleansing and purifying the body were sound, over time these laws had become filled with minutiae and grew too complex and cluttered to be followed sensibly. The Essene teachings urged a return to relaxed simplicity in following these rules. We did adhere to a basic premise that to consume certain sea foods and also some particular products of the earth would go against God's will that the body be healthy, because these foods were contaminated and could introduce toxins into the body.

Unlike the Eastern faiths and traditions, which allowed obedience to a variety of gurus, our schools taught us obedience to the one Master. This was sometimes interpreted as an obedience to our rabbi or head teacher, as it was believed by some that he clearly and distinctively represented the human authority of God.

We were not taught to fear God but to sincerely honor and be obedient to His will. And this was key: the only way to know God's will was not by following written law but by profoundly knowing what was written in our own hearts. And this was the core of the Essene teachings. This idea marked a profound difference from all teachings that had gone before, because this message shifted authority from outside the individual to the individual. Its implication was that everyone could have a personal relationship with God. No temple was needed to intervene and set down rules.

Not all Essenes aspired to fully receive the depth of these teachings. But because my mother had exposed me to these concepts earlier, I was conditioned to them and avidly soaked them up.

My school was not all work and study. School was play and fun for me as well. I was able to make new friends as well as form deeper bonds with children I had already met. I was able as well to reconnect with a few of my relatives.

The one you all know was my cousin John, son of the priest, Zechariah, and his wife, Elizabeth. John was sent down from the city of Capernaum, where he lived, to be schooled in the Essene tradition. Because we were being taught together, the two of us developed a close relationship.

I loved being with my cousin John: we had much in common. John and I were competitive in our quest for knowledge. However, he tended to daydream and, consequently, often got into trouble with the rabbi.

I also became close friends with a boy named Lazarus, from the city of Bethany. You have heard me speak about him frequently. Lazarus had a good heart. We shared many interests and loved the challenge of successfully,completing our studies. We engaged in some good-natured competition: who could quote the most from the Torah? Which one of us best knew the laws of living taught in the Essene culture and why should we follow these laws?

I will now tell you about an incident that occurred when I was seven years of age. My strict religious teachers always gave me most difficult assignments that included mastering certain forms of religious law, forming the letters and writing them down. (Reading and writing were not assigned to all the students, only to those who were in the "inner circle" of the Essene community. I was a part of that community.) This particular time — and my memory serves me well — I was given a particular lesson. I knew that my father and Uncle Joseph would sternly check my work before I handed it in to the head rabbi; they would judge my attentiveness, knowledge and accuracy. My assignment was to read a passage, then attempt to record it from memory, much like a book report. I had been studying my subjects in both Hebrew and Aramaic, and I began to imagine what the letters and words would look like. You could say that what happened to me next was like a hallucination. The words began to animate in my mind and then move all over the page to form letters and words I didn't recognize or know how to read.

When this happened I wrote the words not in Aramaic or Hebrew but instead recorded the symbols that I was seeing. I was also preparing myself for possible harsh words when I turned over the printed text to my father and Uncle Joseph.

When I finally, and very hesitantly, gave the material to my uncle he looked at it, was silent for a moment, then said softly, "What have you written?"

I looked at it and thought, I don't know; I can't even tell what this is. *And I thought,* uh oh, here it comes. I'm in real trouble now; fire bolts from heaven will be down on me. *But instead of chastising me, Uncle Joseph amazed me by breaking down and weeping.*

He said, "I know these signs. These are the signs of our future. These are the signs that tell of all of the stories we have just read. God must have touched you."

I did not know what Uncle Joseph meant. Neither did I know that God had touched me. I only knew that I was having a fun, playful vision. Even so, I stored these words in my memory, because they rang true to me, and I knew there would be a time when I would understand them.

Since I had been learning many languages, I did know that these new words represented yet another one. What I later learned was that these were letters similar to those of the Gaelic language but not exactly the same. These letters were of a language not yet known. They were translations of my Hebrew and Aramaic text into this strange, as yet undefined language. And these words gave new meaning to many of the Hebrew words that I held so dear. This understanding was revealed to me in the many initiations that followed in later years.

The memory of my fear of being completely devastated by the wrath of my uncle and my father, juxtaposed with the playful aspect of my vision and resulting joy, these extremes of emotion, stayed with me, and this experience was etched in my memory in all of the coming years.

This was just one of the many experiences I had that caused me to appreciate the fact that I possessed highly unusual, rare talents. There were more. I could actually see into people's souls. I could read their thoughts and understand their deepest feelings. I could see auras, and I marveled at how they could sometimes change color and intensity, depending upon the individual's mood, or state of body, mind, and spirit consciousness. At times, and sometimes disturbingly, I could even foresee what was going to happen to them in the future.

I had another profound gift, an ability to heal with a simple touch of my hands. I first became aware of this with small animals. Once, I saw a bird fly into the side of our house. By the time I reached it, the poor creature was lying on its side with an obviously broken wing. I picked it up and held it for a few minutes. Then I heard God's voice in my head: Visualize a whole and healed creature that can fly perfectly. *I did that and before my eyes I saw its wing quickly straighten. Then it simply flew away as if nothing had even been wrong with it.*

I now had three brothers and was completing my second year of school and had made many friends there; however, James continued to be my best friend, and we got into a fair amount of trouble from time to time.

My brother and I once caught a mouse while playing in the fields near our house. We brought it home, hoping to keep it as a charming new pet. But before we were ready to announce this new addition to the household, we decided to have a little fun. We mischievously stuck the mouse into my mother's sewing basket when she wasn't looking. We knew the mouse would be nice and warm, and we also wanted to watch Mother's reaction when she reached down for her yarn.

Well, things went just as we had anticipated ... up to a point. Mother reached into her basket; she heard a loud squeak and was so startled by that particular "surprise," that she jumped up, grabbed one of her cooking pots, and hurled it at the mouse. Fortunately, nothing was boiling in it. This particular pot had been purchased in

India by Uncle Joseph and presented to my mother as a gift. Forged of copper, brass and lead, it was exceedingly heavy. The poor little thing didn't have a chance. It was quite sad, not only for James and me but for my mother. It really wasn't her intention to hurt the mouse. Many times these little creatures would come in, and when they did, Mother would shoo them back out. But the mouse had given her such a jolt, particularly when it squeaked, that she reacted spontaneously.

My mother wept over this incident, at the anger she felt as well as the taking of that little life. When she got over her weeping, she made certain we knew that our behavior was not acceptable. She said, "A joke is fine, but you need to be very aware that you can hurt people when you do things like that."

Mother never raised her hand to us. Rather, her stern, disappointed look was enough. My father would occasionally take a small branch and make a switch to be used on our bottoms. It was hardly a beating, as he was gentle, but he punished us just enough for us to know not to mess around with Mother.

One time I even brought a rat into the house, and Mother, seeing it, quickly ushered it out with her broom, saying that if I were going to keep the little rodent, it would have to stay out in the barn.

When James and I got in trouble, we were both remorseful, but I the most, for I was older and at the age where I felt the responsibility much more keenly than James. The mouse incident taught me a lesson: I now know that all creatures, no matter how big or small, are of the Father.

My mother taught me so much. I received a real lesson about my mother's role when I was eight years old. Curious about "woman's work," I asked my mother to explain just what her job was. She told me that women create a home, a comfortable place for the man to do his work. Assuming a masculine role, I asked her, "How can I learn to order you how to work?"

She responded, "But you do not see your father telling me what to do. No. Do you see your mother telling your father what to do? Yes. Well, there is your answer. You must strive to be true within your inner being, and you must not listen to what the world wants you to do."

During this same year when my grandmother, Anna, was making one of her regular visits to our house, we noticed smoke coming from over the horizon in Sepphoris, where she lived. The sight mystified me. My Uncle Joe headed out for the city alone to see, I assumed, what was happening. He returned home quickly and told the family that an uprising was taking place. He had sped back to keep from getting caught up in it. Uncle Joe waited until he thought it safe, and then collected me, and we set out for our neighboring town. He didn't say anything to me along the way, but I could see by the set in his jaw that the situation was serious. I intuitively knew that he wanted me to see and understand.

We traveled a brief time to Sepphoris and saw that a group of political zealots had lodged an insurrection against the Romans. By the time we arrived it was obvious that the Romans had exerted their power to teach the rebels a lesson. While some of the rabble-rousers had escaped, others had not and were suffering mightily for it. The Roman soldiers had razed the town, raped the women before forcing them into servitude and beaten and enslaved the men. And a truly horrifying sight: the most extreme of these rebels had been left to hang by their hands on crosses, crucified for their misdeeds. It was an agonizing sight indelibly imprinted in my heart and mind.

When I returned home, with all of my attention still focused on the hideous sights in the town that had been Sepphoris, a new thought added weight to my concerns: could the Romans inflict their horror on my own family and my own friends in this my own town? *I had reason for concern: after all, my family and I had once before been threatened with death, which had forced our flight from Bethlehem.*

When I expressed my worry to my father, he replied, "Jeshua, no, violence could not happen in Nazareth because God is protecting us." I couldn't help but think that God had surely protected my grandmother, because here she was with us safely away from the mayhem.

I soon learned that protection came in practical terms too. My Uncle Joseph of Arimathea was one of those who were politically maneuvering to keep peace. There was not much room for dissension in the community; it was well run politically and people of power were respected. As a consequence, a serious opportunity for rabble-

rousing, which could have brought undesired or violent attention from the ever-controlling eyes of Rome, never came.

After the terrible destruction of Sepphoris, as time allowed, my father, because of his accomplished skills in masonry and woodworking, volunteered when he was able to rebuild the city.

I was in my third year classes and loved my studies. I had memorized major portions of the Torah to the amazement of my fellow students and the rabbi and could lead the class in recitation. My father often took me to the temple where I savored the teachings of the priests.

This year a girl was born to our family. Her name was Ruth. She was so sweet. She hardly ever cried. Mother called her our angel. We all took turns caring for her and she always commanded our attention. I loved Ruth. Two years later, my parents had a second girl. She was called Elizabeth. By now, ten years had passed. I was ten years older than my new sister.

When I was nearly twelve years old, my fourth and youngest brother, John, was born. And several months later our entire family went to Jerusalem. It had been a long time since we'd visited the big city. First we stopped at my Uncle Joseph's second residence — he had homes in both Jerusalem and Nazareth. Several days later we attended temple services. I saw the merchants who had set up shop right outside the temple, who were selling doves and other objects. I was incensed, because I felt that trading on the temple steps was a defilement of a place that must be kept holy to honor God with prayer.

We all entered and listened to the priests. After the teachings were finished, my family left. However, I wished to learn more so I stayed behind. Soon I was involved with the priests and elders in a discourse on the laws of our religion. I surprised and intrigued them with differing interpretations of religious law.

About this time my father and mother noticed that I was missing and hurried back into the temple to find me. When they located me with this group in a quiet alcove away from the larger crowds, they saw that I was in deep discussion. My knowledge made an impression on my parents, but Mother, of course, with her maternal instincts in full gear, admonished me, "Jeshua, don't go off on your own again."

My reply was, "I was doing my Father's work; that is what I am here to do."

As for the priests and elders, I was explaining details of the Torah and offering interpretations that they had never before heard and lacked the wisdom to understand. While they were impressed by these new thoughts, they also were a bit irritated and, even more, threatened by what my speaking out could mean to their beliefs and futures.

During this time, I was still close to my cousin John. But, while I was delving deeply into the work that would define my future, John, on the other hand, was giving his parents many fits and starts. John was considered the wild one. He was always venturing off on his own and causing worry about his whereabouts. There was much more to John's character, however, and it would be brought forth soon in matters involving me.

On the day I turned thirteen, I went through a traditional, ceremonial rite of passage, which represented my transition from boyhood to manhood. A reading from the Torah was customary during these ceremonies, and, indeed, I had learned my lessons thoroughly and recited the passages from memory. All who attended — a rabbi, elders and family members alike — found my abilities and insights profoundly moving, for I had brought new clarity to these divine passages. They all just felt that it would not be long before I was teaching at the temple. This moment was significant, because it marked my entrance into a more public role.

During this ceremony, which also represented for the family and community the confirmation of faith, John pulled me aside. John could also see deep into another's soul and know that person's inner truth. He could see many things about me, even future events that would manifest in my life. And having received from Spirit the message that he would enter the ministry, John symbolically baptized me by anointing me with the oil of frankincense.

This ceremonial milestone marked the end of formal studies for both John and me. John's mother and father had been living in Capernaum primarily because it was reasonably close to the Essene school, but now with John's education complete, they could indulge their own desires. They decided to move to Ein Kerem, a small town just outside Jerusalem, in order to be close to their home temple. Ein Kerem was a picturesque little town whose name means the spring that flows from the vineyard.

As for me the decision was made to send me along with Uncle Joseph to receive a more worldly education. A powerful turning point for me, it would be a journey lasting fourteen years, one that would be expansive beyond what I ever could conceive.

I packed my most cherished belongings and Uncle Joseph and I set sail on one of his large merchant ships. She was a grand sailing ship. My quarters were a spartan cabin below, next to my uncle's. I would call it home for some time.

We sailed from a port in lower Judea from the city of Ezion-gerber, located on the Gulf of Aqabah, into the Red Sea, and were guided by the sun, moon and stars.

Our route would take us into the Gulf of Aden and then to the Arabian Sea. Destination: the Indian States.

If I had any idea of slack time, my uncle soon laid those plans to rest. I was expected to pitch in and work side-by-side with all the hands on board. My uncle saw it as the beginning of my learning process. While he was seeing to it that I was developing mentally and spiritually, he also wanted me to build physical strength and to know what it was to be a sailor.

There was much work to be done on board, scrubbing the decks, washing dirty laundry, mending the sails, cooking for the crew, and cleaning up dishes in the ship's galley. I gave it my all.

The sailors were different from anyone I had met before. They were uneducated, rugged and crude. Some of them had even been pirates before they reformed and signed on as members of my uncle's crew. The sailors lived their lives according to a set of superstitions that had been handed down from their fathers and their fathers before them. I was determined to set them straight and began challenging their false beliefs with facts. They were most curious about where I had learned so many things at such a young age. I responded that I knew these truths in my heart, that I had learned them from my mother, and at school. They chided me, saying that I was like a girl because I had learned from a woman. They too were determined to make a man of me.

But I challenged them back: "How do you know that these things you've been told by your fathers are true?" And I added, "What if I teach you what your fathers and grandfathers forgot to teach you?"

They were amazed. "How could they forget?" they wanted to know. "They gave us everything they had."

I responded that there is always more to know, that even though they had learned many lessons from their ancestors, there is deeper truth, deeper wisdom, which can be accessed by reaching more deeply into oneself.

We sailed for more than three weeks. During these days I learned much from the sailors and they from me. I talked with everyone, and it was here that I learned that in all of humanity there is equality. While I was growing up, I had seen those who lived humbly and without education. I had been exposed to the ostracism that the lepers endured. But I had not lived among them. I had been sheltered, privileged. My mother often encouraged me to be grateful for the things we did and had. She also expected us to understand that just because we had been blessed by God and made comfortable in a way that honored our purpose, it didn't make us better than anyone else.

I could appreciate this concept, but it wasn't until my time of interaction with the sailors that taught me much about humanity, about giving and receiving, about speaking and listening, that I could fully integrate her words.

We landed at a port in the northern Indian States, then traveled by land to the mountains. Along the way, I was shocked to see such poverty, so many beggars. Their suffering moved me to tears. This brand of poverty was entirely different from what I had been accustomed to. Yes, there were the poor, the beggars, in Nazareth, and the townspeople pushed them to live on the outskirts of town. But, with an attitude of some humanity, our people always saw to it that the poor had enough food and adequate shelter.

But here in the Indian States, with a rigid caste system, under which people were suppressed, there was no help.

Our destination was an Indian Ashram. Nestled in the mountain foothills, it was a different world, peaceful and seemingly in harmony with every element. The chelas who lived there spent their time in education, prayer, meditation, chanting and singing. We spent two weeks at the Ashram studying their religion: Hinduism.

I learned of Lord Krishna, the evolved avatar known in the book, Bhagavad-Gita, who spoke to Prince Arjuna of spiritual truths when the Indian States were involved in civil war.

I also saw the students conducting amazing rituals, such as placing large needles into parts of their bodies. The remarkable aspect of this achievement was that they appeared to experience no pain, and there was absolutely no evidence of bleeding from the puncture wounds. I was committed to learn their techniques, and while there, I was able to master some of these feats. I learned how to detach from my body, so that I felt no pain. There was so much knowledge and wisdom at the heart of this Ashram. What a contrast to life in the rest of the country. Leaving this idyllic scene, we formed a caravan and traveled high into the mountains of Tibet. Uncle Joseph and I reached a place called Shambala, which contained a magnificent temple and many wise teachers that he called Masters. They told me of the great teacher, Buddha, who had lived many years before I was born and who had brought the highest and holiest consciousness to this culture.

The story I was told is that four thousand years ago, a child was born in China. As was the tradition at that time, an astrological chart was drawn for this child, so that his parents could know his purpose and assist him on his life path.

The astrologer's findings were taken to other experts who confirmed his results.

Finally, the announcement to the family was that the child was a great soul who would bring enlightenment to the world. Knowing this, the parents took special steps to educate the child.

Consequently, when he was nine years of age, his parents helped to pack his bags and sent him on his mission, that of going to the temples of Tibet for higher learning. He had a few relatives to stay with as he traveled through China in the early years of his journey.

He worked at numerous jobs and for one reason or another, his journey was delayed at times. He traveled south through India and Nepal before reaching Tibet. This journey as it unfolded was part of his education. He was very courageous, although many nights he cried for his mother. And when he grew into a teenager, he was wishing for his father's presence.

At last, he reached the northern border of the Indian States and began the long, cold trek up the mountaintop through Nepal and to the spiritual temple of Tibet.

Finally, Tseng Tsing, as he was called, now twenty-three years of age, arrived at his destination. Seeing the large temple at a distance, he ran the rest of the way with great anticipation. Observing priests standing on the front temple steps watching him, he ran up to them shouting, "I am here! I have arrived!"

As he approached, the priests at first just stood studying him. They considered this behavior arrogant and quickly handed him an empty rice bowl, requesting that he turn it upside down and place it on top of his head, then go over to a tree and sit beneath it for a period of time. "You are just a little Chela," they said. It was a shock. For he was bringing to this planet and that temple the energy of the cosmic Buddha.

At that time, there was much occurring on the planet. During the last one thousand years or so, from a spiritual point of view, Abraham was chosen by God to form the tribe of the Jews. Throughout the planet there was a shifting of consciousness. The temple was a combination of a philosophy similar to present day Buddhism, as well as Hinduism and Toaism. The temples were not for religious teachings, but rather for spiritual evolutionary teachings with a focus toward worldwide prayers and meditation. Many people would eventually come to these temples from the surrounding areas. Their reasons would be to study in the temple. Their studies would be to learn the languages so that they were able to meditate and pray and participate by traveling to reach the people in the rest of the world and interact positively with them, creating a peaceful environment.

It was here that Tseng Tsing became a great world teacher. He is known by God as the Cosmic Buddha.

They also told me of a prince in the Indian States, who came thirty-five hundred years later, a master named Siddhartha Guatama, who took up the gauntlet of Buddhism, refining and spreading it throughout all of humanity. Born of royalty and wealth, Siddhartha was taught and protected by those surrounding him. But when he finally went out into the world and encountered the poverty and suffering, he renounced his wealth and the throne and became an ascetic, which was an extreme sect of Hinduism. He went off into the wilderness to meditate and pray, to deny his flesh and reject material pleasures. But one day, while fervently praying in solitude, a group of people walked by. They were laughing joyously. And Siddhartha had an epiphany: he immediately recognized the validity of all aspects of the human condition, joy as well as solemnity, abundance as well as denial and friendship as well as solitude. He turned away from his extreme discipline. As he integrated all of his experience, he became enlightened at the age of thirty-five.

My perspective about God and life was expanding. I now knew that God was a universal presence and that His love was an unconditional commodity that encompassed all people, all societies and all beliefs.

Despite the remarkable and rich experiences I had had, I dearly missed my family, particularly my mother, and was glad to be returning home. I had purchased beautiful silks and jewelry to bring back to my mother. I felt she deserved to be adorned by these. I also brought back magnificent wood and ivory carvings, but when I presented them to my father, he said, "I do not have the time for such finery."

Knowing that he was showing the jealousy of competition, I replied, "But indeed you do, Father, especially if it brings you pleasure."

Our next voyage took us north toward Britannia, after first sailing through the Mediterranean Sea. We landed in the southernmost port. Here we traded our aromatic oils, spices and silk. After replenishing our food and water supplies, we sailed north, then traveled inland to a mystical city called Glastonbury, which was surrounded by twelve hills representing the twelve astrological constel-

lations. Uncle Joseph and I planted a tree on one of those hills.

Leaving Glastonbury, we headed up the coast to Tintagel where my Uncle Joe traded his wares for the tin that was mined in that region. We met with some mystic alchemists who were able to transmute metals into various other forms. They astounded me by turning lead into gold.

We turned inland to find the Druids and learn more about the Celtic culture. The Druids were the keepers of an ancient wisdom and were the center of religion in this culture. The Romans called the Druids "Holy Ones." They drew on invocation and prayer and had profound respect for the earth, calling upon and blessing the nature spirits. Unlike almost any other sect, they included women in their Celtic priesthood.

Here, I learned about the energy of the earth, the forces of nature and how to work with the mineral and plant world in conjunction with weather to create a perfect harmonious balance.

The Druids were deeply aligned with the structure called Stonehenge, which was a focus for their religious ceremonies. Stonehenge was constructed in Britannia many decades before the Druids inhabited the region. It was built on lay lines, electro-magnetic lines of force that surround the earth. In fact, most of the Druids' ceremonial sites were built where lay lines crossed, because these locations were considered to be "power points." These energy lines extended from their numerous sacred sites all the way into the country of Gaul.

After a brief respite at home during which I helped my father in his shop, we set sail again, this time well stocked with food and water for our longest trip yet, a southern route over a vast sea. I was now eighteen years old.

This was a particularly enjoyable trip for me, because the warmth of that route with its tropical breezes was a brand new delightful experience. The fact that this trip took six weeks was no problem for me. I wanted it never to end!

When we landed, it was on a warm, sultry shore in a land called Yucatan. Here we disembarked and met people who looked different from any I had seen before. They were short and stocky, with red tinged skin. They wore bird feathers about their heads and worshipped in large stone-blocked temples. As we continued our journey inland, we encountered many amazing sights: several great cities, in use now but built in a much earlier time. We saw signs that the earlier civilization had been much grander; this was evidenced by images of magnificent temples overgrown with thick vegetation.

These cities were beautiful and well thought out. Taking the Druid use of lay lines a step further, these people had connected their cities, which sometimes were miles apart, with very straight roadways, built on these electromagnetic lay lines. Based upon the knowledge of their ancestors who understood the energy grids, they developed communications systems along their roadways, wherein the drum's sound would carry from one city to another, and travel distances by foot were direct and of ease. The temples featured carvings and inscriptions decorating the outer walls. Pyramids, which had also been constructed in a much earlier time, were smaller than those in Egypt, and they featured flat tops upon which sacred religious ceremonies were held. They practiced sacrifice, as had our ancestors.

My Uncle Joe had actually visited this area once before; he possessed maps showing the route from the Mediterranean to these shores. This then was the Mayan culture that had been part of the old Atlantean civilization. There were not many people left here, but those who remained laid claim to an incredible, almost unbelievable history.

They told us that their ancestors had come to this region from a grand, obviously advanced world to the east, called Atlantis. Because of Atlantean disobedience to God and a misuse of their powerful weapons, there was a great flood, and their enormous land mass sank. While there were few survivors, so total was the devastation, some did manage to escape to the highest mountains.

Now, these descendants were determined to please God, in order to keep themselves safe from His wrath. In so doing they ignored the Atlantean technology of the past and lived as best they knew how in harmony with the earth. And for full measure, they often made human sacrifices in solemn and lavish ceremonial rites, in an attempt to prevent a disaster like the sinking of the continent of

Atlantis from occurring again.

They told us that many of their ancestors had not remained there in the tropics but had migrated north into cooler climates, never to be seen or heard from again.

We learned from the priests that certain herbs were valuable not only for healing but for inducing vision, or second-sight.

And they learned from Uncle Joseph and me the truth about the ritual of sacrifice. We explained that in the culture of that early time, through superstition and confusion over the concept of paganism, Abraham and his tribe felt that animal sacrifice was the way to appease angry gods. By engaging in this practice, they were in a sense proving themselves worthy in the eyes of the gods.

Then my uncle and I shared with them the story of Abraham, father of the Jewish tribe. This story portrayed a kind of test, the purpose of which was to break people free of the barbaric custom of sacrifice. It also would reveal that if a person trusted God completely and implicitly he would be spared all sacrifice.

And so, God spoke to Abraham, saying, "Do you love me enough that you would sacrifice anything, even your own son?" Abraham interpreted these words as an order to sacrifice his son, Eskhak (Isaac). Anguished but determined to show God that He was supreme, Abraham led Isaac to the mountaintop. As Abraham raised his hand with a knife enclosed in it, he heard the voice of an angel.

The Angel said, "No, Abraham, this is not the Father's will nor His directive. He would be neither pleased nor honored by your superstitions."

While Abraham was profoundly relieved, he still held to some misinterpretation. Instead of sacrificing his son, Isaac, he substituted one of his best lambs and sacrificed it in order to honor and praise God. Some superstitions die hard, as they say.

Uncle Joe and I reiterated that it is not God's will to sacrifice anything and that neither the Mayans nor anyone else need strive to please or appease God for the acts of their ancestors.

We were also able to enlighten them on how profound was the sinking of Atlantis, that that event affected the entire world. Uncle Joseph explained how the pages of "our own holy book," the Torah, described the intense flooding in the far reaches of the world, and had it not been for Noah, the tribe would have been lost. But he was able to save his sons and other family members. He also saved many of the regional animals that might have been forever lost. Noah built an ark and saw to it that his family was aboard, then loaded up the animals, two by two. Indeed, the tribe survived and so did many species. Of the animals Noah was unable to take onto the ark, many of them were able to escape to higher ground in the mountains.

We traded our fine silks and metal goods, knives and tools and such, for their precious gems, gold and silver.

My next trip, landing me closer to home, was to a country just north of our home on the Mediterranean Sea, in Asia Minor. There we disembarked at a seaport called Ephesus, which was a magical place, full of trickery and bustling with activity and trade. We walked up the neat cobblestone streets, through the center of the city. My uncle had business in Ephesus, and here I received additional education, learning how to negotiate in matters of commerce with the city's merchants.

I went to the library and read enlightening histories of the region. Most particularly, I read about the workings of Rome, which controlled much of the world.

I met once again with someone who had been influential in my early life in a profound way. One of the three wise man who had come to welcome me at my birth in Bethlehem lived here. Quite old now, he nonetheless retained all of his faculties, and I was able to hear first-hand of his experiences in those long ago days. He was eager to know about where my life had led me. I was deeply touched to see him, and he seemed moved by our reunion.

Later we climbed the nearby mountains and found a peaceful, soul-rejuvenating garden setting, amidst many flowers and varieties of herbs. A wonderful place for retreat when needing to nurture body, mind and spirit. We visited a location where aromatic oils were being produced from plants. Uncle Joseph traded for some of them.

After so many years of stimulating, strengthening life experiences, I was ready for a different kind of challenge near my home. I decided to go on a solitary retreat and endure a cleansing fast, dur-

ing which I would pray and purify myself in order to best integrate all that had happened to me. I hiked up the mountain peaks and remained for a period of forty days and forty nights, taking into my body only what I could find in the wild. I discovered a beehive and collected its honey; I sucked the nectar from the essence of flowers and ate a few leaves from the shrubs. I drank much water. The process of purification was intense and involved my entire being.

My fast contributed to a foggy, almost muddled state, and my inner devils came forth to tempt me. This energy was simply the hidden aspect of my ego-driven personality. Some might say my "dark" side was emerging for me to view. I was fascinated with these "devils" for a time and consciously played with them. Since I had mastered many initiations, I considered myself somewhat invincible, but this attitude — some might call it arrogance — provided a perfect framework for a greater force to come forward. This force was called Lucifer, a fallen angel of God. Lucifer approached me and first tempted me with food. Since I had been fasting and was hungry, he dared me to turn stones into bread. But I easily met this challenge and would not be tempted. Satan then tried to tempt me with a more difficult challenge by trying to convince me that I was somehow better and more divine than other people, indestructible even. So when he goaded me to throw myself off a precipice to test this invincibility, I was tempted, because I strongly felt that I would not be injured. Another aspect of me actually hoped that my life would end because of the trials that were ahead of me. But I realized just in time the truth of these temptations.

The episode at the edge of the precipice taught me that frivolous activity does not serve and God is not to be tested.

Why I allowed myself to be tempted was that I thought I could stop at will and bring these dark deeds into the Light. But I was deluding myself, because everything is already in the Light. There was no need for me to allow their expression. All I needed to do was to say, "Stop! There is no room for this."

That is a lesson for everyone. When we are thrown about by "what if's, can't be's, how come's, if only's, why not's, it's not fair," and "not enough," all we need do is say "stop."

Whatever is your devil, just say, "Stop! There's no room for this." And then go on to the thought of your divinity. "Get behind me Satan. I AM that I AM."

I said "stop" to the mind, my own mind that was trying to control me. These devils are not known outside ourselves. They are our own thoughts manifesting.

> And now, "May the God I AM and the God
> you are to be one and be blessed in all things
> formed and unformed."

Now twenty-seven, I received word that my father was ill. I headed home to care for him, but I also very much missed all my family members, particularly my dear mother. Shortly after arriving home my father died. His death hit the whole family hard, devastating my mother and leaving my youngest brother and sister, particularly, bewildered and heartbroken. After a period of adjustment, though still grieving the passing of my father, I embarked on what I decided would be my last journey with Uncle Joseph. I needed to turn my attention home; my mother needed me more than ever now.

We headed for a place not so far from home: Egypt. This was my third trip there and it was in a way a culmination of all that had gone before. It was to mark the end of my mentorship with my beloved uncle. I was to go through an advanced initiation .

We sailed up the Nile to the pyramids. First, I learned about Isis and Osirus, Egyptian gods, who had had a son who was sacrificed, because the priests feared his enlightened ways.

Then I was led to a place of initiation, at the site of the great Sphinx, a statue with the face of a man, body of a lion.

The sphinx had been built in the year of Ei-Aw, about six thousand years ago. When I first gazed at this magnificent structure, I was aware that through the years of wear and tear, the pharaohs, one by one, had undertaken its reconstruction to keep it well preserved. I could see that just recently it had gone through some exterior changes, with straw and mortar used to make repairs.

The sphinx represented a composite of various aspects of godly embodiment. On the outer plane, or surface, was a representa-

tion of human divinity. Its inner planes represented direct connection with God and were made up of a matrix of tunnels and inner chambers, where initiations were held. The underground tunnels were also connected to religious temples in the area. A main underground link was to the Great Pyramid.

I was taken to two different chambers. They were located under the sphinx's left paw and were reached by a stairway leading down to them. The first was an instruction chamber: it contained records of the history of the world. On its walls of stone were symbols. By touching the symbols a vibration flowed through me, and the most astonishing images appeared all around me. They were of pictures revealing the creation of the earth and the souls who inhabited it, and they all moved, as if these events were taking place right before me. What an amazing history lesson!

In the second chamber, the initiation chamber, I was placed into a sarcophagus, the lid then closed and sealed. I was to be left there without light or sound for three days and three nights. I was in complete darkness and silence, an environment of total sensory deprivation.

I was given only a little water to sustain me. For the first twenty hours, I was terrified. But soon my inner voice began to speak to me, and I began to listen. The I AM presence dominated and I achieved a state of calm and peace. That inner voice clearly became my guide. I began to astro-travel beyond my physical body. Before the end of the third day, I had dematerialized my body and moved through the sarcophagus to rematerialize on the outside of it. The priests directing my initiation were stunned by this feat. It was far beyond their experience or expectation. They had never seen an initiate master this process, even though the possibility had been taught.

I was next moved through the underground tunnels to a second initiation in the ten thousand-year-old Great Pyramid. I was taken to the King's Chamber in the center of the pyramid. Whereas the sphinx represented man's direct connection with God, the Great Pyramid was a place to focus a soul's link with universal forces. Here you could feel the power of universal energy as it reached like a beacon through the universe to other dimensions and planetary systems.

My initiations at this locale were meaningful because they returned attention to a place where the spiritual significance of these magnificent structures had long been forgotten by everyone, even the later Pharaohs.

My journeys had both overwhelmed and challenged me. Through them I had not only integrated my earlier Essene teachings but had expanded upon them. I could see beyond the teachings of the Hindu and Buddhist ways, past the Druid, Mayan and Egyptian knowledge, even beyond my own Judaism. I could see how all of these spiritual teachings were connected and that there are many, many ways to surrender to God's will.

The end of my travels marked a new phase in my life and was symbolized in a dynamic way when I joined again my beloved cousin, John, at the river Jordan.

John was a channel for divine wisdom, divine energy, and he had a divine purpose. He was to call for the coming of a new consciousness and give people an opportunity to be washed free of their past false beliefs. His vision was simple and pure. By immersing the body into water one could become symbolically cleansed of all it held that is separate from God.

John's teachings were similar to mine but much more limited because he had not yet understood or fully integrated God's message. Still, he gave what he had to give, and for him it was enough.

I was now twenty-nine years of age. John instantly recognized the important implications of my return and knew that a second baptism to highlight my advanced growth was in order. At the time of this momentous event, John, appreciating my highly developed spiritual state, humbly said to me, "I am not worthy in this role; I am not worthy to tie your sandals."

I reassured him that I would be honored by his participation, and John submerged me into the water at the site of the Point of Dedication, where the Jews had crossed over into Israel in their flight from Egypt. This was the place where the banks were wider, the water shallow, and the Jews were able to get to Israel.

At the moment John pressed his hands to my shoulders I had a vision that this one baptizing me was the reincarnation of the prophet Elijah, who had foretold my coming.

And then, the Holy Spirit entered my being, imprinted itself upon me, and delivered to me enlightenment. A light was seen shining forth from me. And I felt a powerful vibration from God. My becoming the Christed One was actually an ongoing process throughout my lifetime. However, the two baptisms marked particular peaks of growth and, further, acted as catalysts to accelerate still more spiritual expansion. I was now ready to begin my ministry with unlimited support and guidance from God.

And for John ... he did not shy away from acknowledging the presence of the Christ energy that dwelled within me, and for that my Father was grateful, and John also became baptized that day in a new way. Because he was willing to dunk me, God embraced him and showed him everything he needed to know so that his life was complete.

John and I spoke of the baptisms that would come and of the people who would need them, in order to symbolically and ceremoniously cleanse body, mind, and spirit in preparation for a new awakening. Ultimately, the Essene teachings added the ceremony of baptism to the cleansing rituals and made them both sacred.

I would like to expand on the subject of baptism with you disciples for a moment. Baptism really need not always be done by a priest or by anyone else holding a certain faith, except that the ritual affords a person to trust and completely surrender, because they feel cared for and nurtured and supported.

I did choose to baptize each one of you individually, some with water, others oil or breath. But, understand this: baptism is not necessary. Some now see baptism as a necessary ritual in order to find their way into heaven. But this is not so; these are erroneous beliefs.

My life had been private up to now, but an event that occurred shortly after my baptism would make it very public. Some of you witnessed this occasion because you — Andrew, Peter, James and John — were there.

I went to a wedding in Cana with my mother and my brothers and sisters. During the wedding celebration, the host turned to my mother and said, "Mary, we're out of wine. What shall we do?"

As a good Jewish mother would do, she came to me and said, "Son, they are out of wine," implying that I should do something about it.

And when I said to her, "But Mother, it's not yet my time," she gave a look and smiled, then turned to the host and said, "Do whatever Jeshua tells you to do," as if my words meant nothing.

I finally agreed and called for the wine vessels to be filled with water. "Bring them to me," I said. And then in a feat, which would astound all present, the clear water became deep red and the rich liquid tasted of the luscious grape.

Word spread about the "miracle." And the story was embellished even beyond the facts, as if the deed were not in itself enough; it was quite fantastic, really.

That by my word ordinary water was turned into the most perfect wine is not what was important. What was important was that the word was spreading about what this man, I, the Christed One, would mean for the people.

At the time, people didn't know what to make of it. My closest friends and even you four disciples didn't know what to make of it. People who were beginning to hear the rumors that maybe a magician was responsible. They weren't thinking "prophet" because they were not in the market for a prophet. They believed they already had one, who was doing quite nicely, out in the wilderness. That, of course, was my cousin John the Baptist.

As I began my public journey, I was reluctant to move forward. Some might say that this reluctance was divine wisdom, a knowledge that it wasn't time. Then, why did I do it? Certainly, it was not that I was being a "good son" to please Mother. I recognized that she was the vehicle that the Father in Heaven had sent to me to open this gift. My hesitancy came from my own human ego, for I knew that the moment I began a feat such as this, my life would be open to all and my world no longer my own. I would have to begin fulfilling the prophecies.

So, what did I do about this resistance?

I took my unwillingness into hand, looked at it, aligned it, and then I moved forward, turning the water into wine. And this is a les-

son for many, because so often we feel that the righteousness of the true path is so hard that we procrastinate and put off, asking God, "Why can't it be easier? I don't want to do it just now. I do not want to!" And then we blame God.

We must realize that if we refuse any circumstance that comes to us, it unfolds before us anyway at another time, in another eventuality. And in that way it only becomes more difficult: we add an extra burden of personal shame because we denied the experience in the first place. The lesson is that it is all right to feel resistance from the ego. But know that it must be surrendered to the Divine Will.

In the Holy Book many prophets have spoken: "Behold, a virgin will conceive and give birth to a Son and they shall call His name Immanuel, which is interpreted as our God is with us." The prophet Jeremiah said, "And a voice was heard in Ramah weeping and wailing exceedingly: it was Rachel weeping for her sons, and she would not be comforted because they could not be brought back." And other prophets have said, "Even you, Bethlehem of Judah[8]*, you are not insignificant in the eyes of the Kings of Judah, for from you shall come out a king, who will shepherd my people Israel. He shall be called a Nazarene."*

Isaiah said, "O land of Zebulun, O land of Napthali, the way to the sea, across the Jordan, Galilee of the Gentiles! The people who dwelt in darkness saw a great light upon those who dwelt in the country, and in the midst of the shadows of death, light shone."

And Zechariah prophesied: "A man of peace will be coming on a donkey through Jerusalem's gate."

The Essenes wrote of the coming of the "teacher of righteousness."

I am now fully aware that I AM here on Earth at this time to fulfill the prophecies of the Holy Book: that a server of God coming from the family line of David is to be the Messiah, that He shall be called a Nazarene, and that this Messiah will rebuild a Kingdom in the name of God. The prophecy holds that this Messiah will survive the tormented anger of the people.

---

8 The region of Judah was later named Judea during the Roman occupation.

Second Spiritual Law

Honor all that is manifest, for all that is manifest is born from the divine unmanifested.

Explanation:

The divine unmanifested is that which is the sea of love and consciousness from which all form comes. In your life on earth, form begets form. Out of your body comes a body that you are birthing. All things are born in thought and in the divine realm of the God/Goddess.

CHAPTER 3

On The Road

Now twenty-nine, Jeshua seemed almost super-human, powerful in His knowledge, abilities, and physical strength. A magnetic energy seemed to attract us disciples to the charismatic Jeshua. We all wanted to be in His presence constantly. Perhaps we were drawn by the sheer power of His balanced demeanor. Some men looked truly old at thirty, but Jeshua had a youthful quality, which He attributed to physical and mental exercise, diet, and prayer.

Daily, He performed His yoga and breathing exercises and balanced His diet with a variety of foods. He was in complete charge of his thoughts, allowing neither negativity nor judgment to invade them; therefore, He was always in mental and emotional alignment and in unity with all things in nature. He was not affected by weather excesses. His skin was particularly supple and smooth, never bothered by our dry heat.

Those of us who had made our commitment to Jeshua and to His ideals followed along with His dietary and exercise regimen; we were convinced of the benefits, and He encouraged our willingness to act in accordance with His routine. Jeshua indicated He was ready to take on the world. Regarding our upcoming travels, He said to us, "Be thou excited and surprised about everything that you see and know that you can do these things I have done as well."

I had missed that first wedding celebration and the miracle of Jeshua turning water into wine; however, there were many other weddings, many other fun occasions that came along where we could all celebrate together.

Jeshua had experienced similar circumstances as had I regarding friendships. While some of His friends didn't have a clue as to what His purpose was, they nonetheless knew that He spoke good words, had good intention and a good heart. And they felt drawn to something beyond His humanness, even though they weren't clear about what it was. Others of His friends, hearing about His miracles and hearing His words, turned their backs and chose not to be friends any longer.

For some of those who chose to go along with Jeshua, it was the miracles that attracted them. They would joyfully anticipate what His next trick would be.

Peter always fell into that category. Peter would ask, "Mariah, Mariah (Lord, Lord), what else can we do?" He would ask for a particular miracle in one breath and in the next deny that such a miracle was even possible.

One day at dusk, Peter's confusion displayed itself at suppertime. In a frenzy, he pointed to the only two fish visible for the evening meal and said excitedly to Jeshua, "We only have two fish and I certainly don't have time to go out and get more."

To which Jeshua smiled and said, "It is not necessary Peter. We will manifest them." And we did.

The political environment was creating tension everywhere. Many people were speaking out. John the Baptist was one of the most well known and most listened to. He had quite a different focus on the prophecy: he felt that the most direct route to God was through cleansing the body with water or oil. Through that, he thought, the soul might be cleansed.

Originally, some saw Jeshua as just an up and coming prophet, one whom they could include in their usual discussions of religion and politics. Others felt the truth of His words.

The people were praying eagerly for the appearance of a messiah and prophet to tell them when and how they would be delivered from their Roman oppressors. The buzz was everywhere. Since most people didn't have the benefit of books, which were rare and hard to come by, their exchanges took place by word of mouth. At the wells the women talked, and for the men, their debates took place in their taverns and businesses. The topic was dominant in the hearts and minds of everyone. It was a rare day when a family did not speak of these things. However, sometimes they were able simply to enjoy life with family and friends. Weddings and bar mitzvahs were great escapes, joyful celebrations, because here they could forget political-religious issues for a while.

Jeshua pointed out that while political and religious issues seem very important, in many ways they are superficial at best. He counseled us that real human spiritual growth takes place in heartfelt, joyful communion with family members and friends. "That is what life is truly about," He would say.

When we set out on our travels, some people wondered what Jeshua could speak of that would be different and still in line with what they wanted to hear? They also wondered if we were just a typical, run-of-the-mill band of prophets.

Jeshua did not always give the people exactly what they thought they wanted to hear, but He delivered His message with certainty, even though indirectly, through parables and stories. Often before the crowds gathered, our group would talk among ourselves. We considered what life would be like if everyone just lived according to God's Law. What if people didn't try to make God's Law something other than what it was meant to be in order to satisfy our priests and Roman rulers? we wondered.

Moses' laws were simple. What happened to these laws was that they became so full of dos and don'ts and deeds and misdeeds that it became difficult to remember all of them, even though it was expected of a good Jew.

Jeshua cut through the complexity, counseling that God asks only two things: first, to know that everyone holds the image of the heavenly Father within them; second, to love God with all of one's heart and all of humanity as oneself.

When the crowd gathered, Jeshua would speak thusly to them, and the crowd would counter, "Tell us when and tell us how we may throw off the chains of the Romans."

Jeshua would respond, "I am not here as a zealot. I am not here for the overthrow of the government. I am here for the living God. I am here to bring you to your kingdom."

But, you see, when he used the word "kingdom," the people thought He spoke of the kingdom of Judea.

Jeshua told these people that there was another kingdom, one more powerful than they could imagine: a kingdom in God's heaven of many mansions. But He added that right here, right now they could have heaven on earth.

The general populace was perplexed by our countenance. We certainly didn't appear to be like the typically pious prophets that they were used to; rather, we seemed like a bunch of free-spirited renegades. These people expected that if we were speaking as rabbis and prophets we should behave accordingly.

For the religious zealots it was another story. They felt that Jeshua's message that the "kingdom of heaven is right here on earth," gave them license to be free from all the Laws and do exactly as they wished at all times. Therefore, we had bands of enthusiastic zealots and rabble-rousers tagging along, hoping to use Jeshua's powers for their own purposes.

Judas fell into this latter category. He became swayed and wanted to use this understanding for his personal agenda and imagined gains. He would say to Jeshua, "Yes, look at all these people. If we throw ourselves in with these rebels and use your influence and power, just imagine what we could accomplish. We would be like an army and could overthrow Rome. Jeshua, you could deliver us from the oppressors."

Then Jeshua would say, "No Judas, I will not deliver you from the oppressors by means of the sword. Instead, I will deliver you from the oppressors through the love from your heart. Then you may free yourself as God freed you."

My wishes concerning my home in Capernaum came true. I did go back, though not to live there in the same way that I once had. We established a home base in my empty old house, and we returned there as often as we could to rest and plan further strategies. But we were away much. Our travels took us to the regions of Crete, Syria (Aram), Ammon, Philistia, as well as the kingdoms of Israel and Judea. When the sun was setting in a small town and our little group of committed men completed a day of joyful teaching and healing, we would settle in for the evening, often at the home of one of our followers.

It would be appropriate to mention that as our journeying continued, we attracted a particular following among women, who were especially receptive to our Master's teachings. As they joined us, they provided welcome companionship and support.

We were traveling so much now that when we had a stopover lasting two or three days, it was a real treat. But at all times, Jeshua was in charge and directing our schedules.

Jeshua would arise just before dawn and engage in prayer and meditation, after which He would cleanse His body and prepare for the day. Jeshua often fasted for several days at a time. If, when He arose, it was a day that He was breaking His fast, He would often have berries and gruel. We would grind khetey (wheat) and other grains into a cereal and He would add a bit of honey. Sometimes He would have a mild tea and yogurt, along with a small piece of bread.

After that, He would, with great gusto and much humor, see to it that everyone who would join Him that day was awakened and ready to go. He would go from room to room and clang loudly with a metal pot or other cooking utensil and say, "Arise and be in the Light of God today. Arise."

There were those who would grumble and roll over hoping to get a few more winks of sleep, while others would reluctantly, even angrily, get up. And some would simply respond with thank you. After all, He was much more pleasant than the rooster.

We started the day with a chanted prayer to God. It was a vocal acknowledgement that said, "Thank you, Lord, for this day and know that you will bless us today wherever we go, whatever we will do and with what-so-ever we encounter."

We might continue our day by just taking a walk to no place in particular and seeing where we might end up. At lunchtime we would sometimes have figs, some dry bread, a date cake, and some soup.

When Jeshua was present with us and with the crowds that gathered, He was very animated. He spoke His wisdom with His whole being, occasionally gesturing passionately and making a stern face, pretending to be serious. And if we were to see Him do that, everyone knew that Jeshua was teasing in order to lighten us up. When people surrounding Him got very serious, Jeshua would show a frown, which became more and more exaggerated, and He would pretend to be very stern, scolding them. Once He had brought them to the ramtha (height) of drama, Jeshua would break out in laughter and say, "Do not stay in these graves you mithamkin (dig so deeply). Be like the birds and fly. Put yourself up in the realm of heaven." And His feigned seriousness became instantly light-hearted.

If Jeshua were engaged in telling a parable, He sometimes would tease His audience by not finishing the story. He would build to an exciting crescendo, then pause, smile, and wink. That wink was a signal to everyone that they were on their own to figure out the ending and find the wisdom within the tale.

Jeshua instructed people about how to pray, teaching them correct posture, how to align their spine to open their whole being. He taught them how opening their hands was the way to receive direct energy from God and how closing them reverently was the way to give a message to God, in prayer. After we taught these techniques, it was time for singing and then our evening supper.

Dinner was usually prepared for us by the family with whom we were staying. We would wash ourselves, then Jeshua would ask the women who were preparing the food not to fuss over it but to come join us in singing songs. And after our songfest, we would eat our food, prayerfully, yet gleefully.

After finishing our evening meal, we all congregated in the main room of the house. Jeshua would offer a prayer of thanks to God for our many blessings. We would ask Him to share His wisdom with us. And He would sometimes talk for hours, words of elegant wisdom flowing from His lips.

Other evenings we would share experiences we had had during the day. Many times I saw Jeshua appear distracted: He would occasionally scratch His head and stroke His beard as if to make a note to Himself to remember something.

When we finished our final evening prayers, we all separated and headed to our beds. Jeshua would often take one of us who needed His private counseling aside for an intimate sharing.

We all considered ourselves especially blessed when we were staying at the home of family or friends, because we were pampered with precious comforts of warmth and service that were not available to us on the road. While traveling we indeed lived the simple life with no luxuries. When nightfall came, we had to seek shelter in nature. And at times, it was cold. When we lay down at night to sleep, we would replace our sandals with lambs' wool in order to keep our feet warm, and we would snuggle up close to the fire. On rare occasions in winter, when we woke, a dusting of snow on the nearby hills would surround us.

One day when there had been a fresh snowfall on the mountain, Jeshua said, "I'll race you to the top." We all hustled up to the snow-covered ground and Jeshua took off his sandals in order that His toes could explore the clean white snow. This tickled us all and just as I was deciding whether or not I was going to brave the cold, powdery stuff and remove my sandals as well, I saw Jeshua bend down and make a ball out of the snow and toss it at Peter, hitting him on the back of his head. Peter quickly turned around and glared at us. Jeshua didn't utter a word, but simply pointed at me. Surprised, I shrugged my shoulders, but before I knew it, Peter hurled a ball of snow right at me. Then, the whole group, laughing boisterously, began peppering each other with snow. James got in a good shot at Peter, who was by now taking most of the brunt of it. Peter's temper flared and he grabbed James and pulled him down in the snow and raised his fist threatening to sock him. In the nick of time, Jeshua bent down to restrain Peter, before the blow found its mark on James' face. He admonished Peter and told him to keep a watch over his aggressive nature. In a way, the fun was over; we were sobered by this turn of events. As the mood shifted, Jeshua reflected on the symbolism of snow, saying, "The snowing is a reminder of God's gift of clearing and cleansing; it is a reminder of our purity."

During most of our days, we would enter towns and speak to all who gathered to hear us. After Jeshua's teaching, we would heal the sick people who had been waiting for us. As our reputation spread about the countryside, the crowds grew.

These travels would be interrupted by breaks during which time we might go home for the holidays and visit family. Occasionally our beloved families came to join us wherever we were in order to celebrate Sabbath dinners. Our women would take good care of us. Jeshua's family, in particular, often came.

Sometimes, our families accompanied us in our travels, but it wasn't always very convenient, and on some of the longer journeys, we would have to leave them behind.

Even though we dearly loved our family members, at times we spoke about them as if they were a burden, and it greatly amused Jeshua.

But the women and children were never neglected. They visited when it was possible and we brought them along when possible. They were given much teaching and much love.

The scene at the religious temples was becoming more and more difficult, to the point of complete disarray, much to Jeshua's chagrin and consternation. Worshippers arrived with their Roman coins, Caesar money, we called it, and needed to exchange them for Hebrew coins, because a good Jew could give alms only with his "God money." This exchange caused a great commotion on the temple steps, with moneychangers haggling with templegoers.

To further add to the confusion, there was always noisy bartering going on over the doves. Doves were a much-coveted commodity, offered for sale to parishioners for sacrifice to God. There was much competition for the best doves because it was thought that whoever bought the most and the best got the most direct route through heaven's front door and the best seat beside God.

These activities to Jeshua were foolish, a thorn in His side. The concept that anybody could buy a way into heaven by purchasing doves was ludicrous. Jeshua saw the temple as a sacred place, one that should be kept quiet and holy for communion with God, not disturbed by these goings on.

While we did not always go to the temple, we always observed the Sabbath. Except for the larger cities, such as Jerusalem, there were no large temples, thus no large gatherings of worshippers for Pesach (Passover). The people would worship in small synagogues or in private homes.

Frequently, when we were in the region we went to one of the disciple's homes to celebrate the Sabbath. Often we were at Peter's. But many times we would have our Sabbath prayers and dinner outside under the trees by the roadside. We would light a lamp and give thanks to God.

Once, the question came up about whether it is necessary to worship under the roof of a temple or other holy place. "Of course not," said Jeshua. "You may worship wherever you are."

Then He pointed out to us that many times people take the Sabbath too lightly and casually, thinking that if they are away and unable to attend services where they are accustomed to worshipping, they could simply forget about honoring God. He told us that always one must find a way to honor and celebrate the Sabbath, that while every day is a holy day, the seventh is set aside for a very special reverence: it should be used not for working but for giving thanks, for appreciating God and observing the sacredness of life.

That some choose to build huge temples to honor God, Jeshua said, was anathema to God's law. "People think that they're showing the Father that they are good and sincere in their faith when they construct these monoliths, but God truly doesn't care about these things." We conducted our services according to God's commandments, not the priests' rules.

My connection with my brother, Peter, was strong and intense. I was very fond of him. He complained frequently about his marital woes, and I had much compassion for him. When his wife berated Peter for being away so much, he would say to her, "Woman, this is the work of the Lord." And she would threaten to hit him over the head with a kitchen pot. While she never did such a thing, she was shrewish, and I commiserated with him.

Peter was an interesting duality: both jokester and tyrant. He had a quick temper. Since I loved Peter so much and always had compassion for people in trouble, particularly one of my close brothers, I often made excuses for his emotional outbursts. I would defend him to Jeshua by saying, "Jeshua, you don't understand! You just don't understand Peter sometimes."

Jeshua was amused, indeed, and would try to keep a straight face during my passionate defense.

I thought Jeshua did not understand Peter because when he (Peter) showed his temper, Jeshua would reprimand him. Such thoughts were clearly presumptuous of me, because Jeshua had a perfect understanding of the human dynamics. He knew that all of our "acting out" was magical and necessary for our deep life experiences.

When Peter and I were having an argument, we would plead with Jeshua, "Lord, Lord, help us here."

Jeshua would sometimes say, "Resolve this yourselves. Be not like children but be like the teachers of Light you are."

And I would say, "But I cannot because Peter is being bullheaded, and we cannot agree when he is in this state."

Then Jeshua would say, "Agreement must come from your heart, not from your mind. Agree that you love one another, shake hands with each other, and therein is your harmony."

So issues were resolved not by trying to create the one and perfect way that things are supposed to be said or done, but by letting go of all the superficial discussion and coming back to the heart.

Jeshua explained that our actions are simply roles we have chosen to play. When we understand this concept, it is easier to let go of the drama, internalize the wisdom gained from our experiences and learn to love.

It might be appropriate to say here that part of Peter's and my interaction had to do with getting Jeshua to notice us. We were all like a bunch of children vying for a father's attention. Jeshua exuded such charisma and evoked such respect that we all clamored to be close to Him. But He held no favorites; He loved all of us equally, no one person more than another. He recognized that each of us had our individual, unique gifts, and He would call upon the one who could best serve.

While traveling I occasionally broke a strap on my sandals and would call upon Peter to mend it since he was handy at these things. After all, he was the one who knew how to repair fishing nets.

Sometimes we wore out our sandals completely. I remember an incident about some sandals that were given to us by Jeshua's uncle, Joseph of Arimathea. Joseph had brought us sandals after returning from one of his great journeys. Brand new sandals from a fine Spanish tannery. What a great gift! The leather was soft and supple; the sandals rolled about our feet and ankles with great ease. Our feet felt that we were walking on clouds.

I remember saying to Joseph, "Thank you, my brother, for this gift. However, these sandals feel a bit tight on my feet. Do you have another size?" Everyone laughed.

Joseph responded, somewhat annoyed, "The shoes fit, Mattai. The more you wear these the more they will form to your feet. Do not ask for what you do not need."

How did Joseph know that they fit? How did he know what my foot size was? He just did. Jeshua's uncle intuitively knew many things. No wonder that Jeshua respected him for the great teacher that he was. No wonder Jeshua's parents placed their son in these expert hands.

My feet were usually slightly swollen from being on them and walking for days. And I was often aware of a painful pebble in my sandals that refused to be dislodged. This pebble began to symbolize my commitment to my Master. Despite the adversities, I continued to walk on with Jeshua. Later I understood that the pebble could indeed be dislodged; I did not have to suffer pain, of any kind.

When we were away from our families, at times it was obvious that other women were eager to fill the gap, so to speak, and we were challenged by the temptations of adultery. Our discussions inevitably led us to consider the subject of "vows," the meaning of vows and how they are used and misused.

We noted the many religious ceremonies that are held, which mark specific events in life, such as the baptismal ceremony after one's birth, the marriage ceremony and the memorial ceremonies, which mark a passing from the earth plane. We knew the significance of these ceremonies, yet we questioned the vows taken during these important times.

We were perplexed because we could see that the time-honored tradition of keeping to these vows often didn't work. Certainly, there were marriage vows that were not kept and religious vows that were not met. I myself had vowed to collect money for Rome, but I had broken that vow when my life veered into a fabulous new direction.

What we came to understand was that the ceremonial tradition is an important one. However, the vows taken within that ceremony had the potential to be problematic. For example, the vow that a parent makes for an infant to follow certain rules and religious traditions might be inhibiting for that person's future growth. The marriage vow to "love, honor and obey till death do us part" leaves no option for other life experiences that might be necessary. And what about the memorial service, where a person might vow to avenge a death of a loved one for a perceived wrong? The vow might lock that person into getting even when forgiveness may instead be appropriate. The inherent problem concerning a vow is that one might spend a lifetime either trying to get out of the vow or trying to fulfill it.

Jeshua led us to understand that a commitment to a vow, unless one is certain that the vow is a life path, is not wise. A vow can become a confining trap, boxing a person in to a life that may be ready for change. A marriage, for example, might be nearing its completion stage, with each partner needing to experience life in new, different ways. The vow, then, that was taken becomes the stumbling block to new growth.

As for myself, I realized that while I was rewriting my career, I was indeed honoring my oath to myself, which was one of ethics.

Jeshua told us that the only oath to be honored was the promise of commitment to entertain life with an open mind and heart.

In what might have seemed a rather strange turn, a single woman arrived to accompany us. Her presence was to become so constant that we would come to think of her as one of us. She was a woman with a past, a woman who had been condemned and ostracized for what was considered her evil ways. But she would rise above her past to become elevated as one of Jeshua's most esteemed students. She would secure a place in the hearts and minds of all as a truly enlightened being. Her name was Mary of Magdala.

Mary Magdalene, as we called her, had been condemned by her community of Magdala as a harlot and was to be stoned. Jeshua rescued her from that circumstance and took her on as a student.

Mary Magdalene was very beautiful, slender, and curvaceous with fine features. At almost eight-and-a-half hands, she was taller than most women in our society, who averaged seven-and-a-half hands. Mary Magdalene was gifted with a big heart and had the capacity to love intensely. She felt that loving everyone, loving deeply and loving sexually should not be a sin. Mary's gift of love was truly heart-centered, forming her true strength, and she wished that everyone could give and receive love from their hearts.

Mary Magdalene had an innate wisdom and knowledge that she was willing to speak out about, which was uncommon in a day when women were trained not to give voice to their thoughts. She wasn't the least bit shy about giving an opinion whenever the opportunity arose, and she made sure the opportunity came frequently.

Mary Magdalene was a complex woman with many different talents. She stood apart from other women. She was independent and powerful, yet soft. She had a peasant-like rough quality, yet she radiated love and compassion. She excelled in home making and was an excellent cook. She possessed all of the feminine characteristics that are so desirable from a man's point of view. All in all, I must say that it was hard for any man to say no to that woman, no matter what she asked. I myself was attracted to her.

Mary Magdalene always was a strong presence within her family. She had not only conquered the household business with ease, but she also had obtained a religious education and thus was well qualified to guide her family members with their spiritual needs.

After Mary Magdalene's father died, the family found itself in deep financial straits. It became up to Mary to support the family. And she saw a way to do it. With the tremendous love she possessed within her heart that she wanted to express, and to solve her family's financial problems, she decided that to become a prostitute would take care of both issues.

After Jeshua adopted her, taking Mary in hand, He gave her a clearer understanding about how to love a man without lying down with him. Her challenge was to realize that her entire being, not just her body but her mind and spirit as well, could be brought into alignment. In time, she was able to be more discerning. And she soon understood that her role was greater than what she had originally thought.

Mary was a catalyst for healing everywhere. The challenge for many women was how to come into balance and recognize their true roles, as Goddesses, nurturers and receptors of truth and in all ways equal to men. As Mary Magdalene's feminine energy was powerful, she was able to raise the consciousness of many men by her unconditionally loving nature.

While traveling with us, Mary Magdalene frequently washed Jeshua's feet with oils and dried them with her hair. She used rose oil and sandalwood and mixed them with olive oil until they formed a cleansing and healing aromatic blend. However, her act of humility and love often turned into conflict.

Judas, among other disciples, believed that the foot-washing ritual was a waste of money, for the oils were costly. He felt that the money used to purchase the oils could be better spent on other things. In addition, this ritual was usually reserved for royalty or someone of high political position. Jeshua, of course, downplayed his royal status, because His emphasis always was on the equality of all people.

Therefore, we were presented with a bizarre situation in which both our emotions and our ideas about prosperity consciousness were being challenged. We decided that we must allow our egos to step aside and to openly accept an act of humility and in so doing become humble ourselves.

So, too, we should accept the generosity given to us and recognize that we can also give to others. For as we give, we receive. This is God's law. Our abundance is without limits.

During our evening get-togethers, when it was Mary's turn to speak, she would share her deep insights, but occasionally she had a special gift for us. She would become quiet, close her eyes, and take deep breaths. Then after a few minutes, she would begin to speak in a deep voice! She would impart the wisdom of a spirit who was the Tibetan Holy Man, Buddha, the one about whom Jeshua had learned so much during His travels with His uncle. He now existed in a dimension of heaven and had not had a physical embodiment for four thousand years. The first time this astonishing event took place, Jeshua explained that Mary Magdalene was an oracle for masters who resided in the heavenly realm and she was able to bring forth their wisdom.

We were allowed to ask questions and she would answer in this man's voice. Much knowledge and much wisdom came through: many of our questions were about events we had seen and experienced. When the session was over, she would open her eyes and join us in conversation. She had no awareness of the events and conversations that we had been involved with a few minutes earlier.

One day, when Mary and I were alone, I brought to her a concern that had been circling at the edge of my consciousness for some time. I told her that I disapproved of the affection she exhibited for Jeshua. I told her that I felt that Jeshua was being distracted by her and may even love her and could consider taking her as His wife. My fear was that Jeshua would lose His focus to her enticing ways. I went on to encourage her to "be like other women," and stay at home preparing the meals in the kitchen, washing the clothes, mending, sewing, and cleaning the house. I continued to tell her to refrain from trying to distract Jeshua from "the work we have come to do." I admit now that at some level I was jealous of her attention to Jeshua.

Mary received my words graciously and humbly, but she was a little angry as well. Like a woman of poise and culture, she took my recommendations into her being and dealt with them, magnificently, too, in my mind. Her response was, "I understand how it is for you men who carry the power. But I love my Master. I love my Rabbi. You cannot take that from me. "However," she added, "I will never give Him an opportunity to use me against His purpose."

Mary knew that despite her momentary desires that Jeshua spend more time with her, He would never be distracted from His purpose. Jeshua had made that clear to her. In turn, though, Jeshua loved Mary Magdalene absolutely, as student and as friend, and positioned her with unqualified equality alongside us disciples.

We all learned to accept Jeshua's beloved, Mary Magdalene, indeed we lovingly nicknamed her "The Magdalene," for there was in this woman the means to serve our understanding and consciousness. Men in our time normally had little thought that women served any other purpose than to bear our children and take care of our needs. Through Mary and also Jeshua's treatment of her we could appreciate that she was a whole being, not simply a body for pleasuring men. We came to know that she had a brain to think with and learn from and wisdom and love to share with all. She indeed housed the Shekinah, the Holy Spirit manifested in the physical body.

As for me, I reflected on my attraction to Mary Magdalene, as well as my great love for Jeshua. I reflected on my feelings of jealousy as Mary Magdalene sat at Jeshua's hem, listening fervently to His words. I realized that if Jeshua were to be distracted by her, it would take away His attention from us disciples, and that was something we could never get enough of, it seemed. I vainly reiterated my point to her that she should "back off" where Jeshua was concerned. I thought about my "instructions" to Mary that she be as other women, bound to home and hearth. And then I saw that at this time while I was still mastering the tools that Jeshua was teaching me, I did not fully understand the concept that woman are equal to men. After all, such a teaching was not part of my cultural upbringing. Only in very small parts of the Essene tradition were women standing with men in equality, although they were trained to be equal in knowledge.

As time passed I could see through Mary Magdalene's presence with us how one could rise from degradation, disgrace and condemnation to achieve a state of grace at an exalted spiritual plane. Mary Magdalene even now inspired people, especially women, as an archetype of consciousness. I could see women looking at her life and seeing that their own had many parallels, that from whatever sins they perceived that they committed in their lives, they could emulate Mary and rise up to be cleansed and awakened to equality with Jeshua's consciousness.

One day not long after we had debated the subject of vows, Jeshua related to us the facts about the gifts we receive from God and the sharing of those gifts with others. He used a beautiful allegory, speaking of the lilies: "The lilies of the field do not toil, neither do they spin, yet I tell you that King Solomon, in all his glory, was not so gloriously arrayed."

He went on, "We all have gifts, and we should share them. The truth is that someone needs to pluck the wheat from the fields in order to make the bread. And someone needs to do the labor of life, and those who do the labor, according to their talents and God-given gifts, must be appreciated, no matter how trivial or insignificant their work may appear to be.

"It is fear and worry that are the toil of man, not the sweat of his physical labor. And what is the fear and worry of man? That he shall not have enough if he does not sweat. But there is the abundance of all things, and they are given unto you when you recognize your wholeness and give of your own gift completely. A gift cannot be given with one hand and taken with another. There is no gift in that."

We continued our journey up a large hill. As we rested on the top, gazing down below at the desert floor with its scattering of trees and large boulders, Jeshua stated that He had awakened us to God's powerful gift. That God had given us the power to heal was not so much something that we received as it was an ability we opened to. It was a gift from the Father rather like an initiation. Jeshua allowed for us to recognize that as we claim our unity with the Father-Mother God, so also do we claim our gifts from God. But it is not for us to grandstand, to perform miracles, thereby proving that God exists. Rather, it is to acknowledge that God is working through us in order for us to serve others. He was quick to point out that it wasn't only we who were gifted with special qualities; no, indeed, everyone has the gift to perform miracles; it is just that in them the gift is not yet fully developed.

Calling to the twelve of us to gather close around Him, Jeshua now gave us authority to heal sickness and disease and cast out unclean spirits, those disturbed, confused souls that might be lurking in people's bodies and minds. Jeshua was our pattern, the catalyst through which our abilities and talents were revealed to us.

I remember particularly an occasion early on as we entered a town at the edge of the mountains.

Jeshua was delivering a message of the love of the Father-Mother God to those who had gathered. He told the people that the kingdom of God was within and that we all have the ability to access the power of God and that knowing this would set us free. He also stated that He was here as the I AM Presence to take on our sins just as our Father does and free us to love unconditionally our fellow man.

The crowd, though small, seemed riveted. But then a group of men arrived and began to shout and challenge us. They became so loud as to interrupt our interchange with the crowd. I asked Jeshua who they were. Jeshua said that they were zealots, religious fanatics. They were stirring up the crowd with accusations that we were blasphemers.

We tried to ignore them and continue on, but they began to threaten us by shaking their walking sticks and moving in our direction.

Clearly, we could not continue, and I felt some fear for our physical safety. Indeed, so did some of the others, particularly when several stones were thrown our way. While no one was hit, I still felt that they were a danger to us. Peter erupted in anger and moved to challenge them to a fight. However, Jeshua restrained him with a firm hand and soft words. Then, He bade us all leave quickly, and we did.

As we withdrew from town, I was troubled. I thought, *is this really worth it? If we are challenged like this in other places we're going, it must mean that the people are not understanding what Jeshua is teaching. They just don't get it. And to be placed in harm's way as well, it just doesn't seem worth it to me.*

I shared my concern and doubts with Jeshua and learned that some of the others also felt as I did.

Jeshua answered my concerns in this way: "When we are rejected by someone, we are to shake the dust from our sandals and depart. Don't look back." He was not saying that we should flee in fear but was speaking symbolically, telling us that we need not carry another's discordant energy with us.

Jeshua reminded us that our message was not designed to save anyone: we were not offering a parokey (savior) to rescue people but rather a messenger of truth. This point was pivotal because, after sharing some of our deepest feelings, we came to realize that Jeshua had come to show us how we could feed our needs and also those of our brothers and sisters.

This had been a time when several of us were considering giving up this mission and going back home. We thought that it was not worth getting hurt or losing our lives. After all, I had thought to myself, I was not skilled in the art of self-defense. I was not a soldier. I certainly had no training in that. For Peter, of course, it was different; he was so big and gruff. He always wanted to stand up to anyone, whether he was afraid or not. But, really, he was not so much aggressive as he was well anchored in his protective nature.

But Jeshua reminded us that He was not asking us to lose our lives, but to stand in our generosity of spirit, and also to stand in the faith that our lives are not in our hands but in the hands of God. He also reminded us that unless a friend is willing to lay down his life for another, his life is worth nothing, that greater love hath no man than to lay down his life for a friend.

"I do not ask of you to be martyrs," He said, "just to stand in your truth and your generosity of spirit. But be prudent: if the crowd is pressing on you, back away."

Peter and I called Jeshua on this particular teaching one time. We were at a point where it looked like trouble was coming for Jeshua.

I said, "Back away if the crowd is pressing."

But Jeshua said to me, "The crowd is not pressing upon me, but the God I AM impresses the crowd. And I am here in the fulfillment of the desire of the promise fulfilled."

Well, I certainly did not understand that. It was long after these events occurred during the sacred ceremonial Passover, which came later that year that I was able to understand how one could be "pressed upon" by the crowd and still maintain control. After Jeshua spoke in soft and calming words of reassurance, we reconsidered our position.

Very soon our Spirits lightened and we were all laughing at the incident. Our doubts were now gone and our enthusiasm was high in the knowledge that we were doing our Father's will!

There were other times during our travels together when I felt afraid. Once was when we were at sea on the Galilee. Normally, we set sail together to escape the crowds who were pressing in and making demands upon us. It was a way for us to experience a little peace and quiet in order to organize our thoughts. At times like these we could share our feelings and concerns and gain solace just being together.

Jeshua was giving to us a teaching about faith. Then very abruptly He stepped off the side of the boat, and after standing still for a moment, began walking through the water. Even though He didn't seem to be sinking, we were alarmed, afraid that ultimately He would sink and drown. Some became hysterical.

But Jeshua simply turned around and with a smile raised His hands and said, "Calm yourselves." With His cool, reassuring manner, we finally calmed down. He turned to us then and simply said, "It is easy. You need only have faith and trust and then you become one with the water."

At that, and before I realized what was happening, Peter stepped overboard and grabbed Jeshua's hand. He stood next to the Master for a moment, and then began to slowly sink. Jeshua held onto one hand and Andrew and I grabbed the other. We pulled him aboard. Peter was shaky from the experience, and then pronounced, "My faith is weak."

Jeshua gently cuffed him on the shoulder and said, "Ah, Peter, all you need is a little more practice." None of us tried to walk in water after that episode. But I was often reminded of that incident, when, on warm summer days I watched the Master joyfully walking along the shoreline, the waves lapping at his feet.

We had another incident at sea. Jeshua had directed us to sail north on the grand Mediterranean Sea to a place called Crete. In our boat on the open seas, we twelve were relaxing, as we usually did, while Jeshua had gone below to be alone in meditation and prayer.

Nightfall came and we were getting hungry. Peter asked, "Should we go get the Master?"

"No," I said. "He asked not to be disturbed."

Suddenly, a fierce squall broke out. While Peter and some of the others, as fishermen, had experienced many storms, I wasn't as seasoned; this was the worst I had encountered. And now, even Peter was worried, because the storm's intensity was increasing rapidly. I was afraid that the boat could capsize and sink. My brothers were afraid as well.

At a critical point Peter rushed below to fetch Jeshua. A few minutes later Jeshua appeared and realizing how fearful we all were, quickly evaluated the situation. The storm had gotten so severe that I had long since lost my last meal and was having difficulty holding on and not slipping and falling overboard.

Jeshua then quickly raised His hands in prayer. I could barely hear Him over the roar of the wind. Then, I clearly heard Him say the words, "Peace, be still." And as suddenly as the storm blew in, it stopped and the seas rapidly calmed. I thought, *how powerful He is to be able to command the weather at will.* We were all amazed at Jeshua's ability; even more, this time, we were much relieved. Here we were in the middle of the Mediterranean in now calm waters.

Jeshua's annoyance was obvious. He said, "Why, may I ask, would you allow an outside force, such as a storm, upset your life? The outer storm that you so fear is merely a reflection of your inner storm. You all have just witnessed me calm this storm. And in the same way, you are able to calm what is within you. You must pay attention to what is on the inside of you, not the outside of you, and master all of the emotions and issues that you are experiencing. You must learn to become calm, still, and in peace where chaos is occurring all about you. When you are able to do this, then you will not become a victim of your environment."

Jeshua had not been affected at all by the storm. He had been munching on some bread and drinking a cup of water down below. He told us that He wasn't disturbed, not because He was God and nothing could touch Him unless He allowed it—no, on the contrary: in His humanness everything touched Him. He could feel the boat sway, but nothing disturbed His focus, His life flow. He knew that He was completely safe.

I could see now that while Jeshua and the rest of us had experienced the same event, we twelve experienced it differently because we were guided by fear. I learned that when one is in balance and at one with

God, even though it might appear to others that there had been a very bad experience, there is no disharmony felt. It is experienced simply as a flow of creation.

So our message from Jeshua was not only about controlling the energy of nature, nor was it that if we are calm and peaceful within, we will never experience a storm. No, the message to us really was that we would never be disturbed or disrupted by what occurs around us or to us, when we have mastered what is inside of us. We will experience all outer things in an entirely new way.

Jeshua was quick to give us another level of understanding about this event. When completely centered and focused, there is a good possibility that one will never be exposed to inconveniences, such as the storm. However, there is never a guarantee that inconveniences will not happen.

We didn't stay long in Crete: a quick teaching, and then we sailed back home. I was happy to be back on solid ground. The trip had been for me a great challenge.

On our next trip, thankfully on land, we were traveling to Jerusalem and spotted a man up ahead lying beside the road. His clothes were torn, and he was moaning softly when we approached. The man was seriously injured: he had scratches and bruises and was bleeding from some of his wounds. He struggled to speak, finally managing to express that he had been robbed. My immediate impulse was to give him water and care for his wounds. And then we noted that he was a Samaritan.

There had been a centuries-long mutual hatred between the Jews and the Samaritans. While the two shared a common heritage, they differed in their religious beliefs. That, along with differences in legal traditions and day-to-day lifestyles, kept them a wide berth apart. They all avoided each other. Some Jews thought the Samaritans contemptuous.

I felt that we should walk by this Samaritan and not get involved because there might be more robbers nearby. While fear was directing this response, the real issue dug much deeper. I didn't like Samaritans; I felt that I was better than they, and in my prejudice and snobbishness, I thought better to simply pass this man by.

The others must have been thinking the same way I had been, because we all hovered about, seeming to weigh whether we should respond. However, when Jeshua kneeled down to compassionately assist the man, a greater knowing inside me took hold. Instantly, I thought to myself, *How could I ever, even for a moment, have thought that we should ignore this suffering person?*

Jeshua validated my thoughts, "We must help this man. Is he not our brother? And why were you all so slow to respond? What were you worried about anyway? The robbers? How many could there be? Look at us. Look at how strong we are. We must never have fear of the robbers."

We all immediately pitched in to help the man. I put my goatskin water flask to his parched lips and bade him drink. Then I asked Jeshua to heal the wounded man.

Jeshua smiled at me and softly said, "No, Mattai, that is your job."

Well, I did the best I could. While he did not become completely whole, his condition seemed to improve. We cleaned and wrapped his wounds with strips of cloth. Then we carried him to the city and took him to an inn where he would receive more care.

It always seemed to me that with every new experience we encountered, there was a lesson to be learned. Indeed, along the way to the city, we received another level of this lesson from Jeshua.

Jeshua posed this question: "Which is the greater sin against God, for you to ignore someone in trouble, whether wounded, sick, lame or mentally disturbed, even though you could help, or to have inflicted the difficulty upon that person? Which sin is greater?"

And He answered, "Both sins are equal in the eyes of God."

When on our trips, Jeshua would sometimes say simply, "Follow me." Occasionally, in my egocentricity of wanting to show Him I could do the leading, I would turn the tables and say, "Teacher, follow me." Then Jeshua would happily comply and off we would go. I never lead us astray, though. Even if I had, we would never have been lost, because Jeshua knew at all times where He was and where we were going next — in more ways than one! God was indeed guiding Him, and He was leading us.

At times, it seemed too much for all of us to figure out all of His intense teachings. Then Jeshua, feeling this tension, would say, "Let's go play." And we would all take a walk and then sit under the olive trees on the hillside with cups of wine. In the cool breeze, we would joke and laugh, and sometimes we would jump in the crystalline waters to bathe. By this action we could break the tension with a cycle of simple, pure fun.

One time a few of us playfully, like children, jumped into the Jordan River at a place that was most accommodating. For once, we were neither bathing nor baptizing but simply playing in the water. We splashed about and swam, then challenged each other to a race. A joyful time it was! We attracted a crowd because we were all behaving like silly children. Disbelieving what they saw, the people confusedly asked, "That isn't the Rabbi out there, is it?"

When we came ashore and wrapped ourselves, threatening to splash anyone who dared come close, Jeshua sat down and addressed playfulness: "When you are playful in spirit and when you become like a child, you open yourself to receive *all* of God's gifts, for would a great and loving Father deny His child anything it needed if it were within His means to provide it? So be as these children in spirit and know that in this place, you are open to receive all that our generous Father can give." We had His permission to be just a little bit silly.

Jeshua was in a playful mood much of the time. The rest of us were usually serious. Once when we sat enjoying a sip of water at a well, Jeshua wanted us to lighten up so that He could play with our minds. Our playful mood made us more receptive to His teachings.

This time Jeshua said, "God is like this well. Our Father God is much deeper than this well and yet this well is full of the waters of life. He who would be willing to dive into this well is diving into the Father-Mother God."

And to my surprise, our brother John took Jeshua seriously and before I knew it, he had climbed to the edge of the well and was ready to jump in. We quickly grabbed him and pulled him back down to the ground, in the nick of time, too, to prevent him from going in feet first. He was so eager and so serious that we nearly witnessed a big splash within the well. Jeshua burst into laughter along with the rest of us. Jeshua could hardly contain himself, but finally He blurted out to John, "Though I am teaching you correctly, I didn't mean for you to be so serious as to take me literally." John felt foolish for his behavior and we all teased him about it.

Jeshua's intent was to show the water and the well as symbols of the spirit of God. He talked further about surrender and commitment, diving in to follow our beliefs. Then Jeshua made an important distinction: He noted that we were already in spiritual water and didn't have to do any diving. We had only to let go and enjoy.

Jeshua then posed this question: "There is a fish in the lake. Does the fish see the water that he is swimming in?"

We all pondered this question for a while and finally Peter said, "Well, of course not, Master. The fish cannot see the water. He is simply in the water. To the fish, his reality is that his whole world is water. He doesn't know the distinction between water and no water."

And Jeshua said, "And you all walk in air. Do you know that you are breathing air? No, you just know you are breathing, don't you? You are living in your air world."

Then He added, "Be in the well of Spirit, be in the water, which symbolically represents the gifts from the universe. And just live it as if for you it is already true. You possess it."

While we assimilated and integrated this wisdom, we noticed someone approaching the well. He seemed most curious about our antics. Jeshua greeted the man, and then set about manifesting an invitation for all of us to dinner at this man's house. It was always nice to be fed a good, home-cooked meal. These were good times, and on the way to this man's house, we again kidded John about trying to jump in the well, but we realized that, like John, we were all ready to follow the Master anywhere, anytime.

The way we lightened our day was through humor, enjoying not only cosmic or philosophical humor but also finding the humor within the challenges of our everyday events. When we could engage humor in these ways, we could clearly understand its function. One example was with the Roman government:

We didn't make fun of the Romans, but we saw that hierarchical structure as like a dog chasing its tail, and that image was very funny. We also saw the Romans as bumping into walls, another funny image. But why are these things funny? Jeshua said, "It is because they remind us of something painful, and there is a need for our humor to be reestablished in the world. When we can laugh at our foibles and constraints, we can release the tension that builds from the pain in our lives.

"But humor can be cruel, too, and one example of when it is most cruel is when the body is in pain and jokes are made about it. It really isn't so funny, then, to laugh when in a state of pain and suffering. In those moments the humor is distorted because there is denial of the pain, and in the denial of pain comes fear."

Human tragedies were certainly nothing to laugh at. But we were not above seeing the humor in some of the minor mishaps. We laughed once when Peter, who had lagged behind us, was running to catch up. He slipped on a loose stone and fell, hitting his bottom hard.

We said, "So, Peter, when you lay upon your ass, you are giving healing to the earth itself."

As Peter slowly picked himself up, he looked at Jeshua and said, "Lord, Lord, how can you laugh at me when I am hurting?"

And Jeshua said, "Because we hurt with you, my friend."

Peter said, "Well, if you hadn't been in such a hurry I would not have had to struggle so hard to catch up. You're lucky I didn't break something."

And Jeshua said, "*I'm* lucky?"
Peter often blamed Jeshua for his mishaps.

Lazarus continued to be one of Jeshua's best friends. He still lived in Bethany, a town near Jerusalem.

Lazarus, now a successful, wealthy businessman, owned a grain mill. He ground the wheat and amaranth used to bake bread. The grain came from his own crops, which he farmed on his many irrigated acres. He also ground the grain that was brought to his mill from others' fields.

When we visited Lazarus at his home, which was often, Jeshua felt a special joy, because the two were so close. Lazarus lived with his younger sisters Martha and Mary. They followed closely the laws of their Essene religion. They were an honest and good family, and they loved one another greatly. However, the sisters were very different. The older, Martha, was content to perform the household duties, making everything run smoothly. We knew we were in for a treat when dining there, because Martha was a great cook, who delighted in preparing sumptuous feasts. Lazarus would brag, "A feast for royalty."

Mary, on the other hand, wanted little to do with household duties, particularly cooking. So Martha delegated to her the cleaning up; however, Mary disliked this job as well.

Mary preferred going to temple and learning the teachings of the religious school. She loved to hear Jeshua speak, and every chance she had, she would run off to listen to Him. Mary was beautiful with long, black hair, lovely eyes, and an infectious laugh. She had a zest for life but still lived strictly within the bounds of the progressive Essene doctrine. Fortunately, the teachings allowed for abundant freedom in the lives of the women, for Mary took full advantage.

Martha and Mary were always disagreeing on something, most certainly on the length of Mary's hair. Mary's hair had a lustrous shine to it, and she like to wear it long. But Martha felt it should be cut short, as was the current custom for young women.

I was very fond of the sisters, particularly Mary. When we visited, Mary always did her best to make sure I was comfortable. "Mattai, did you get enough to eat? Are you sure you don't want more pie?" she would ask. And then she would smile at me and her hazel eyes would sparkle. It was very apparent that Mary doted on me. While Martha and others, friends and neighbors who came to help prepare the meal had to be coaxed to join us in after dinner conversation, Mary was only too glad to abandon the dishes and come in. Sometimes soon after dinner, we would hear a crash in the kitchen of a dropped plate and that was a clue that Mary, having upset Martha, would soon be asked to leave the kitchen before she destroyed all the pottery. She would then join us.

Mary would always find a place next to me, even if it meant squeezing into a tight spot between one of my brothers and me. Then she would turn to me and smile her beguiling smile. She certainly was a distraction.

On one particular evening after we had finished supper, a beautiful event touched me greatly.

In an act of great humility, Mary approached Jeshua, knelt down and took his feet in her hands. With her own tears and some rare oils, she washed His feet. Then Mary applied sandalwood that came from India; rose oil, from Asia Minor, and frankincense, gotten from Arabia. She had purchased these expensive oils on a trip to Jerusalem. The oils had a particular significance, because they transmitted to various parts of the body a blessed energy. What a splendid aromaticity they emitted. After washing Jeshua's feet, Mary dried them with her lustrous, long hair.

The next morning we left Lazarus' home and went on our way, feeling uplifted and blessed by their graciousness, so blessed, in fact, that we decided to make Bethany, and Lazarus' home, in particular, our home away from home, our alternate "headquarters" for rest and relaxation. Our frequent, carefree days were less available to us now. Things were changing drastically in our lives at this time.

THIRD SPIRITUAL LAW

Keep holy all that is given unto you. Rest in the cycle of rest knowing that you are receiving. Open and give in the cycle of serving, knowing that it is all moved through you as the divine hand. Keep all that is given as holy and sacred.

EXPLANATION:

The Sabbath is a day to take time off from regular chores and duties to pray, to reflect inwardly and to allow the body to rest. Many people do not honor the Sabbath; they do not make time for this divine endeavor; rather, on the Sabbath, they continue in their habitual life patterns and habits.

What defines rest? Remember the challenges and tricks that the high priests would try with Jeshua? They questioned that if a man were ill and bleeding, should you heal him on the Sabbath? The laws are very strict within the sacred books. The truth is you must balance your life. Do what you do, but find sacredness during the day in which you must be busy doing things because our world does not honor the Sabbath consistently. But perhaps on the day of your Sabbath, at the start or at the end of the day, you can enter into deep prayer and rest for yourself. You must find a balance.

Most people continually excuse themselves for their busyness and think that when their busyness is all over, then they will rest. Then when their life is over, they still haven't done it. They haven't yet balanced themselves.

If the whole world would honor this law, there could be a new reverence for the Sabbath. It doesn't matter if it starts at sundown on Friday or on Saturday or if it starts when you wake up on Sunday morning. There needs to be an overall pattern consistent with the honoring of your process of life on earth. Eventually, all days are the Sabbath days that you simply and reverently do the things you need to do and you do not separate them from the acts of spirit and love. But to merely pay lip service to that as the truth will not gain you anything but merit for your ego.

CHAPTER 4

The Miracles Continue

Jeshua's reputation had spread like wildfire. His was now a household name in Israel. Our intimate little group was experiencing dramatic change: the only peace we had was when we slept at night or traveled far from home, but even then, the crowds were tracking us down.

When we arrived at a village, the streets were full, and not just with people waiting to hear Jeshua's words, but also with those who wanted simply to touch Him or receive a blessing from Him. When He finally stopped to speak, large crowds gathered to listen. At times, the streets were lined with the sick, as many townspeople would bring their ailing family members hoping that when Jeshua walked by, He would perform one of his miraculous healings.

Not only did they wait, but many followed us as well, and our ranks grew. And now, our families and extended families accompanied us frequently.

One day we came into a town and immediately recognized that something was amiss. No one had come to greet us. No children were playing in the street. When we asked the few people we encountered what was wrong, we were told that nearly the entire population was sick with an illness that had swept through the village.

Jeshua hesitated for a few moments and then told us that their drinking water had become polluted. He went on to say that the well they relied upon contained tiny life forms, which among other symptoms caused dysentery.

Jeshua, knowing that the condition here, where everyone was sick, was a microcosm of the nature of illness, used this opportunity not only to provide a healing mechanism to the townspeople but to teach us, His disciples, about why some people get sick and how disease works.

He told us that disease could lurk in the body in two ways: first, there are those with obvious illnesses, such as a weak heart or lungs, those with digestive problems. Second, there are those who have inherited through the genetic structure weaknesses that may not have expressed yet into illness: these weaknesses are simply lying dormant.

In both cases, when an external event, such as the well water being contaminated with tiny living creatures, erupts, the weaknesses in the body are attacked and conditions worsen. "It is like a wall that collapses: it begins with one brick tumbling, then another, and another," He said. "Because of the pre-existing conditions, when an epidemic hits, the organs become weaker and the body cannot defend itself adequately."

When we arrived in this town, we came upon those suffering paralysis of the arms and legs. We also heard complaints of gastrointestinal problems, bloating and diarrhea. There were some who were extremely weak, whose breathing was labored, which Jeshua told us was a consequence of a swelling in the heart. And there were still others with conditions not yet expressed. He was able to see these things.

Jeshua pointed out to us how these life forms, too small to see, had seriously invaded these people's systems and were concentrating where the weaknesses were presenting and where there were reduced body defenses.

Jeshua observed, "I see we have some real work to do in this town." He added, "In our lives, there is a time for joy and laughter. However, now is the time for blessing and healing. We must bring our joy into the healing of these people."

While Jeshua was utilizing His healing techniques, He was also speaking to the people, adding certain lessons. For some, the message was that through their faith, their knowingness that they could be made whole, they were healed. For others, Jeshua gave instructions about what to do in order that their bodies accelerate the healing process: He told all about the importance of keeping the body clean on the outside as well as the inside, and He encouraged them to keep their thoughts clean as well.

These were a very busy few days.

What I observed was that many of the sick were healed by their faith alone, while others were healed through cleansing, along with prayer and blessings. Others chose not to live through the experience, and they died.

In one poignant case, a weeping mother came to Jeshua and said, "Why did you not heal my child? Why did my child have to die?"

We disciples were disturbed by her questions. We hoped the woman would be pushed aside and ignored, as if we hadn't heard her. We preferred the praise and gratitude of all the others who were healed.

Instead, Jeshua responded, "Speak again, lovely woman."

And the woman said, "You, Master, are a great Rabbi and a great healer. Why have you allowed my son to die?"

And Jeshua said, "Woman, it is not I who does the healing, but the Father in heaven through me. All of those souls that are called home by Him will be healed in Spirit, for their bodies shall return to dust according to the Father's cycle. And the Spirit shall return to the wholeness. You may weep for the loss, but let your heart praise the Father. Let your body and emotions be cleared of the grief. Let the Mother God hold you as you experience this release. Let the mother you are within become whole again."

We were all very impressed and relieved when Jeshua spoke these words because it felt to us as if we were getting a lesson as well. We now felt that we had permission from Jeshua to feel okay when the healings that we performed for others didn't appear to work. However, Jeshua, sensing our thoughts, clarified our understanding.

You see, we held the point of view that if someone came to us for healing but did not respond the way we thought they should, which would have been to get up and walk away, healed, then we would need to consider that there was a good reason for that, so that we could feel okay about the outcome.

Jeshua provided a clearer understanding for us of the concept of healing. He reminded us that healing of the body, mind and spirit was of God's divine will and timing, not of human prerogative. He also explained that healing is an ongoing process that could take form in many different ways, even through a person's death. He encouraged us to forgive ourselves for our expectations and our ego's attachment that healing be done in a way we think it "ought" to be done.

After the healings were complete, we set about cleaning up the drinking well. We always carried with us an array of therapeutic minerals that we had collected from a mountain site. Now we had a situation where we could put them to use. We ground up all we had and added them to the well water. We followed this addition with plenty of crushed leaves and bark from the lemon tree. Then we asked that no one drink from the well for seven days. At the end of seven days, the water smelled sweet. It had a slight lemony taste and was now pure. We were able, through the essence of lemon oil combined with the minerals, to transmute and transform the microbes and parasites that were present in the water into a harmless substance.

Some months later, we returned to that town and were received with great celebration by the people. There was much rejoicing and feasting. A delicious supper was prepared for us. At these times, we felt so thankful to God for the gifts that we were able to share with others.

There was a time when we were invited back to the house of Lazarus for Seder with him and Mary and Martha. Seder, the dinner celebrated on the first night of Passover, commemorated the exodus of our Jewish ancestors from Egypt. We chose to accept their invitation and proceeded to Bethany for an overnight stay in their home.

Lazarus, as the host, was performing the role of rabbinical leader and was giving the ritual prayer from the book of Haggadah. But there were protests among several people present, who said to Jeshua, "But Master, you are the greater teacher and, therefore, should you not be the one to lead the prayer? It would be an honor for us if you were to do this."

Jeshua replied, "We are here as Lazarus' guests and all are equal. He is to be the leader of the ceremony, as he is the head of this household."

Then Jeshua appointed Martha to light the Chabbat candles and perform the ritual prayer, a ceremony usually assigned to the women. This event now upset Mary, who felt left out. So agitated did Mary become that when it came time for reading the passages of prayer and drinking the wine, Mary refused to serve more wine. Behaving like a petulant child, Mary said, "If Martha is so special, let her do it."

The prayer ritual was completed despite Mary's outburst, and everybody settled in with a peaceful feeling, glowing a bit from the effects of the wine and satiated with a great meal. Jeshua then went to Mary and said, "Mary, count the days of your life in which you will light candles. Could you not offer this day for Martha?"

Mary replied, "But Lord, but Lord, am I to always be second?"

Jeshua, with a twinkle in His eye, mimicked Mary's fervent plea, "But Mary, but Mary, there is no first or second in God's eyes. You are equal and all one. And our Father loves you all with the same breath."

Mary cried and asked for Jeshua's forgiveness. And Jeshua, as an act of forgiveness, poured her a glass of wine and asked Mary if He could pray over the wine as a gift to her. She graciously accepted.

The animosity Mary felt toward Martha was an example of sibling rivalry, which Jeshua later explained was an interaction that was a reflection for all of us. He pointed out that like sheep upon the earth someone is usually feeling left out or left behind. He added that there is always someone who feels that he must measure up to achieve approval.

Jeshua emphasized, "We do this with earthly parents, siblings, or our colleagues, but at times, we even do this with God, our Father-Mother. We believe that somehow we must beg for favors or beg for special status instead of recognizing that we are all of the same breath. We think that God will love us only if we perform well. So we strive for so much faultlessness: to dance elegantly, speak eloquently, behave politely and pray without error. In our fervor to be loved by God, we even pray louder and still louder at times. In this belief and struggle to perfect our rituals, we miss the point. God does not notice the ritual. All God notices is the intent in our hearts. And there is equal love and equal measure for all of us."

We ventured into Jerusalem once during this Passover period. As I later reflected, the recent observance of this somber holiday might have been what provoked Jeshua.

We entered the city with Jeshua leading the way with firm steps and a fierce look. He walked straight to the temple and charged up to the steps. There the moneychangers were noisily going about their usual business. Jeshua strode intently toward the nearest moneychanger and in a fury threw over his table, spilling coins all over the ground. Then He roared, "How dare you defile my Father's house! This is a temple of worship, not a house of commerce! Red-faced now, he stomped toward each moneychanger, flinging each table over as he went. With the exception of Peter, who stayed right by his Master's side, urging Him on, we disciples were aghast, hovering together in wonder and fright at the sight of a Jeshua we had never before seen. Jeshua then picked up a whip, cracked it into the air and yelled, "Leave my Father's house now!" In one fleeting moment the grounds were empty: the moneychangers had scattered, the dove merchants had fled, and worshippers, quivering with fright, took to hiding behind portals and columns.

Jeshua at once became still and seemingly focused on some far distant object. Shortly, He asked to be left alone, then went inside the temple where He stayed for a long time, praying, I surmised. My brothers and I dared not interrupt Him. Thrown for a loop we waited patiently, yet we were aware enough to open the birdcages and set the abandoned doves free.

While walking from town to town, sometimes we just wanted to get away from it all and get close to the earth. At these times, veering off the main road, we might find ourselves in the middle of a wheat field. We would pick off a stalk of wheat, stick it in our mouths and chew it up. Real hayseeds, we were, sometimes. It felt so good; we felt so free. Returning to the road, we thirteen would spread out, at times taking turns to walk alongside Jeshua and ask Him questions. As we entered a place, Jeshua would then position Himself a little ahead, leading the way into town so that He could greet everyone and give them His complete attention.

Rarely now, was there no one at the entrance to welcome us when they heard we were approaching. But on the few occasions when that was the case, Jeshua would greet everyone He met, whether they knew who He was or not. He was always very friendly and enthusiastic. Children would sometimes be waiting to see the man their parents had spoken about, even though they did not understand the full significance of Jeshua's blessings. Sometimes the children would run along the road intent on keeping up with us. Jeshua loved children and always went where we needed to be in order to encourage, bless, and heal them.

I remember a child about five or six years old who tripped and fell while running after Jeshua. Jeshua stopped and turned around even though He hadn't seen what had happened. The child had scraped his knees. One knee was bleeding, and the child was now crying in pain. Jeshua knelt down and took the child's knee between His hands. He bowed His head for a few moments, and then He removed His hands and picked the child up. There wasn't a mark or blemish, no evidence of any injury to that knee. The child, with unabashed joy on his face, didn't want to leave Jeshua when he was delivered home, and after Jeshua bade him farewell, he continued to follow us down the road.

Amazed, we asked Jeshua how that child's knee could be a bloody abrasion one minute and a perfectly normal, smooth-skinned knee the next. Jeshua claimed that He simply was able through His gifts to accelerate the healing process. He stated that healing does not need to take an hour, days, or months but can happen instantly, when we believe it can happen and know the power of who we are.

Jeshua spoke so lovingly of the children, perhaps partly because they mirrored so His close connection to God. He explained that children at an early age are more at-one with God because they have a clearer memory of Him, their souls having just come from His realm. They have not yet been swayed by parental and societal influence, succumbing to limitation and bias inherent on the earth plane.

We were walking along the road between the Seaside Village at Galilee and the hills outside of Jerusalem, when we began to talk about whether it was better to eat fish, or the lambs, which some people still sacrificed for God, or the wheat and the berries from the earth. Some of us felt that we should not be having this conversation at all, since Moses and the laws of Leviticus had already prescribed our diet, as ordained by God. But others were eager to "test" these laws through a discussion, and our exchange turned lively indeed.

On the subject of consuming flesh, because of the understanding that there should be love and reverence for all life, I pointed out that the law stated, "you shalt not kill." I said, "And so it has been understood and written for all these years that thou shalt not kill another human. However, are we not all but the same creation of God? So then how can we kill an animal and consume it?" I was now a vegetarian and passionate on the subject.

Peter brought forth a different point of view, his own fervent perspective. As the fisherman, he said, "If everyone refused to eat flesh, there would be no livelihood for people like myself and my family. Think about the shepherd who raises sheep. How could he live?" Peter also believed that the animals came to the planet to sacrifice themselves for human consumption.

On another side of that argument, Bartholomew pointed out that by consuming meat, one could not ascend into heaven, because the fear and pain that the animal experienced during its slaughter would transfer to the human, and that particular density of vibration was sufficient to negatively affect man and his relationship with God.

We talked about those who felt free to consume anything and everything placed before them, without concern for how it might affect their bodies. They would abuse themselves by drinking and eating too many rich foods, which harm the body. That philosophy would embrace the idea that God didn't want one to lack anything that He had put forth on earth. We noted that these people didn't realize that applying moderation to all the things we consume is better tolerated by our bodies and much more consistent with God's desire for us.

Then a new thought crept into the discussion. We were reminded of the Genesis teaching that "these things are yours and you are the keeper of the domain," which we interpreted to mean that all things were put on the earth for us, but we were not to abuse any of them.

We could come to no agreement.

Finally, when the argument was becoming heated, Jeshua silenced us with His words: "Whatever you shall bless truly, not with words, but with your own hearts, then whatever you bring into your body for nourishment and fulfillment and pleasure, so God blesses you."

Jeshua went on to make clear that as far as the best diet was concerned, one needed to understand that the diet is not a primary consideration to highest consciousness. But one must attune to the needs of the body and its function. For some people, it is avoiding pork. For others, it means avoiding meat altogether or for just a period of time.

"What our people fail to acknowledge and understand," He said, "is that there is no wrong in anything that you consume. It is, perhaps, that the higher the energy one has, the less need there is for meat for the bodily functions. But at the same time, there also is a much lesser need for quantities of all foods, less need for consuming much of anything.

"So people will tend to let specific diets be a belief rather than an actualization of what the body needs. When you feel in alignment in your body, it is being fed appropriately. When you feel excessively bloated and are not digesting well, then you know you must shift your diet. So often, though, my beloved friends do not put these changes into practice in their lives. They think they can eat anything as long as they don't have a fear that a food can hurt them and they remember to bless it. But their body becomes ill from congestion. So there is a misalignment of the truth."

Jeshua also told us that fasting can be an important part of a diet. "It can lift you mentally and spiritually as well as physically," He said. "Fasting allows an opportunity for the body to realign itself to a powerful choice point: whether to live as a healthy demonstration of life or whether to live as a consciousness that is stuck. During a longer fast the body is able to cleanse three areas: the colon, the liver, and the lymphatic system. These are the major places where foods and poisons are held. A fast allows these products to be relinquished, removed from the body."

He added, "We also know that the body stores the poisons of thoughts and beliefs. A clear fasting at the physical level also symbolically allows the opportunity for the mind to heal its attachments to food, to life itself. People who participate in a prolonged fast often find themselves in an altered state of mind where they may be facing their fears and personal demons. They are able to align and heal the things that are stored in their bodies, such as adverse memories and emotions. They certainly can heal many fears.

"Humans can take the opportunity to fast once a week on the Sabbath, for example, to allow the opportunity to experience a different way of feeding the body and the spirit; this feeds the soul more completely.

"I sometimes recommend a three-day fast. But one could also do a seven-day, ten-day, or even a forty-day fast. Fasting is not to be considered as something negative. It is not to be viewed as a purification of the body because the body is in some way bad; some religions have made fasting a punishment to the body, mind, and soul, believing that they are not pure. Rather, this can be perceived as an opportunity to clear what is incorrect or unwanted within us. Clearing means recognizing clearly the choices that are available to us.

"The foods that you may eat or drink during fasting are multiple. I fasted with honey, leaves, insects and water. But it isn't only the things you eat, it is also how you eat them. It is to eat with conscious reverence in every moment with every mouthful of food chewed and every step of the process of consuming. The further you go into a fast, the more liquid it can become. I had my goatskin flask filled with water, and I had the moisture from the dew on the plants as well as the moisture within the leaves of the plants. There is much nourishment in these leaves.

"When fasting one does not usually eat meat, bread or other cooked foods. One can squeeze the juices from fruit and add nuts, such as almonds, but these are not necessary.

"I do not want to create a formula for fasting, for there is none, certainly none that should be considered of a religious nature. Many people claim after a prolonged period of fasting that they don't feel hungry anymore. I do recommend that no one do a prolonged fast if he hasn't previously mastered one full day of fasting."

He went on, "Nutrients are very important for the body, especially when you are feeling the need for minimizing certain kinds of foods. So I encourage you to bring more minerals into the body and continue to clear and refresh with the wholesome nature of water.

"Some say that it is a sin to consume anything that is of an intoxicating nature. Others say that intoxicating nectars are harmful only if used in excess. But these are only rules laid down by man.

"Some people think that they may not eat anything that was once living, yet they consume our plants of the earth. Are not those plants alive? People do not comprehend that even the rocks upon the earth are alive. They are inanimate and appear to be non-living, but that is not so."

In summary, Jeshua said, "Ultimately, it is not so much what is consumed that is unhealthy or damaging, but the mindlessness with which these things are consumed. What happens is that one becomes consumed by what is eaten."

On our debate about animals, Jeshua broadened the scope of our understanding, "Some people feel that man is in charge of the beasts and as such may rule them and do whatever he will with them. People feel that they have license to be cruel and abuse them. But this is not so. It is an arrogant view. Mankind is given charge over all only for the honoring of it. Just as the Masters who rule from the heavenly planes of Light are to serve and protect and honor their brothers and sisters on earth and consider themselves as equals, so too must humankind do likewise with the earth and all its creatures, for our planet is a gift from the Father-Mother God."

He continued, "That which is given unto Earth is given unto all.

The beasts of the earth are the brothers and the keepers of the earth. The humans, the Adamic dwellers of earth, are the way showers for one another and the caretakers of the beasts. It is God's plan that if the beasts are cared for and the earth is cared for, and when we acknowledge and honor one another, all live in harmony."

As we looked at Him in wonder, Jeshua explained, "There is a lot that can be said that humans are to care for both the earth and those who reside upon it. They must be good stewards of the earth and walk in its beauty and be empowered by the awe of it. But the earth is given for all."

All of our discussion about food must have made us very hungry because the next thing I knew we were all settled in underneath the olive trees diving into a meal of bread, dried fish, nuts, and figs.

Peter asked Jeshua a question that unmistakably turned our attention elsewhere.

"Lord, ask me any question for I would like you to test my intelligence," he said.

Jeshua answered Peter with a riddle for all of us to consider. It went something like this: "What is it that comes between the desert and the hillside? What is it that comes full and yet empty? What is it that has the face of glory and the face of laughter? And what is it that with all these dimensions will carry you upon command and drop you at its own choice?"

Peter responded, "Lord, I have the answer to that question. God is in all things: our Father, our Creator, has breathed life into all matters."

And Jeshua said, "Peter, what a wonderful answer."

Just when Peter was preening with pride at his "correct" answer, I piped up. "Peter has missed the point; he doesn't know what he's talking about," I retorted. "Rabbi, Peter's answer would be true for all things, so that doesn't count."

Jeshua considered me, "Is that so, Mattai? Then what would you say is the correct answer?"

Just as proudly I answered, "My Lord, it is a camel. Everyone should know that."

And Jeshua, smiling, said, "Yes, but Mattai, you didn't tell me whether your camel had one hump or two."

We all laughed and Jeshua commented, "Oh, my friends, you bring such amusement to me."

My friend, Peter, who was giving great and serious contemplation to this riddle, now thought that he should have answered "camel."

Jeshua turned thoughtful, pondering our responses, and with a sigh said, "I wonder if you understand anything I have taught you?"

Peter and I both sobered immediately, feeling chastised. But shortly after, we were seeing the humor in the entire situation and able to cut loose with a few laughs. We realized that there was more to Jeshua's questions than what appeared on the surface, that many stories do indeed have more than one answer and one meaning.

Devastating news came that would dampen our heady days. We learned that Jeshua's cousin, John the Baptist, was dead. We were all in shock to learn that John had been sacrificed for the vanity of a woman. He had been arrested, jailed, and then beheaded for speaking out in criticism of Herodias for marrying her husband's brother, the second King Herod.

We had not yet recovered from this pain when a messenger brought word of another upset. Our friend, Lazarus, was very ill, and his family was asking for our immediate return.

Jeshua mystified us by going about His business as if nothing had happened. After awhile, I asked Jeshua when we were going to the house of Lazarus.

He replied to me simply, "Soon."

I didn't quite understand what was going on. Why wasn't Jeshua going to His friend? I wondered. I knew how much Jeshua loved Lazarus. I surmised that Jeshua might still be grieving over his cousin and not ready to respond to any other request.

Finally, a full five days after the messenger had come to us, Jeshua dispatched us, "Now we will go to Lazarus' home."

As we neared his house, Martha spotted us at a distance from her window and dashed towards us in a rage. Mary followed a few moments later; she approached quietly and somewhat tentatively.

Martha screamed to us that Lazarus was dead, and then she shook her finger at Jeshua. "He would not be dead if you had been here," she said. "Why didn't you come sooner to warn him that he was dying? Why didn't you heal him? Why didn't you do all these things?" she wept bitterly.

But even in Martha's misery she was remorseful, because she knew that her acting out was not appropriate: it was not her place to accuse. Still, she blamed Jeshua for Lazarus' death. During Martha's outburst, Mary had stood by quite silently.

Jeshua wept, mourning his dear friend. We were all sad. Yet we wondered how Lazarus had died. He did have some bad habits: eating too much rich food and drinking too much wine.

As things settled down, we began to pay attention to our private thoughts. While we were all silently blaming someone else for this seeming tragedy, at the same time we were feeling guilt and remorse that somehow if we had done something differently, our friend would not have died. I realized that this was a most common reaction to death.

Then Jeshua said to Lazarus' sisters, "Take me to his tomb."

This provoked further outrage in Martha, who, after all she had been through, did not want to confront her brother's gravesite, for after family members had died, it was the custom to leave it be and not visit, except, perhaps, only once, after the seven days of prayer. She most reluctantly, and with a fury inside, took her place beside her sister and they led the way. Jeshua followed, and we all filed behind and walked to the burial site.

A large stone blocked the tomb. Jeshua asked that we pull it away. We were all silent as Jeshua bowed His head in prayer. After a long period, Jeshua looked up, raised His arms and spoke, "Lazarus, arise and come out of your tomb!"

Murmurs rose from the crowd. Then, another shrill cry came from Martha, behind me, "No! My brother is four days dead; his flesh is already rotting."

Mary silenced her sister, and a hush returned to the group. The stillness now was palpable. We had no idea what to expect. Our emotions ran high.

After what seemed like an eternity to me but was really only a few moments, a figure suddenly appeared. It was Lazarus, standing in front of his own tomb . . . and looking very much alive! I flinched at the sight of him, still partially wrapped in his burial cloth. As he took a step toward Jeshua, Martha fainted. Sweet Mary fell to her knees, weeping. Lazarus embraced Jeshua; both were in tears.

Jeshua had brought Lazarus back from the dead. We had the feast of all feasts, inviting perplexed, amazed friends and neighbors, to celebrate the miracle and to honor Jeshua.

Mary was joyous, radiant. As the wine flowed, I became more relaxed and at ease with her constant presence near me. After the feast she called me aside and presented me with a special sweet, which she claimed to have created in the kitchen just for me. I noticed Martha glancing our way. I could almost read her thoughts. *Why, I have never seen you so intent on cooking anything the way you doted over that sweet for Mattai ...*

Given with such love and enthusiasm, I had no choice but to sit down and eat it right then and there. It was difficult for me to refuse her anyway.

I found Mary beguiling. She was so full of charm that she created an appealing distraction for me. This was particularly so when I had been brooding over such things as the death of Lazarus, the constant fear for our safety, or whether we would have enough funds for our travels. I would think, *wouldn't it be nice to have someone like Mary with me whenever I needed a comforting feminine touch.* But good sense would take hold and I would realize that Mary might interfere in my commitment to Jeshua as His disciple.

After I had eaten this delicious morsel, Mary bade me walk outside with her. It was a star-filled evening, cool and breezy, with a light scent of night jasmine filling the air. My senses were alive in this lovely environment with one of the most beautiful women I had ever known. Mary must have sensed my mood, because she began a line of questioning that I recognized immediately as a serious inquiry on the subject of marriage. When she reached for my hand, I noticed that my palms were embarrassingly moist.

This was a most difficult occasion for me. But despite my mood and my attraction to her, I told Mary that I had no plans to marry, ever; I had committed my life to learning from Jeshua and teaching others. I could feel her anguish, though with dignity, she struggled to hide her disappointment. For both of us, however, this subject was not at an end. I was still musing about my choices, and I perceived that Mary sensed it.

Mary and I had both been deeply moved by the happenings that day, and, more than that, we were charged up. Neither one of us could think of sleeping, so we talked well into the night, sharing our innermost feelings. I couldn't remember ever being so open with or feeling so close to a woman, certainly not with my mother and not even my sisters. It was nearly dawn when we parted and went to our respective sleeping quarters.

I felt elated and definitely attracted to Mary, so a great deal about that evening troubled me. Should I break my vows of celibacy and take Mary for my wife? After all, some of my brothers were married and even had families. But I thought to myself, *look at the turmoil they are going through. They're separated for such long periods from their families and then when they return, they face inquisitions from their wives and children who want to know why they've been gone so long and what they've been up to. There were also always so many duties around the household which needed attending to. While they are comforted by knowing that they're needed, still they also know that they will be leaving again. And the wives are so angry, particularly Peter's. She is downright antagonistic.*

We were all basking in the glory of the day before and decided to stay one more day. I accepted another invitation from Mary to meet again and talk, but first I sought out Jeshua. After dinner, I told Him that my emotions were being torn asunder. I confided the conflict I felt between my chosen path of celibacy and my feelings for the lovely Mary. He nodded his complete understanding for, after all, He had known Mary since childhood and was acutely aware of her beauty and charm. Then after listening patiently while my tormented heart spilled out its dilemma, He spoke, "Mattai, you have every right to possess those feelings.

"It is natural for a man to desire to commit to a relationship with a woman. That is the Father's wish for us here on earth. It is as if we are seeking the other part of ourselves. It is also our Father's choice that we have *free will* here on earth to do as we choose.

"We as His children should strive to serve our Father in the highest manner that we are able to express. Therefore, only you, Mattai, can choose in this moment which road would serve best our Father and consequently serve best your soul's growth. Now go pray on your choice that it truly be for your highest good."

And with this, I was excused to deal alone with my tormented emotions.

After much prayer and inner reflection, my decision was formed. I sought out Mary and together we walked into another beautiful desert night that might have been accented with the romance that only lovers can know. But it would not be. I told Mary how much I cared for her, but that despite my feelings, I would not take a mate. I was seeing my role clearly and had chosen to serve but one master and that was God, the Father.

My decision was a painful one, and I felt even more distress as I looked at Mary and saw her heartbreak: she had bowed her head and was sobbing softly. My heart was wrenched from my chest but my decision was final, determined as I was to follow what I knew to be my course in this life. The following day we departed Lazarus' home, I with very mixed feelings of both joy and sadness.

Because of the intensity of our experiences over the past few weeks, our emotions were at a raw edge, and we needed a break. Despite the long distance, we decided to return to Capernaum, to headquarters at my home, to catch our collective breaths.

Soon after we arrived, Jeshua summoned Peter, and the brothers, James and John, and said, "You three, get ready: we are going to Mt. Tabor." After they left the rest of us waited in Capernaum. They were gone for a week.

When they returned, Peter, John and James appeared stunned by whatever had happened, almost as if they had experienced an epiphany. Usually we were all eager to share every detail of each event, but this time the three were practically mute. They seemed unwilling to explain what they had witnessed.

After I prodded Peter relentlessly he opened up some. He told me that when they had ascended to the mountain top, all of a sudden Jeshua's face became like a glowing, radiant sun and his entire body transformed into a brilliant white light, with His physical form actually fading, then disappearing, in the intensity of brilliance.

And then, Peter said, "Two others appeared beside Jeshua. These apparitions were Moses and the prophet, Elijah, and they began speaking with Jeshua."

Peter continued, "Once I recovered from the shock of what I was witnessing, I asked Jeshua if He wished me to build three shelters, one for Him and another two for Moses and Elijah. But before I received a response a cloud descended upon us and from out of the cloud came a voice: 'This is my Beloved Son with whom I am pleased; listen to Him.' I was so scared that I bent my head down. I was afraid to look up. Finally, I heard Jeshua's voice: 'Get up, do not be afraid.'

"We all three stood and then saw only Jeshua."

Peter stopped speaking. When we asked him to tell us more, he merely said, "I cannot."

We were far from satisfied with Peter's rendition; we hungered for more information, but none of them would say anything else. We chose not to pursue it further.

Directly after returning from Mt. Tabor, Peter took off for Bethsaides to see his wife and children. It wasn't long before he returned to us with a surprising announcement: he would be moving his entire family to Capernaum. Peter confided to us that his wife was displaying a snarling anger and complaining incessantly about his prolonged absences. He felt that by relocating his family, at least he would see them more consistently when we returned to "home base."

Unfortunately, Peter, on his fisherman's savings, could not afford much, and he had to settle for small, temporary quarters until he could manage something better. Unfortunately, this move did little to alleviate his wife's disgruntlement, and she retaliated, much to Peter's consternation, by moving her mother in with them, even though it was a squeeze to do it.

I was spending so much of my time during this stopover period reflecting on my own complicated emotions regarding Mary. But it was not the only subject on my mind. I was trying to come to terms with my relationship with our brother, Judas. Because of my role as overseer of the finances as well as the so-called PR director, Judas was jealous of me. He saw me as wise and smart, particularly when it came to managing the money for our little tribe. He often came to me asking my advice and counsel on many issues, such as how he might better recognize the needs of and be more available to our Rabbi, and how he might help out with the growing crowds.

While Judas wasn't quite as intellectually astute as I was, he was a deep thinker and felt things very intensely. I would often have to calm him down; in the process he would sometimes stir me up.

Judas worried about how we could better prepare ourselves for our travels and what we could do for the families of our own fishermen and merchants, for now the fisherman could no longer fish and the merchants could no longer sell goods. How could we replace their resources? He often looked to me to come up with a way to create this lost income.

Judas also very much wanted all of us to take full advantage of the growing crowds in order to solicit an army. From time to time, he would say, "The Rabbi has said that we must not fight with our swords, but this is such a great opportunity. Perhaps it would be wise to at least be prepared for defending ourselves and our nation."

Often he came to me for counsel regarding these issues, especially because he thought I had the inside information concerning the Romans. Then I would calm him down and say in a stern voice, "Judas, we cannot go against the Master's wishes. He will provide for all of our needs."

Then Judas would say, "I know, I know. But I cannot help thinking that there has to be a way that we can use all of these opportunities."

There were moments in which Judas could actually sway me to be in favor of corralling Jeshua to take political positions. It would seem to make sense to me; I would be mentally stimulated and convinced by his passion. But in the next moment I would fear his zeal and possible disloyalty.

Perhaps I understood Judas better than the others did, but I did get angry that he, always the opportunist, was forever looking to find a political edge. I wanted so completely to be finished with the politics of Rome now that I was gone from there.

I realized that there is nothing more fanatical and opinionated than a convert. From a moral and ethical point of view, I now had a complete disdain for politics, even though it had once been my way of life and my means to achieve wealth. Still, it wasn't as easy to shake as I had believed.

Jeshua never questioned Judas' loyalties, not ever. His choices may have been questionable, but Judas' decisions were truly based on his own interpretation of Jeshua's role, which he never fully understood. He believed that he could use Jeshua to his own purpose, forcing His hand to quicken the process. In a certain way, he was correct. However, his actions would prove not to produce the results he had anticipated.

Jeshua and I had our first argument, well, a discussion really, about whether we could financially manage another trip to Jerusalem.

I said, "Well, Rabboi[9]," as I often referred to Him, "We cannot afford it."

And Jeshua replied, "And by what means are you measuring affordability? Of course, we can afford it."

Not getting it, I forged on, "Well, it would be far better to take another healing trip and receive the alms and gifts from that before we attempt another trip to Jerusalem. Jeshua turned speculative, and rubbing his jaw, said, "Mattai, I think it is time for you and your brothers to have a very special lesson."

9 The term "rabboi" was often used to refer to a "way-shower," one outside the temple structure who could assist others in their spiritual pathway. The title "rabbi" referred to a temple priest. While there was a technical distinction, they often were used interchangeably.

Fourth Spiritual Law

Live in the cleansing of the body, mind, and spirit. Honor your flesh. Honor all flesh as a manifested vehicle of spirit.

Explanation:

People really need to honor the cleansing of the body. In fact, this is where some of the kosher laws come from: from the idea of not eating certain kinds of foods or avoiding certain kinds of unclean things. Bathing the body, as is the custom in our culture, is important. Just be cautious not to overdo and wash away too many skin cells, which contain our natural oils that the body needs.

It is also important to perform internal cleansing in the process of fasting. The spirit is cleansed by way of the breath, which is the fire of life. These three: outer, inner and spiritual cleansing, maintain our essence.

CHAPTER 5

Manifesting

Money, or the lack of it, was an issue that came up for us many times. We had some coins, but we also had expenses: for travel, for food, and for the replacement of our worn-out clothes, sandals, and blankets. Then there were the inevitable, never-ending taxes to be paid. I knew about the taxes only too well. It looked like the expenses certainly were going to commandeer the coins and then some.

Jeshua had been waiting for just the right moment when we would be ready to know the truth about this concern: where the resources were going to come from to finance this grand crusade we were on. He stepped in to teach us on this subject when Judas raised a question about the taxes.

Judas always had the biggest issue with money, much more so than the rest of us. "Why must we pay monies to Rome?" he would ask. "They are doing nothing for us."

Jeshua would remind Judas that one must give unto Caesar that which is Caesar's and to God that which is God's.

However, Jeshua's explanation was not good enough for Judas. He was still not satisfied and refused to let go of the issue. "What about the taxes?" he would ask again. "What should we do about that?"

Then Jeshua would patiently say, "Here we go again! What about us paying the taxes? How many times do I have to say this, Judas? Now, let me clarify it one more time: you pay to God what is God's and to Caesar that which is Caesar's. It is very simple."

Then I would ask Jeshua, "What should we do if we give all of our money away and then don't have enough for our travels?"

Jeshua answered with a parable that began with a question:

> *If a man has two coins to buy food for the day, and a beggar asks for one of his coins so that he can eat, and the man gives up one*

of his coins to the beggar, has the man lost anything? The man says to the beggar, "Here my friend. Be full and bountiful of God in this." What has he lost?

The coins of your earth represent not only your daily bread, but also the manifestation, the manna, that is given unto you. As you give what is given to you, freely, in faith, you are given more.

If it is given unto you, my friend, that you have one coin and you give it unto another, when you know that that one coin was meant to feed your child, then perhaps you feel you have given unto the beggar an opportunity to steal from your son! But when you know that unto you is given all, then nothing has been stolen and there is nothing but receiving in all parts of life.

He explained, "This, my dear ones, is my lesson and a lesson that I give to others. For there unto this day, I present you with two coins. And there on this day, I present you with an opportunity to be graced by the request of others. If you give freely, you shall receive freely. But if you withhold in fear, you will be withheld from.

"There is in you no greater gift than the gift of love, and love is the source of all things called money and coin.

"Money comes forth from love and can be multiplied in love. Money held onto is disguised as fear and shall be indeed buying you more fear. So, bless every coin in your pocket and in your savings. Bless the home where you live and the things that you wear and the grandeur of your transportation. Bless every coin that comes to you from where you see it and from where you do not see it. And give it to all, for you are not to be bound by coin, just as you are not to be bound by love. The love of your life is the great I AM."

Then He revealed how our abundance comes at times from very unexpected sources:

There once was a fisherman who had but a small boat and a net that was weak from many years of wear. The knots had been retied so many times that they were only able to hold a very few fish. Yet he had faith that this was the only thing that he had to offer his family, his only gift to sustain them. He had faith even in his own fear that he had no power to provide in any other way. One day, this fisherman put his net into the boat and rowed his boat out to sea, just deep enough to enable him to get the early morning catch. As he placed his net into the water, a large fish came swimming toward him as if to be fleeing from something else and got caught in the center of the net. In its fury and its fierceness and swiftness, it ripped through the net, leaving, unbeknownst to the fisherman, a very large hole. The fisherman gathered in his net, thinking that it would be full of fish, but what he saw instead was but one small fish, which somehow landed in a small spot where there was no rip.

Sitting down in his little boat, the fisherman yelled angrily at this little fish, "Who are you to be in my net which has many holes? There is not enough of you to feed my family. How dare you come into this net when I am not able to provide for them. You are not enough."

To the fisherman's amazement, the little fish spoke to him: "Master, I am but a symbol of all there is. There is enough of me and enough in this sea for you and for your family. Kind sir, if you will allow me to bless you, I will feed you and your family, and there will be no lack and there will be no dishonoring of you and your profession. Take me to the shore and sell me to a hungry man, who waits there."

And so, the fisherman, with nothing else to do, rowed his boat back to shore and to his amazement, a hungry man waited, a beggar man on the corner of the crossroads up beyond the shore. The fisherman walked up to the man while thinking to himself, This man looks so poor. How could he possibly buy this fish? He is but a beggar.

And the hungry man said, "Sir, I have this coin to give to anyone who will give me a fish. Give me something to eat. Kind sir, I see you have a fish. Would you please give that fish to me?"

The fisherman, because he had been so instructed, gave the fish to the hungry man. And the man gratefully handed the coin to the fisherman. The fisherman looked at the coin and saw that it was a gold coin worth a great deal. It would feed his family for a month! He said to the beggar, "But sir, do you not know the value of this coin? You could have bought yourself new clothing or a place to live. You could have bought yourself many meals with this."

The beggar responded, "But no one believed that I had a coin to pay. No one would give me or sell me anything. No one would even approach me. Sir, what I have in that coin is of no value unless there is someone to share it with." And with that, the beggar took the fish and quickly disappeared.

Then the fisherman sat and wept and thanked God for this illustration of abundance. And with that coin, he bought a new net; he repaired his boat, and fed his family well for many days, and not just with fish but also with many other fine foods he now was able to purchase from the marketplace. They enjoyed chicken and lamb, and they celebrated, for now, the fisherman knew there was indeed great abundance and God our Father is without limits and so it is.

I was beginning to understand, but the big challenge for me was about to occur.

Jeshua's next teaching was at a spot outside of Capernaum on a hilltop where He could be seen and heard.

And indeed many came, nearly three thousand people. They listened attentively, but as the day progressed, I noted their restlessness. A few of us disciples went down into the crowd; we circulated among the people, inquiring about any problems they might be having. They told us that they were hungry but did not wish to leave and miss out on any of the Master's words.

Jeshua, observing the matter, called us into a huddle and said, "We must feed these people. After all, were they not hungry for my words? Now their physical bodies require nourishment." He instructed us to walk through the crowd and collect all the food they had brought and bring it to Him.

The total amount we could scrounge up was two fish and five loaves of bread. Even so, Jeshua said, "Distribute this food among the multitude."

I thought to myself, *has He lost all reason?* Although I dared not speak my feelings aloud to Him, I did say, "That cannot be done. There isn't nearly enough food to go around."

Despite our skepticism and without hesitation, He commanded us to break off pieces of both the fish and bread and give them to the people to satisfy their hunger.

And to me, He requested that I stand with Him. He looked at me and said, "Mattai, you will be the cornerstone of this manifestation." He bade me visualize the Father standing next to us and to know that our loving Father God would fulfill all our needs. Then he instructed that I proclaim, it shall be done! and give thanks to the Father for His gifts to us, as if we had already received them. I did as I was told with enthusiasm and faith.

As my brothers continued to break off pieces of food and hand them to the outstretched hands of the people, I noticed something very strange: the size of the fish and number of loaves were not diminishing but instead remained the same, yet the people were consuming the food and appeared to be satisfied.

My lesson that day was firmly anchored from then on: a bounty can be created out of a small amount. We can multiply material goods, whether they be money, food, clothing, or other treasures.

The act of faith or anticipation of the abundance is the initial catalyst. Then comes the act of knowing and proclaiming it can be done. One must *believe* that it is already done, and finally, and most importantly, one must *thank God* as if it is done. These are essential to seeing the completion of this manifestation.

In order to manifest we cannot simply want for certain events to happen. It's not wrong to want something or wish for it; however, that is not the catalyst for manifesting. Instead, manifesting is acting in the moment of faith and declaring intent. We all encounter moments when we're absolutely certain that a thing can be done. And that's the golden moment of manifestation. Along with my faith, it was my intent, which helped to create the manifestation.

The process of manifestation, then, becomes a very simple five steps:

1. *Knowing that the manifestation can occur.*
2. *Proclaiming that it can be done.*
3. *Setting intention to have it happen.*
4. *Believing that it is already done.*
5. *Thanking God as if it is done.*

My experience with the loaves and the fishes answered many of my questions and simplified my role as keeper of the money. I now felt that we were like a commune, and I no longer had to hold tight to the purse strings. But I did wonder why we had to wait until we were in dire need of something before manifesting and then go through complicated ceremonies to get it. Why not just manifest everything we need right here, right now? But Jeshua was quick to point out that we only need answer this moment's needs. And He reminded us that all abundance comes from the Father; therefore, we must be grateful and show respect for all of our gifts.

I realized that the episode with the loaves and fishes was my initiation by Jeshua and that what He offered me had much to do with simply "being" and having faith in my own power.

I became clear and knowledgeable about how to call forth a manifestation, not for the sake of earthly glory for myself and/or others but for the sake of completing a piece of work that needed to be done.

With the loaves and fishes I learned about what had to coalesce in order for the manifestation to take place. While Jeshua held the knowing, I was a key player: Jeshua called upon me to help create with Him. Jeshua was the anchor; He asked for my vision and my faith, and He asked for me to hold the power of manifestation in my breath. There were two others involved and in that we held the unification. We blessed the loaves of bread and the fish in such a way that they would distribute themselves perfectly to feed all those hungry people. We often participated together in manifestation in this way.

This event was for me more awesome than for anyone else, partly because I had gotten it: I understood. I saw clearly that the manifestation would not happen unless I participated in it. I also clearly understood that I might have been the cause that kept it from occurring. What a powerful awareness! That I might fail was an awesome fear, but it did not stay with me long, for I shifted into the absolute acknowledgement that when I hold in faith and command from the power I AM that God be present, all is given and is completely available *now*.

And so it was done and of this I am reminded: that I need call that ability forth for everyone in my reality, not to appease their ego's need to show off its bounty but to fill the need inspired by God.

Jeshua told me that God makes no judgment of the fancifulness of human life, for extravagance is provided as grandly and abundantly as is the simple piece of bread for the beggar. It is all given in equality from the

Father. So there is no judgment about anything that life can offer.

Whose power is it then that brings glorious wonderful things into one's life? It is the unification with God that brings these gifts. Humanity has yet to see how this works. When people awaken and remember that it works within and through oneself, then there will be no more hunger in the world, no more cold, no more disease. Then no one shall walk this earth wounded again.

A common pitfall one encounters in this consciousness is the need or desire to figure it all out. That foray into intellectual territory actually keeps one from experiencing the wholeness. It is to simply "be." In the beingness state, the "doing" comes naturally, without any effort at all.

One day we were walking along the desert road feeling hot and thirsty, and we started to complain. Jeshua reminded us that our needs are always fulfilled.

As He was speaking, we saw an oasis up ahead. Reaching this refreshing spot, we were quick to guzzle down some water, then we sat down in the cool beneath the shady trees. It was easy then to reflect that our physical needs were always satisfied.

Jeshua, of course, was one step ahead of us: "Not only are your physical needs always met, but so are the needs of your soul. You can think of it as your physical need for water: as you drink your thirst is quenched. So too, when you thirst in your spiritual quest, the answers are revealed unto you. The answers come in the form of spiritual words, experiences and understandings. These gifts cause you to feel uplifted, fulfilled and complete, as they assimilate into your being. And then you can share your newfound joy with others. In doing so, we are instruments of God in assisting others to fulfill their soul's quest and enrich their lives. So be it!"

As we were continuing to walk down the road, I shared a troubling observation with Jeshua, "Master, I know that God gives abundance to all that ask and yet, I see people who have many needs. Some lack enough food to eat and some lack shelter. There are many poor. I have seen them. Surely they ask the Father, but still their needs are great."

Jeshua gave me a compassionate look and said, "Yes, you need ask for it, but you need also to be willing to receive it. And there is a difference between the two. How many times does the human ego cry out 'give me, give me, give me. God, why does the universe not give me this or that?' Well, you simply haven't opened up to receive it. You just need to quit complaining, and step into your power. We don't always want to do that because down deep we feel that we don't deserve His gifts. But it's not true. However, those are the manipulative games we play to support the ego's survival. Remember, though, all of our earthly activities serve our soul's growth, so never consider that any of the games played are wrong."

He added, "Along with this is fear, fear of not having enough. Or even, 'what if I get what I want? What will happen to me then? I will have no excuses. I would have to change my self-defeating attitudes and beliefs that there is not enough for all of the people. I would have to believe that I have the power to create and I have responsibilities to shape my own life.' These ideas are scary to many."

Jeshua always said that an obstacle to manifestation can be contained in one little word: resistance. I knew that there were those who did apply these laws but who were not able to bring into form that which they desired. Jeshua counseled me, saying that lying within us many times is a resistance to receiving what we want — perhaps we feel undeserving — or simply resistance to accepting a specific universal truth. He advised me always to acknowledge and honor any form of resistance that might be present. In that way the soul keeps moving ahead. When our circumstances seem to be breaking down, it is not really so: it is simply that a breakthrough is occurring. This is the ongoing process of the universe giving us always just what we need.

He illuminated me further: "Whose power is it then that brings glorious and wonderful things into my life? It is my unification with the Father's gifts that brings these. There are periods of time when I cannot see how it works. Yet, when I awaken and remember how it works in me, with me, through me, and for me and for all who come unto me, then it shall be!"

Jeshua went on to tell us that tithing is a facet of receiving. "A good demonstration of faith is found in the concept of tithing," He said. "It is a very necessary part of your concept of abundance.

"Remember," He continued, "our ancestors recognized and taught the importance of tithing, that we must tithe ten percent of what we receive and give it with an open heart to God. You may give it to the temple or you may gift it to God's people who are in need. In tithing, when we give, we receive back and our lives become enriched. The amount you tithe will multiply and come back to you tenfold."

Jeshua had allowed for me to see that my abundance does not come from Rome. As a tax collector I believed that my income depended upon my collection of the tax money. But now I understood instead that my abundance came from Father-Mother God, the Infinite Provider.

I was now functioning as a manifestor, recognizing how all needs are always met in perfection. I knew that I was able to manifest because I held as truth my personal ability to do so. I also knew that it was not only I who could manifest but everyone else could as well, and I committed to teaching people this truth, not merely by my demonstration but by my words to them that they held the same power as did I. While I knew that I was not responsible for seeing to it that everyone else develop his or her God-given rights and skills to manifest, I could be helpful in this regard and could provide them with a valuable gift. To teach the people how to manifest for themselves would be a greater service than providing a miracle. But looking at it another way, teaching people how to manifest might be the greatest miracle of all. I likened this idea to teaching the people to fish instead of manifesting the fish for them.

Fifth Spiritual Law

Be thou knowing the Father as that source which gives breath. Be thou knowing the breath as that pulse of energy, which is thought. And with thought be one with the Creator. Be thou knowing that you are more than thought, for thought moves through you. You express through the breath, which is the intent of thought, a frequency shifted by desire to a frequency that is the cause for all you experience.

Explanation:

Simply, the act of desiring something to manifest in your life causes it to happen. Particularly, when that desire is felt deep within the heart and expressed through prayer and affirmation. Then it is answered by the Heavenly Father. Of course, the desire will always occur in God's perfect timing.

An example would certainly be when one deeply desires to serve God and do His will. God hears that intent. There should be no fear or hesitation attached to that desire, for fear blocks the fulfillment of God's promise to us.

CHAPTER 6

The Blessings

Even larger crowds appeared now. People were flocking in droves to see Jeshua. So many desperate people were pleading to hear words of hope, even though some did not fully comprehend the depth of Jeshua's teachings. Many of these people sought healing from physical ailments: chronic pain, seizures, blindness, deformities, and infectious diseases. The mentally ill approached us, and so did those who were possessed by spirits of the dead, and they all begged for help. Throngs of people awaited the latest miracle, some of them asking for their loved ones to be raised from the dead. There were so many people asking for help now that it was overwhelming to me at times.

Not only did large numbers of people greet us when we arrived at their towns, but now we even had them at times following us wherever we were going. Jeshua accepted with grace and ease the challenge to serve everyone who asked, no matter what their needs were.

One day we entered the outskirts of Bethphage, a small town close to Jerusalem. Jeshua said, "It is once more time for the blessings. Go into town, my brothers, and inform everyone you meet that tomorrow morning we will assemble at the town gate and walk up to the Mount of Olives where I will teach them."

Again? I thought. *This will be the eighth time for these blessings.* The first time Jeshua had spoken the Blessings was on a hillside in Galilee not far from the sea. This kind of meeting place seemed to serve well the people's needs.

Even though this event had been repeated, I realized that each time Jeshua spoke the Blessings I felt more uplifted. And each time He spoke them I learned and understood more deeply their full meaning.

The next morning a large crowd gathered at the edge of town. And when some of those people caught sight of Jeshua, they shouted out, "Behold, here is the son of David."

Jeshua informed us that we should head for a specific place in the mountains, a spot He knew would be perfect for all to be able to see and hear. We began our trek along a path into the mountains. As I glanced back, I saw a long line of humanity twisting and turning like a giant serpent along the trail up into the Mount of Olives. Finally, we arrived at a flat knoll atop a rocky outcropping. Jeshua pronounced, "This is the place."

We settled ourselves next to our Rabbi and waited for the journeying audience to arrive and position themselves just below us. As they took their places, I could clearly see that there were thousands of people who had come; I would estimate at least five thousand. The crowd quieted down, and Jeshua began to speak.

I was amazed at how Jeshua's voice projected, booming out so that all could hear. He was wise indeed to have led these people to this particular place where there was a canyon below. The canyon helped to move the air currents so that everyone could hear His Word.

Jeshua blessed this place, and He blessed all the peoples of the world, then began his teaching of the eight blessings, that came to be known as The Beatitudes.

The Beatitudes seemed a bit enigmatic, but they were not meant to be unsolvable mysteries. Rather, they were stories within stories and messages within messages, each level meant to stand and be understood on its own.

On this hillside where we were witnessing a gift of nature with her echoes and her beauty, Jeshua brought forth a message of truth and of healing. Of the thousands who were there, hundreds received these messages in their fullest meaning. They got up renewed, free and clear in their minds, whole and happy; they went on to share Jeshua's concepts with their families and friends. There were also those who left in a hurry to return to their daily affairs. They hadn't really heard Jeshua's words. Still others heard only a word or phrase, hardly Jeshua's entire message, but they gleaned enough meaning to move onto a new path in life. They were now able to see beyond Jeshua's words, even to the effects they had on others. Indeed, they could see those around them shining like lights. In their awe they were able to find God in new ways in their day-to-day lives and experience their own connection with the Divine Light.

When Jeshua had stopped speaking, I realized that this was the most important, profound teaching He had ever given to His largest crowd yet. And now there were those coming to me asking whether I could help them understand what Jeshua's words meant.

So here I stood before these hungry people ready to teach them a new way of living, a new way of loving. As I received His assignment to teach, I found that His words deepened in me and I could give them with more definition in more complete ways.

The Beatitudes are eight spiritual laws for living. Taken to heart and followed with passion, lives are enriched, made easy and filled with joy.

The First Beatitude

Blessed are the humble for theirs is the kingdom of heaven.

This spiritual law espouses that one should not allow a personal view of another person to dominate. Rather, if asked an opinion of a particular person or his actions, one might say, "I know that he has within himself the ability to choose the correct path and do the proper thing; that is, he is capable of doing the right thing as he contacts his inner God self."

We are sometimes self-inflated with our own knowledge, excessive desires, wants and lusts, influence from family, public honor, dogmatic religious teachings, and material possessions. We become prideful. These worldly things prevent us from exhibiting our humility; hence, we are prevented from truly experiencing the kingdom of heaven. In the kingdom of heaven we know the love of and Oneness with God. The kingdom of heaven is found everywhere, including here on earth.

The Second Beatitude

Blessed are they that mourn, for they shall be comforted.

This beatitude needs to be clarified in its understandings, especially in reference to its implication about suffering. Most often people suffer because of the loss of a loved one. Erroneous interpretations find that since Jeshua blesses those that suffer, he encourages people to take on a role of suffering. But that is not His intention. Jeshua blesses those who have chosen the path of suffering, so that their suffering can become worthwhile and transformed into positive outcomes.

The concept of mourning may be confusing, leading us to wonder where it fits in, when God wishes for us to be joyful, rather than sad. But accepting the challenge experienced when we mourn deeply allows us to reach out more profoundly to God in order that we might be comforted by Him.

It is sometimes human nature to go to an extreme degree in pain and suffering before getting to the truth. But the Father informs us that to suffer any pain at all, whether physical or emotional, is entirely unnecessary. Instead, we can embark on a search for truth through spiritual means, by disciplining ourselves and by expressing unconditional and unlimited love towards all life. Through this, we can find spiritual enlightenment and receive the many blessings of God with ease. These truths ultimately will set us free.

The Third Beatitude

Blessed are the meek for they shall inherit the earth.

This rule seems contradictory, for those who seem to be the opposite of meek are usually the ones who appear to have the most power and are the most involved in controlling worldly things. But here Jeshua referred to a state of meekness, which means to be open-minded and, as such, to allow our faith in God to predominate, to sublimate our will to God's will so that His will is done in all things.

To do this it is important for us to step out of our own way to enable His will to manifest. After all, He knows what is best for us. And the end result of His manifestation is but another level of "inheriting." What do we inherit? We inherit much through the manifestation of good health, abundance in our businesses, and harmony in our lives. In fact, we may receive riches in all of our life's experiences. Amazingly, as we relinquish control and hand it to God, we receive complete dominion over our lives. We truly "inherit" the earth and all thereof. The glory of God and all of His riches are poured upon us.

The Fourth Beatitude

Blessed are those who hunger and thirst for righteousness
for they shall be well satisfied.

Righteousness infers right living and right conduct, but righteousness is far more than that, for it includes right thinking. Right thinking means having a loving attitude toward others and maintaining thoughts that would promote joy and harmony in every aspect of our lives. Think of Jeshua and how He demonstrated to all how He thought.

Our external life is but a reflection of our inner state of being. Whatever you wish for in your external world, you must first really believe it deeply within yourself. Your moment-to-moment thoughts must encompass this belief, for what we are truly about inside, in our deepest being, is reflected in our external world. This is true in all things — our health and wealth, satisfaction and fulfillment. To receive more love, we must first love ourselves and then love those around us. Do not be confused. The individuals we choose to love may not be the same specific persons who return our love. But according to divine law, love will always be returned sometime, by someone, somewhere.

The Fifth Beatitude

Blessed are the merciful for they shall obtain mercy.

This simply means that you should not judge others, and by not doing so, you yourself will not be judged, for if you were to judge others harshly, then you will in turn be judged harshly.

It is easy to find fault with our fellow men, but we should not do so, for as he has encountered difficulties in his life, it is felt by all. Those difficulties are experienced at some level by everyone because we are all one. We are all God's children and are living on earth together in the same kettle of fish, so to speak. A very important aspect is that until we walk in another's sandals, we cannot know the reasons for those acts with which we are finding fault.

Keep in mind it is not merely what we do and say or write as expressions of our judgment, but it is also what we think. This is another important aspect of judgment. In our thoughts we find fault and judge others that we presume have committed incorrect actions.

We all also play in the arena of self-judgment for words and acts of the past. Self-judgment is just as incorrect as our judgment of others. We must never judge ourselves harshly for anything we have done, because this is not consistent with self-love. Sometimes, of course, self-assessment is valuable for reviewing behaviors that seem not in accordance with the unconditional love that Jeshua expresses moment to moment, in order that we can change and improve these in a positive, loving manner.

More people are suffering from the pain of self-judgment than might be realized, and this pain interferes with their spiritual growth. So with every thought and deed, we must constantly bless completely not only all others but ourselves as well, all aspects of the self: body, mind, spirit, and we must pray for the highest good of all to prevail. In this way we are merciful to ourselves.

The Sixth Beatitude

Blessed are the pure in heart for they shall see God.

Those who are pure in heart are souls whose hearts know not anger and hate but are full of love, and they know that God's love will sustain them, no matter what. Whether sickness, loss, or sorrow should touch them, it matters not, for God is there at all times. They feel and know profoundly His love and support. Their reward is that they achieve a personal relationship with God and grow in that relationship ever more. Every day they know God as a friend, not simply a casual friend but an intimate companion that they can depend upon without fail to supply their every need.

The Seventh Beatitude

Blessed are the peacemakers for they shall be called
the sons and daughters of God.

Beyond the obvious, in being peacemakers for others, we must see ourselves as peaceful within. When there is a storm of conflict within our hearts, there will usually be chaos around us. The greatest advances can be made in our spiritual growth when we are creating an inner peace and are serene within, for at this time more than any other time, we are open to receive God's gifts. It is like readying a vessel so that the essence of spirit may flow in freely and fill with God's energy. As this occurs, we become as His children. And our heavenly Father is heaping His gifts upon His innocent children.

The Eighth Beatitude

Blessed are those who are persecuted for righteousness sake,
for theirs is the Kingdom of Heaven.

Here is a good example of the many layers of Jeshua's teachings. The first understanding of this blessing is that people have been persecuted or killed for speaking God's truth. Because these martyrs so bravely went forth to share with others the truth, as they knew it to be in their hearts, this is a particularly poignant understanding of this particular law.

To clarify it, though, Jeshua broadened the interpretation. He said, "Blessed are those who live through their commitment to serve God." This, then, is the meaning with the most relevance for the most people.

Subsequently, when He said, "Blessed are they which are persecuted for righteousness' sake, for theirs is the kingdom of heaven," it was never prescribed that any of us be martyrs. That was never intended, and how sad that the words and ideas are interpreted to mean that mankind must follow Jeshua's path of sacrifice.

The concept of persecution needs to be better understood. Each person's kingdom resides according to his individual state of consciousness. One can focus his consciousness in the kingdom of the lower earth, under dominion of the kings and other rulers. Or one can live through the kingdom of the mind, ruling others. Still another kingdom is the emotional one, where there are many levels of domination. But to live in the kingdom of heaven means living in the belief of God's omniscience. And they who do choose the kingdom of heaven are most blessed.

Why could one be persecuted by man for speaking the truth? Because others are arrogant in their belief that their God is the only God and their way is the one and only way. The truth is that the One God reveals Himself in different ways to different people. So we must have respect and tolerance for other people's beliefs. Some people think that there is no room for other people's beliefs; others reject people who seek to live the path of correctness and alignment with the Father-Mother God.

In reality our inner selves set up our own persecution when we need it. Why? Because the soul desires perfection and to achieve perfection we require spiritual growth. By bringing to us challenges that feel as if we're being persecuted by others, we might change and grow. Our greatest soul desire is to have a close relationship with the loving heavenly Father. Consequently, the soul continually strives for that, whether we consciously recognize it or not.

Since our souls continually strive for Oneness with God, we are continually given opportunities to achieve that state. Sometimes these opportunities feel very good to us and we welcome them; at other times they feel painful and we might wish that they had not come to us. However, they all are blessed events; they all represent our rightful due, giving us exactly what we need in order to grow in our relationship with God.

God brings forth our gifts always, even to those who do not recognize the Father or know what their spiritual path is. There is blessing even for those who live within the threat of a curse, for God presents Light into their specific choices and removes the darkness and confusion. It is for people to understand their true blessings, that their sufferings are only illusions that fall away as a result of the many gifts from the kingdoms of the Father.

Jeshua was well trained in the mysteries of the Kabala, which explained the many kingdoms of heaven. The Kabala refers to the Tree of Life, which can be thought of as a blueprint containing four dimensions, or layers, that are sometimes called the four kingdoms. Within these kingdoms are still more layers of understandings; one can think of these as a superimposition of layer upon layer upon layer.

While I never studied the Kabala, I received its gifts like a sponge. Jeshua taught us portions of this great spiritual philosophy, giving its teachings in parables. Jeshua was clear that one kingdom was not better than another, that each one served equally and justly the level of awareness and consciousness of its path.

Jeshua said, "When you are persecuted for following my teachings, be glad, for you will inherit the kingdom of heaven. Even though you may be persecuted for doing God's work, you should rejoice because your rewards are great and you will know God's love in all the spiritual realms." He explained that the other part of this gift held that if it is one's goal in life to know righteousness and keep positive thoughts, then God's promise is a reward for the sacrifices.

If we do not continually entertain loving thoughts foremost in our consciousness, then a loving God provides a wake-up call for us.

One of the great aspects about the day Jeshua taught the Beatitudes was the party we had afterward. We finally dispersed all the people, but in order to do so, we had to repeatedly say to them, "Please, you must go now.

The Master needs His rest. Please you must go. Come to hear His teaching again tomorrow."

At our insistence the people finally departed and we were alone once again, just the thirteen of us, to celebrate the day's happenings.

As we sat back with our cups of wine we animatedly looked back at the miracles and laughed in delight at the people's profound joy. Thomas said, "Did you see the man who amazed himself by dancing on his once crippled legs?" And Simon remarked on the woman who fainted after seeing light emanating from all thirteen of us. I noted the antics of one woman not so pleased by the occasion: this woman, who was crippled, screeched in anger because all around her were those experiencing miraculous healings, yet still she could not walk.

As we replayed the events, we smiled, mindful that we were smiling with our people, not at their expense. Their joy filled our own hearts; we appreciated each person's uniqueness and perfection, as the words and miracles touched them in different ways. We also realized that while each person had his or her own personal story, truly, no one was very different from another.

As Jeshua joked right along with us, I finally said, "Master, after speaking to all of these people, how can it be that you still have a voice?"

"Calm yourself," He said, "There is nothing that will be drained from me; no life force can be taken from me except that which I give unconditionally."

And I quipped, "Then at least have another drink of wine so that you may clear your throat."

And He said, "I cannot argue with that, Mattai." And so He did imbibe the wine. We ate and drank wine until the early morning hours, when we fell asleep under the trees.

The evening had been grand fun; the spirit of the evening and the drama of the people's response was the essence of our purpose, for this wasn't labor for us but simply a joyful expression of a joyful day. Oh, from time to time, Peter would grumble about not being able to fish. Thaddeus might try to stir up some heat for getting organized. And Judas was up to his old games. He repeatedly said, "Let's get them going. Let's make zealots of all of these people. We have thousands here. We can create an army." He was so full of passion and still continually talked about taking up arms.

Jeshua could command an audience because that which He spoke was so different from what the people had been hearing from their leaders. They also came to us because of the miracles they hoped for: those who lived in fear desperately needed the miracles because they provided for them a link to their wholeness. And simple curiosity drove some to His audience: these people had heard the stories of Jeshua and the promises He made, and they became impassioned in their quest to personally experience His presence. Jeshua would forever be known for having touched these souls in these sermons.

One cold evening around the campfire, we got into a heated argument about who should, or for that matter, could, enter the kingdom of heaven and what did they have to do to enter it. Our thoughtful Phillip conveyed that only certain people, who had proven themselves special in some way, should be able to enter the heavenly kingdom. Jeshua reminded everyone that the "humble" shall inherit the kingdom.

In many religions, like ours, where disagreements were voiced and unresolved, there were divisions from which new sects sprang. These sects dictated behavior among their pious people and determined their levels of learning. These levels of learning were particularly important: through them some felt that they would be exalted to a higher position in God's kingdom; others proclaimed that by passing more tests or engaging in certain actions and rituals they would gain an improved access on their pathway to God. It was perceived that initiation rights gave one a better "key" to enter the sacred kingdoms. Pointing to the false nature of this understanding, Jeshua said, "You do not need to produce results to prove worthiness. The greatest and only requirement is love."

He continued, "If a man be humble and open in his being to be one with all that lives, all that breathes in God, then he is already in the kingdom of God. For where is the kingdom? The kingdom of God is within. It is not that which is elevated to a place that is beyond this earth. But it is that you are aligned with that which is the hosts of all living God. And there in the kingdom within, you dwell in peace. You dwell in joy. You dwell in love for there is a unity."

And then He added, "We make no mistake by assuming there is a difference now between being humble and being proud. Here I am only saying that the humble are open and willing for there to be the merging.

"And let it be known that for all of those who wish more understanding of this that the inheritance is given to all. It is not withheld from anyone. However, it is only those who are open to receive it that shall know it. So there is no one that is denied an inheritance from the Father-Mother God."

The discussions became heated then because someone would say that God certainly would not allow certain elements to exist in His kingdom. For example, some believed that the Romans would not be allowed in, neither would be the Samaritans. Many groups were thought to be excluded. The younger James said, "Well, let those groups have their own kingdom then, because they have their own God."

Then Jeshua would remind us that there is but one God, and that their gods being true or false are all part of the one God, whom we serve. Then we would all have to consider once again that God is displeased of nothing and no one. He illustrated this truth with the story of the prodigal son:

> *A wealthy man had two sons. As they grew to manhood, one wanted to be independent and go off to experience the world. So he asked his father to give to him his inheritance so that he could do the things he wanted. His father blessed him and sent him off with a good sum of money. The young man went to distant places and had many experiences. One day the reality hit him that he had spent all his inheritance and he was now penniless. Because he knew no one in this far away region and his only skills were those he had learned from his father growing up on a farm, he had difficulty finding work. At last he was offered a job, that of feeding and caring for a herd of swine. It was a lowly job and did not pay much; however, he was hungry and desperate. After weeks of his demeaning duties, he became so hungry and sad that he decided to eat the food that he was throwing to the swine. Having done that, he was only further depressed because he could imagine that even his father's servants were eating better than he was. That night he asked God for assistance from his sufferings. The next morning the answer came to him. He should go home to his family and ask his father if he may work in the fields as a servant. He thought that in his father's employ, he would eat better and live better than he was*

at this moment. He thought, I will throw myself on the mercy of my father. With his mind made up, he set off to see his family.

When he finally reached the road leading up to his family's house, he was spotted by his father who shouted, "My son has returned to us. Kill the fatted calf and prepare a feast for we must celebrate his homecoming."

So they welcomed their son and threw a great party.

After the son explained that he had spent his fortune and wished only to work as one of the servants, his father pronounced his decision. "No, you shall work as my son by enjoying your position with all the privileges you had before you left home."

Upon hearing this, the other son, who had remained with his father and faithfully performed all of the tasks required for running the farm, became annoyed. He was upset and said to his father, "Father, why would you do this? I have been a faithful son who did as you asked and I never demanded nor spent my inheritance."

His father replied, "This day is a glorious day, for my son was confused and had become lost. Now he has seen the truth and has come back home to me. This is a time for rejoicing for my lost son's newfound understanding and for his return. I will bless him with all that I have and so it will be."

Jeshua said, "The heavenly Father will always take us back even when we stray and deny and separate ourselves from Him. He will always bless you no matter what. For we are His beloved children and will always be such in His eyes."

Jeshua told us that the key to all of the Beatitudes is *the blessing.*

Blessed are they and blessed are those.

Blessed, blessing, and blest.

He told us that instead of just eight blessings, He could have delivered hundreds of them, because, truly, the Father blesses everything. But He chose these eight because within them were contained crucial tenets for living in harmony with all of life.

He also reminded us that the key to understanding lies in deeply exploring why and how it is important to bless. This is true whether you choose to bless that which you wish were true and proclaim it in its truth or bless that which you wish were not true in your experience and proclaim the healing of that through the blessing.

I then understood that the key to these blessings was not to dissect the eight verses to the point of philosophic analysis. Yes, they had meanings that were pertinent to the politics of the day and could be considered in that context. But the higher, unlimited understanding lay in the gift of blessing from God. He who proclaims blessing regularly is showing gratitude regularly, and, as a result, he receives more blessings than he can even measure, and, therefore, his blessings overflow his cup.

Consider the beatitude "Blessed are the meek for they shall inherit the Earth." The kingdom of God is in Earth as it is in Heaven. Those that shall open their beings in meekness, and surrender to the power of love, as they master the physical life on earth, they shall indeed be the keepers and the dwellers in the *new* heaven, the heaven they create right here on earth. Even greater, the earth becomes transformed through them.

Our very involved, intense conversation that evening about the meaning of the kingdom of heaven, who could reside there, about the messages of the beatitudes and the experiences of the people in Jeshua's audience ultimately resulted in a grand clarity of perception for all of us.

We all thought that the event was hugely successful, and afterward, we were in a joyous, celebratory mood. The holiday of Passover was approaching. We were pleased when Jeshua stated to us, "You twelve along with Mary Magdalene will go to my house and spend some time with my mother, Mary, and my brothers and sisters." I know He missed them.

Sixth Spiritual Law

Forgive all things. Give all in joy. Forgive all who walk with you. Forgive your words. Forgive the words of others. Forgive the deeds that you have done, and the deeds that others have done. Forgive and live in the gift of our Father-Mother God's love.

Explanation:

It is a way of saying turn the other cheek. Sometimes to turn the other cheek sounds like martyrdom, suffering. It isn't to say, "Gee, I really like that. Let me have it again. I'm a masochist." No, forgive and start fresh.

CHAPTER 7

A Family Like All Others

As we approached the home where Jeshua grew up I remembered that it was more elaborate than others in the area, owing, obviously, to Joseph's design and construction wizardry. The house was constructed primarily of stone and mortar, and it featured extraordinary, decorative exterior masonry. It certainly showcased Joseph's creative artisan talents.

A group had gathered at the door, and they greeted us warmly. Jeshua's mother, Mary, stood in front, her kind face and gentle smile a welcome sight. Jeshua's brothers, James, Joses, Simon and John were there, along with His sister Ruth and a new face, little Hannah. Elizabeth, a neighbor and also close confidant of Mary, was also there. I noted that even though Joseph was now gone and some of Jeshua's brothers and sisters had moved away, this house still bustled with activity.

As we moved inside where this remarkable family had anchored itself, I found myself again fascinated with the intricate ornamental woodwork. The structure had two stories with open beam ceilings and wood floors. The upper floor contained a large gathering room. Off to one side was a smaller enclosure, which served as a family meditation and prayer room. On the main floor there were three bedrooms: Joseph, when he was alive, and Mary had occupied one; Jeshua and His brothers had shared the second, and the girls, Ruth and Elizabeth, had slept in the third. Now, Hannah occupied Elizabeth's bed in the girls' room. A large kitchen and dining area served as one great room. Only light cooking and warming were done at the kitchen hearth. The major cooking was accomplished outside. Here rocks were heated for food preparation in a small fire pit. Some were then lifted into the bread oven for baking, and the rest were put onto an open cookery where meats were roasted on spits. Overhead branches of dried palm leaves weaved together to cover the outdoor cooking area and form a semi-enclosed ramada. Stone covered the floor surface.

After washing up we settled in to talk. As was the custom in Jeshua's household, both the women and men took part in the conversation. Everyone was eager to hear about our latest adventures; they took particular delight in the humorous stories we were able to relate, and often their laughter was occasioned by the telling of good-natured wrangling between Peter and me. This day was no exception: Philip related a story, which caused Jeshua's family to break out in gales of laughter.

He said, "You guys missed out on a good one. We were all walking beside the Galilee, and the sea air smelled particularly fishy. Mattai was in a very crabby mood that day, and he grumbled loudly, 'This air smells like bad fish!' Peter, ever the fisherman, with a sublime expression on his face, stuck his nose in the air to take a sniff. Then he replied serenely, 'It smells like honeysuckle to me.'"

Later James led us all in prayer. With Jeshua away most of the time now, James held the position of eldest son and acted accordingly as head of the household.

We were served a fine feast, certainly comparable to what we had come to expect of Mary and Martha's culinary talents at the house of Lazarus. At the meal's conclusion we settled into the gathering room for more sharing. And then the time grew late and we all retired.

The following day I was up early and encountered Jeshua outside speaking to His brothers. I joined them and James asked me if I would like a tour of the grounds. While I had visited Jeshua's home before, this was the first time I had been offered a complete tour. I quickly agreed and off we went. We came to a large, open field in back where James recalled, "This is where Jeshua and I played our childhood games." Large trees lined a walkway leading straight across a field to the back of another house with a patio facing us.

James said, "That is where my mother's closest friend, Elizabeth, lives. I often went over to see her when I was just a boy. She was like an auntie to me as I was growing up."

Then James gestured to a building and said, "Come with me." We meandered over to a wooden structure and entered through a large door.

He explained, "This building is divided into two sections. This part was my father's workshop when he was alive. This is where he did his woodworking. These benches are the ones he used to carve the furniture he created and over there are his tools."

James looked up and pointed to the rafters, "Up there are the racks where my father stored his precious wood. He would lay out his wood in straight rows, and he always sorted the different types separately. Over to the side he stored the new furniture. My father was always very organized. Now, my brother John has taken over. He was well trained by my father for this wood crafting profession."

Moving on to the other half of the building, I could see that it served as a barn. James said, "Here we keep our animals: these two donkeys serve as transportation and these two goats give us plenty of fresh milk." He added, "When He was old enough to take on household responsibilities, it was Jeshua's duty to care for the chickens and other animals. As my brothers and I grew, we too shared in these duties."

We moved outside of this combined barn-shop, sat down and James recalled, "When our family traveled, my Mother, Mary, rode on her special donkey. She liked this particular donkey because it was gentle and surefooted. The younger children would ride with Mother or sometimes by themselves on the other donkey. Sometimes even my father joined them on the donkey. Our trips were great fun: we always laughed and joked along the way. Jeshua would often run ahead of us just so He could see over the next hill and be the first to spot an interesting view of the city of our destination or maybe just to explore the land and look for wild creatures along the way. We constantly had to keep calling Him back. All in all, we had great times together."

Our talk was interrupted by the appearance of Jeshua's sister, Ruth. She greeted us and asked me if I was enjoying myself at their house. "Indeed I am," I responded. "More than you know. But one thing would add to my pleasure, and that would be getting to know you a little better."

"But of course, Mattai," Ruth replied sweetly. "What is it you wish to know about me?"

James got up to go inside, and Ruth and I moved over to the largest tree in their yard and sat down underneath it. She smiled and said, "I have spent many hours under this tree. It has protected me from the sun and the rain alike. I feel very safe and secure here in this spot."

I focused my attention on Ruth, now twenty-two years old. She was slender and quite lovely, with fine facial features and like her mother, she was very feminine and graceful in manner. On this day she wore a long, lightweight, blue-green skirt made of an elegant fabric. I complimented her choice of dress, and she said, "Thank you, Mattai. When you say that, I feel like a pretty woman."

She then recounted, "My Uncle Joseph brings beautiful fabrics to us from faraway places. I sew them myself. I love to sew." Ruth also wore a long, silky scarf around her neck. It was hand-painted with flowers done by a professional artist. It accented her face to advantage.

"I have a wonderful life," she started out. "It is filled with so much fun and happiness." Laughing now, she added, "I admit that I love to get really silly sometimes, especially with my brothers and sister, but I have a great family, and they always understand when I seem to bubble over in jest or enthusiasm.

"When I was younger I helped take care of my grandparents before they died. I was very close to them. I always felt that they knew of their special purpose with my family. Through their love they formed a strong foundation for all of us to accept our destiny and be able to grow in ways that we needed to."

Ruth told me that her mother and father had given her a spiritual education starting when she was very young. "My mother was particularly influential in my life," she said. "She is able to heal with her hands, you know, with the energy that comes from her heart, and she passed this gift along to me through her teaching. I feel so close to her. When I think about my mother I always hear her melodic voice, because she loves to sing as she goes about her household chores. I love to hear her voice."

And about Joseph she added, "My father started work early and ended his day late in the afternoon. For part of his day he trained my brothers to be woodworkers. I had little interest in Father's workshop, but once in a while I went there just to be near him. He would be working on several pieces of furniture at a time, carving one piece while the other was being dried. My father loved his craft. He did a big business and received lots of orders from the townspeople. He learned his trade from my grandfather and he assumed, I think, that his sons would learn from him, but while he tried to influence my brothers to enter into the same profession, only John continues on with it today."

Ruth said that her father's work always afforded us a good living. "We always had plenty of what we needed," she told me. "We ate well. Our chickens offered their eggs, and our goats gave us milk. I learned when I was young to milk the goats and I got to be very good at it, but the milking had to be done very early and it wasn't always so easy to get me up."

She spoke of their mealtime. "The diets we got accustomed to when we were children continue today. I always drink goat milk for breakfast and eat goat cheese at noon. We eat lamb and chicken several times a week, except on the Sabbath and when we are fasting to cleanse our bodies. Then we eat mostly fruits and grains; those are particularly enjoyable for me."

And they weren't always alone for meals. Ruth explained, "I remember when we were growing up that we often had other family members over to join us for our meal, and the women all got together in the kitchen to cook. How noisy it got. Our family was always very important to us and we had many celebrations together. Mother knew how to bake tasty pies and other desserts and she loved to cook. Fortunately for all of us, she still loves it and hasn't lost her touch. I love the scent of her sweet treats; when we get wind that one of her luscious confections is about to pop out of the oven, we certainly all gather round. She taught me well for I too have the art."

Ruth then described her daily life: "My parents established a household routine to which all of us children were expected to adhere strictly. We always rose early in the morning, washed, and got dressed. Then it was time for our prayers and meditation. I was disciplined to sit for quite a period of time. 'Forgive and breathe,' my parents trained me. 'And be one with God; serve the family and God before serving yourself in selfish ways.' When I was old enough, my job was to do the daily sweeping. Everything was to be kept very clean, particularly the terra cotta floor tiles in the kitchen. Later, when my sister, Elizabeth, was old enough to help with the chores, I began to assist with the cooking and dishwashing. When not helping around the house, I loved to play with my sister."

Ruth entered school when she was six. "I went to the Essene school at the edge of town," she explained. "I walked there and back every day, rain or shine. Along with learning writing and reading, we were trained to discipline our minds and to know the blessings in all things. Our training also included how to channel divine energy, and we had classes dedicated to teaching us how to be oracles.

"As my Essene education was progressing, my long daily prayer and meditation turned into even longer periods. We were trained to be able to focus our minds and to sit in silence for up to three hours at a time and to be in communion with ourselves and with God.

"I had to memorize many of my lessons. After school I would meet with Mother and discuss the teachings with her, and she would regularly offer explanations. I received daily direction in my life from my teachers, my parents, and during my silent time of prayer and meditation. At night I studied with light from an oil lamp."

Later on, Ruth lived at her school. She said, "When I was eight years of age, I was given a room at the Essene school, where I would stay for two week periods, for special training and initiations. There were times when we were not to leave the sanctuary in order to deepen our spiritual awakening. My spiritual activities were my love and my wish. The Essene teachers told my parents that that was my calling.

"Each student was assigned a counselor, a special teacher and guide. We would have a one-on-one relationship with that guide: student and mentor. In my case my teacher guide was much older; he was very kind and had a wonderful sense of humor. He supervised my education and consulted my parents on what kind of homework I was to do and what disciplines to focus on. His name was Solomon."

And then she said there was a culmination of her education. "I had an ordination in the Essene school when I was fourteen. I was blessed and received a special head cover, which I still sometimes wear. "Our schooling was complete at age fourteen. Then it was time to get married, have a family and keep a household. I haven't married, although I do have a very special friend in my life, with whom I have a close and abiding relationship. I guess you could call him my sweetheart."

But she added, "Early on, I made a commitment to my spiritual life, and now I, too, am a teacher at the Essene school. My work keeps me very busy. In fact, nearly half of the time I live at the school; the other half I spend here with my mother.

"You know, Mattai, it might be said that I have had an easy time of it, and I cannot argue with that. Everything seems to have gone my way." Laughing again, Ruth said, "Perhaps I inherited my mother's special ways!"

And then sobering slightly, she added, "I cannot say the same for my sister Elizabeth. It seems she always has struggled; she has not always been so happy and carefree. I often think how interesting it is that members of the same family can have such different experiences." She smiled and said, "Well, Mattai, that just about sums up my life."

Later that day Mary's friend and neighbor, Elizabeth, invited us over to her house for refreshments. Elizabeth had a fascinating background. She was trained with Mary in the Essene school as a handmaiden of God. When Mary was chosen for a particular and very unique mission, the two of them became close friends. Elizabeth said, "We bake, sew, market, and even counsel each other when an intimate friend's guidance is needed."

Elizabeth was married to a wealthy member of the Sanhedrin. The couple never had children and were always at odds regarding their religious views.

Mary and Joseph's children were always in and out of Elizabeth's house; she disciplined them like an aunt would, while acknowledging that Mary would always have the last word in that. Elizabeth often acted as a co-hostess at Mary's. In a sense Elizabeth's life was lived through Mary and her family.

On the third day of our visit we twelve had decided that it was time we heard from Mary herself. I was particularly interested, because I had always wondered about her life. We had always heard such wonderful things about Mary; her manner was so soft and gentle, always filled with compassion and kindness to others.

I said, "Now, Mary, we all want to know about your life, about your intimate experiences with God and our Master Jeshua. We want to know everything about you."

She replied, "Let us all gather in our great room and you shall hear my story."

We went upstairs and sat down in a circle. Mary's eyes literally were shining with the love and the reflection of her glorious life.

She began, "I remember when you all first came to visit and I couldn't remember all of your names. I thought that I would not be involved with you or be burdened by having to converse with all of you." Mary laughed. "It was silly of me to believe that I could just ignore you guys, that I could simply put the food and wine on the table and leave you all be. At the time I was thinking, *after all, I really have enough to do! I have been taking care of this family for all of these years, and now my children are bringing their children for me to teach and to bless, as a grandmother would do. When do I get a break?*

"But my idea of just ignoring you certainly did not work. There was a point when I knew that there was no way you were going to let me get away with that. You guys were so animated, so intriguing. I was really tested to know you in depth."

Mary began with little-known facts that preceded her birth. "Much of who I am today I owe certainly to my mother, Anna, who molded the early part of my life.

"I did not know for a long time the parameters of my destiny — by that I mean all the circumstances of my future — but my mother understood only too well. While she was growing up, many future events were revealed to her and also to her brother, my uncle, Joseph of Arimathea.

"As my mother related it to me, she and my Uncle Joseph were like two sides of a coin. They each contained the same spiritual knowledge, but they came to it in different ways, and they would play out their roles differently too. By the time they came to be adults, their lifestyles were quite different. Joseph of Arimathea became a world traveler; my mother stayed at home.

"Both Uncle Joseph and my mother knew from an early age that their lives were not destined to be ordinary. As children together they had visions, often seeing things simultaneously that foretold a future, one of hope but one also of forbearance and pain. They were schooled early about preparations they needed to undertake in order that I would be well prepared for what was to come.

"My grandparents really didn't know what to make of their children. They were peasants, you see, unschooled themselves and not capable of seeing to their children's education. So Anna and Joseph's schooling came in different ways that were not so understood outside of their own experience. From an early time my mother seemed to be rather 'out of herself' and her brother would hear words spoken through her that he knew were not hers.

"Through this vehicle Uncle Joseph gained knowledge of future events, as they would unfold. My mother received information in a different way: she saw pictures flash into her awareness. For example, she told me that even when she was a girl, she saw me, her daughter, large with my child, Jeshua, and knew that I had not lain with a man to become pregnant. She also saw me in the stable with a bearded man called Joseph. She saw my baby as He was humbly born. She saw many things, but I had the feeling that she did not reveal all to me."

Mary continued with her early life: "After my mother married my father, Joachin, and I was born, they turned their attention to my training as their first priority. As a child I was shown many things that other children were not. Because my parents were visionaries who knew my special mission and purpose, they devoted themselves to my preparation and training and saw to it that I was brought into the inner circle of our community to learn.

"When I was six I was sent to the Essene school to study the religious traditions of the Torah and learn about life. My school sat at the outskirts of Nazareth, near the one where Jeshua was educated. This was a day school exclusively for girls. We all returned home each day after classes; we never lived at school. Very few girls had the opportunity to be so elegantly and completely educated, and I considered myself one of the lucky ones.

"I learned to read and write in Aramaic and Hebrew and learned many other subjects that for the most part only our men are taught. While we girls were trained to be on an equal footing with men, it was only in a certain small segment of our Jewish society that true equality existed. By taking up these subjects, I was truly stepping out of the cultural mold to get my education.

"Beyond these courses, I was selected for another most unique training. Because of the visions and prophecies that our people had been told about, it was believed that a Messiah was to be born in our community, born of a young betholta (virgin). Seven young girls were singled out as possible conduits for this Messiah's birthing. I was one of them, and we seven entered a period of intense training to become handmaidens of God. The Romans would have seen us as vestal virgins, or goddesses. I guess we were so-called goddesses in training.

"We were taught the meaning of the sacred rituals and how to correctly carry them out. Our training was full-bodied: in other words, not only were we growing spiritually but we were also developing the energy of our bodies and minds. We learned how to focus all elements of the body, mind and spirit for healing purposes. While I always had an innate knowing about how to heal others, these studies intensified and better directed my abilities.

"We also learned about the Kabala, which, as you know, is seen as an expanded thought of the Hebrew religion. We learned of the many facets of God, how God is not just a male figure but encompasses the widest spectrum of male and female attributes.

"By the time we in this inner circle of training had reached the age of eleven, we were much refined, very learned and most obedient young women. At age thirteen we went through the traditional rites of passage, marking our entrance into womanhood, where we were prepared for life as wives and mothers but more importantly as tools of God. While all the young girls in our culture were initiated in this traditional ceremony, for the seven of us, the preparation was much more rigorous."

And then Mary said that things became even more intense: "As the time approached when we would renounce all earthly pleasures in order to serve God completely, four of the handmaidens abdicated, leaving three of us to continue on. We three were sent into seclusion for an intense period of deep prayer and personal cleansing. My beloved confidante, Elizabeth, was one of the four to leave training, and she, along with the others, assisted and supported we remaining three during our isolation.

"And then one day I met Joseph!" With this rather abrupt change of subject, Mary grinned and paused, as if teasing us about whether she would continue on.

We were on tenterhooks with our curiosity, John, so much so, that he pleaded, "Oh Mary, you're not going to stop now, are you? How was Joseph chosen to be your husband?"

Her smile now becoming wistful and her gaze distant, Mary continued, "Joseph held a position of note in our community as well as in the temple. He was chosen for me as a result of the visions of our priests, and our engagement was arranged according to our community traditions. My mother and father were instrumental in these preparations, as was the custom, and my Uncle Joseph of Arimathea, who was always active in our family activities and also a leader in societal affairs, acted as the marriage broker, bridging between all interested parties.

"Just after my engagement was announced a miraculous event occurred. I was nearly fifteen at the time and in a deep prayer state when I saw before me a great shimmering Light. A voice sounded from that Light and spoke, announcing that this was the Angel Gabriel appearing as a messenger. The voice said to me, 'Hail Mary, Beloved One, handmaiden of God, we greet you. I have been sent by God to beseech you to open yourself in order to receive the Holy Spirit, for this day we proclaim you the mother of the Child of God.'

"At this I wept and in my own way blurted out, 'Wait a minute. Back up and stop a moment. What are you saying?'"

Mary laughed at herself as she recalled the episode and went on to relate what she said next, "Of course, I know I am the handmaiden of the Lord. Of course, I am here to be the mother of all of God's children if that is what God asks of me. But I am betrothed now, and I do not understand your message.

"The Angel Gabriel responded, 'Your betrothal is sealed in the heavens and, behold!, the child will be in you now.'

"And with that I felt an extraordinary heat radiate from inside of my body. My womb began to pulsate; my heart fluttered, and I became faint. I started to weep, for I felt within me an energy that was so great it seemed almost impossible to contain.

"I felt my soul consciousness actually rise up out of my body. As I continued to rise up, I spun into a whirling energy where I was in the essence of a beautiful dance with the Holy Spirit of God. I don't know how long I was in this state, but when I became conscious of my physical surroundings once again, I was slumped in a prayer posture, and tears were soaking my veil. I knew then without a doubt that my purpose had been given to me.

"Yet even though I now knew what my purpose was, I had no clear understanding of it, nor did I know where the path would lead me."

Mary said that after this momentous event and completion of her prayers, she hurried to tell Joseph, her betrothed, what had happened. "After hearing my story, he wept and kneeled before me. He kissed my feet, then my hands and stomach. He stood and kissed my lips and said, 'I am honored to be your husband.'

"We then made plans for our upcoming union and I left to visit my cousin, Elizabeth, whom you all know as the mother of John the Baptist.

"When I arrived in Capernaum Elizabeth greeted me with a warm knowing. I had not told her I was coming, nor had I told her of my pregnancy. What a surprise it was then when she instantly proclaimed, 'Blessed are you among women, and blessed is the fruit of your womb.' Some say that knowing these things is women's intuition, but in Elizabeth's case she had received her own vision; that is how she knew.

"Elizabeth perceived a holiness and sacredness about me. I say this in all humility; I do not claim to be special in any way other than to honor the God that dwelled within me.

"It was obvious that Elizabeth herself was in a family way with John. She gave me some tips and pointers of what to be aware of as I went through my pregnancy, because you'll remember I was still a young girl, and I'll admit to being a bit fearful of the upcoming birthing event. Elizabeth told me that she, along with other family members and friends, would be there to help in my son's birth. At that time it never occurred to me or to Elizabeth that my blessed event would take place somewhere else entirely, away from my hometown. I was eager to return to Joseph and left for home forthwith."

When Mary returned she said she found much discussion about the coming Messiah: "The other handmaidens, through the telling of the prophecy and by their own visions, were aware that the Messiah was to be born among them. While they had some doubts, they surely thought it to be true, and each wondered if it would be she who would bring forth the Blessed One.

"As the time for fulfillment of the prophecy drew near, ritual blessings took place and conferences were held in our temple. There, after much rumination and, I admit, great suspense, it was confirmed that I was the one carrying the child, the Messiah. This was a period of much jubilation, that what had been so sought after for so long, prayed for so long and so devotedly, would come to be.

"Now, you may be wondering what the effect of all this was on a newly betrothed couple. Well, actually, Joseph and I went on quite as usual, doing all the busy things couples do to prepare for their futures. And along with that, Joseph was being specially trained for fatherhood by the Essene priests now that my role had been so clearly defined.

"As you know, a betrothal is considered like a marriage. While not yet sanctioned by temple ritual, the engagement is a first step in the marriage confirmation process. We had vocalized our commitment to each other. Joseph and I were assembling our home, getting together the things we would need to begin a marriage. Within two months we completed the temple ceremony and shortly after that we were united in marriage at a community service. Joseph was nineteen years old at the time, I just fifteen."

Mary then told us of Joseph's unique qualities. "Joseph possessed strength and quietness, traits needed to allow and support God's plan. He made no demands on me and always considered that this child was his child. There was no doubt of his feelings on the matter. Joseph possessed no egotistical attachment to the concept that for this to be his child, it must be conceived from a seed from his physical body. Moreover this impregnation by the Holy Spirit could not have occurred without the blessing and energy from Joseph. It was the gift of his vibration of energy and could not be separate from him.

"Though the act was not a physical act of procreation that caused my pregnancy, still the baby's genetic patterning was Joseph's pattern. It would be silly for me to believe that Jeshua looked just like His Father, our Father in Heaven, because remember His Father has no physical body. So, while Jeshua contained Joseph's hereditary background, Jeshua's actual Father was our Father Divine in Heaven acting in a spirit of direct alignment within my womb."

We were spellbound by her words. While this story was developing, Jeshua was out and about with Mary Magdalene. Mindful that we were away from Jeshua's hearing we encouraged Mary to go on, telling us some of the family tales.

She began, "Life wasn't always easy, you know, because our family was fragmented. We picked up and ran for the first few years of our married life. We didn't land in any one place for long. We were moving all the time. We were first in Bethlehem, then we fled to Egypt and stayed for a few years before returning to Jerusalem. Finally, we settled here in Nazareth. It was so good to be home. My best friends, Aunt Hanna and Elizabeth were close by, and my mother lived just a morning's walk away.

"The family fragmentation didn't stop when our moving stopped. It continued as my other children were born and as my husband, being such a busy man, had literally no time for the family. It was not an easy family life. I did not have a husband full-time and my children did not have a father full-time. The times we did share were wondrous because Joseph always talked about the principles of our faith. He helped to guide me through our Essene traditions.

"I suppose my family might have been considered dysfunctional. But we were simply a family, a perfectly normal family, like everyone else's. It would have been easy to find fault and complain about what didn't work, but I learned to celebrate what does work.

"And so, in our family, while there were problems and issues to be worked out, truly, there was not much friction. But that was not the case in some other households. Some of the wives were so discontented that their husbands would take long journeys to get some freedom away from the screaming women. That has always been approved by our society."

Of community life Mary said, "We women always supported each other, though, and that made life more harmonious. We would congregate together to share our loaves and do the laundry. We baked together and all communally cared for the children. There was no isolation, and this was very nurturing.

"During the hard times when the women were feeling unsupported and overburdened by their mates, I could counsel with them, because I understood their issues; indeed, I had the same ones, but had found a way to work them out. I urged them toward a remedy, which, in truth, was simply a healing of their own heart. I encouraged them to take more of a leadership position within their families, to call a gathering at the family table and lay out the issues and tell of their importance and then to humbly and with vulnerability declare their own needs.

"Surprisingly, when one does that, they find out that their mates' needs are much the same as their own. It isn't so hard to come to agreement when these questions are raised: How should we deal with one another? What needs to be done? And to admit that sometimes we cannot do for another, because we can barely do for ourselves.

"When a request is made to share the load, not only with household tasks but emotionally as well, and agreement is reached, then no one has to feel that there is a lack, because everyone is pulling his or her own weight and receiving support. It is important to stand firm for truth, for there is unity despite its seeming fragmentation.

"Unfortunately, some take the tack of abandonment, putting asunder the family unit. But that does not really solve the problems, does it? My husband, Joseph, never abandoned us. He did not go away. He stayed home, except that he was busy in his shop a lot, like you guys are often busy with your work.

"And now it is necessary that we bless that you thirteen are a family unit and a holy one indeed."

She spoke of her personal trials and of her children: "One of my greatest challenges was with my beloved daughter, Elizabeth. She was not completely aligned to our family's purpose or my Son's teachings. She became angry with Jeshua because she perceived that her brother had abandoned us and was wayward with His wild, crazy ideas. Her anger spread to encompass the entire family, and she left to prostitute herself on the seamy side of town. My heart was broken, for I thought that not only had I failed Elizabeth but I had lost her as well. I prayed and prayed for her redemption, and now Elizabeth has seen the Light. She recently returned to us. Elizabeth heard the stories of Jeshua's work and that He was offering forgiveness for all, even the prostitutes. She came and asked for my forgiveness and also Jeshua's. I have welcomed her and continually thank God for answering my prayers. Today, she is with her husband.

"Except for Ruth and John my children are all married, and some have children of their own. John is very sensitive and very much heart directed. He has a wondrous balance of his feminine and his masculine sides. As you know he is a master carpenter and works in his father's wood-making shop. He earns money toward our support.

"The last to join our family was Hannah. I knew her spirit and considered her part of the family, and I brought her into the household. She is only five years old and such a Light. Her eyes sparkle as they reflect God's love. She reminds me of an angel."

Hannah remained a mystery to me. Mary had introduced her hurriedly into the discussion and had quickly moved on. Somehow I knew that how Hannah had come to be part of the family, where she had come from, was not a subject to be probed.

There was a rustling as we shifted positions to again get comfortable, anticipating Mary's portrayal of her eldest son, Jeshua.

"He is of a royal bloodline, you know, truly a prince," she started out. My father's family is descended from our beloved King David. Joseph's family are descendants of King Solomon. So you see, when two royal family lines come together, this is an undeniable evidence of a royal lineage. Our Jeshua, the Jeshua you know, is truly royal by all standards.

"My feelings for Him are most heartfelt. Jeshua has been both my greatest joy and my greatest agony. What mother would not be proud and pleased with her firstborn? What mother would not be nervous and having doubts about her ability to do the right thing with a firstborn who is precocious enough to speak truth to you before His age of wisdom and also precocious enough to say that He will not be your child but rather the child of God? This is a most perplexing thing. One feels at the soul level that this is a perfectly wondrous idea, but from the human perspective it seems at the very least preposterous but if true, then full of great pain.

"So the pain for me began for my ego at the moment of conception when I knew that I would constantly be surrendering the ownership of this child. In the end I could do so only because I had faith in God's plan and felt deep down within me that it would lead to an expansion of the consciousness in our land, indeed throughout the entire world and for all time to come.

"Many parents feel that they own their children, just as it is a belief by some that husbands own their wives. It is part of a certain consciousness. My soul always knew better than this: that one person can never own another, but still as I acknowledged that Jeshua's relationship with me was not the primary one, it was hurtful. Every mother hopes that she is the first and the last love of her children's lives. I do know that Jeshua loves and respects me deeply. During those years when I was unable to understand

His mission, I prayed constantly and surrendered. The period when the idea of losing my beloved Jeshua began to be particularly intense was when He set sail with my uncle, Joseph of Arimathea. He began to be away a lot and I was feeling the pain of that separation."

Mary related to us a somewhat amusing little story about the authoritative Joseph of Arimathea: "Everyone knows my Uncle Joseph as a successful man of the world, a merchant capable of wheeling and dealing with the best of them, a truly powerful man. In his capacity as a world traveler, he was able to be a way shower to Jeshua. Joseph took my son to all these different cultures and introduced Him to so many master teachers. He was indeed responsible for Jeshua's education in this way.

"But, interestingly, as able as he is in the world, he is all thumbs when it comes to the family. He seems not to know sometimes how to handle some of the issues that come up. What is little known, and I think quite amusing, is that Joseph has always had to answer in family matters to his brother, Zachary's, wife, Hanna. My aunt Hanna is very slight of build, you know, but that certainly didn't stop her from keeping Joseph on the straight and narrow. She was a constant reminder to Joseph of his contract with God and his responsibilities with Jeshua."

Then she returned to the subject of Jeshua: "When the time came for Jeshua's life to become public, when He would go forth to teach and when He gathered you twelve and others around Him, there were moments when I became very angry that He would not be the leader of our household in a more prominent way. I have felt cheated at times that He would lead the world but not lead His family. I shifted my expectation to have James fulfill that role, and now I fear I put quite a burden on him, or so it seems. So that is my continuing sorrow, which is an ongoing healing process.

"The funny part is that I feel much joy at the same time I feel sorrow. I wish that I could now tell you all that I have risen above it in every moment, but I have not. I have worked diligently to rise above it. I have asked God to help heal my pain, and I have had healing. But it is not complete. The challenge continues for me and also for everyone else who loves Him.

"Everyone who loves Jeshua feels a personal deep soul connection that is more profound than anything they have ever known, and everyone wants to possess that feeling. They want to own Him, to claim that they are His best friend. But you all know that only too well. I hear about the jealousy and competition among you. You strive like children to get His attention. He is like the father whose children vie for attention and say, 'Don't you love me the most? Look what I can do? Am I important to you?' You all still play that game in some fashion. Everyone does who wants to be part of Jeshua's life. What we have all learned is that He never ever chooses favorites. He loves us all the same, and with the same profound divine completion that we long for with one another.

"I would love to tell you all a story of Jeshua as a boy." We all shifted in our seats and smiled expectantly.

"When Jeshua was eight years old, He was beginning to learn the Roman language. So when He would tell jokes, He would use the languages of Roman, Hebrew, and Aramaic and mix these languages while making puns or plays on words. It was quite a mental exercise for Him. He was far more mentally advanced and sophisticated than most children His age. He was far more deep and satirical in His renditions. He often got frustrated with His classmates as well as with us, His own parents, because at times we simply didn't understand His jokes. And He would say, 'Now listen. Listen to what I have said,' and then He would repeat the joke, believing that if He said it one more time and slowly enough that we would all finally *get* it.

"One time I said to Him, 'Jeshua, the joke is on you if you think that all the Father in Heaven wants of you is to belittle people for their lack of knowledge or for their slowness of thought.'

"And he said, 'Mother, I belittle no one,' and then He said, 'It is with your spirit that I give these words.'

"And I said, 'Jeshua, what in the world is that supposed to mean?'

"And He said, 'It is you, Mother, who has taught me my humor.'

"About that time I wanted to disappear. But I said, 'All right.' And we had a good laugh. But I added, 'You must be sensitive towards others who do not receive that in the same spirit.'

"And Jeshua said, 'Yes, Mother, I shall remember that.'

"That episode was just one example of the many moments when He was getting the best of His mother. He had extraordinary wit and He certainly knew how to get me."

I chimed in, saying, "Well, I'll admit I still do not get some of His jokes, and I've remarked to Him in a humble way, 'Master, you simply can't tell jokes.' He just smiles at me."

Mary continued, "Jeshua has always had the gift of language and an innate understanding of the subtle nuances. It was the way He learned to put words together. In retrospect I see that this was one way He could confirm for Himself that all things are connected and that there is truly no separation, that all languages are a part of the one language, the language of Love, the language of the Divine. And that, my friends, is my Son at His greatest seen from my eyes."

We all thanked Mary for taking the time to fill us in on the things we had had so many questions about.

That evening before we retired I went to Jeshua with a request, "Master, during the last several days I have communed so much with your family and friends and have heard so many personal stories. Now I have some questions for you. May I have some time alone with you, for you to assist me in understanding more clearly some of your teachings? I have many questions as to how they apply to me personally."

Jeshua smiled and nodded, "Yes, Mattai, I believe it is time for you to receive a deeper understanding of issues that dramatically affect you in your life. In the morning after our prayers and breakfast, come to the prayer room, and we will talk, just you and I. This will be our time."

SEVENTH SPIRITUAL LAW

As thou art in all and in wonder of everything present in your world, so are you in heaven and heaven is in you. Therefore, behold your world in love, in radiance. For thus only is God's purpose fulfilled.

CHAPTER 8

Jeshua Speaks to Mattai

Ateh, Malkuth, Ve gebura, Ve gedula, Leholam. Amen.

Thou Art the Kingdom, the Power and the Glory, Forever and Ever. And so it is.

Jeshua had just given me His unique blessing and anointment. As He faced me, He touched two fingers that He had dipped in frankincense oil to the middle of my forehead, then moved His hand down to my stomach, after that to my left shoulder and finally across my heart to my right shoulder. He finished by opening His arms wide.

During this sacred moment I murmured my thanks and then was prompted to ask Him, "Jeshua, you have often anointed us and others with the oils of frankincense and sandalwood. I know that you have spoken of the value of these oils in treating and protecting us against diseases. Are there other benefits for their use?"

Jeshua replied, "Yes, these oils contain powers that not only stimulate healing of the body but also protect us in spiritual ways. They act as an invisible armor, sealing individuals from negativity that would harm them. I use the oils both to accelerate the action of physical healing and to trigger openings so that people can receive gifts from Spirit."

I had many confusing issues in my life and many haunting questions about His teachings that I passionately wanted to have clarified. I had been waiting patiently for His undivided attention, and now I finally had it. From His holy and wise lips, my burning questions would be answered. I considered this time He had set aside as sacred indeed. And He was committed to teaching me personally.

Jeshua greeted me, "Well, my friend, are you having a good time?"

I answered, "In general, I am having a good time. However, there are moments when there are not such good times."

Jeshua responded, "Yes, well, these moments present an opportunity to ask the Father-Mother God for peace. And now, I do command the peace within you, just as we calmed the water, 'peace, be still.' This is the simple request of your own inner being. You have the power. You even have within you the energies to create peace, and please remember the power and the glory are yours forever. Peace be with you. Enjoy, knowing that all that has come before you is for your peace and your pleasure.

"When something appears to disrupt that peace, blame it not, nor have anger about it, unless you want anger to be your friend, to be your breathing companion day and night. Let anything that disrupts your peace at any moment be breathed in as a gift that does not disrupt peace but is a realignment into deeper peace. Let that disruption be blessed in the creation of peace where it has previously not known peace. Like a moth to a flame, there are moments that occur which disrupt the peace in order to restore the peace.

"In other words, a disruptive force can become trapped in its own anguish while seeking peace and not knowing where to find it. Then it finds that its anguish might lash out at times where peace is very present, because this force is drawn to that peace. But its anguish instead is exhibited.

"Is this confusing for you? Let me give you an example: if someone comes into your peaceful sanctuary and argues with you, that argument may be amplified because of past unresolved situations. And it may be magnified as that soul runs its anguish against the Light. The anguish reveals itself in order that there may be an opportunity for it to be cleansed and aligned into a great peace. It might seem that this soul exhibits this behavior in order to control and change the environment into its own hateful hell. But there is no greater power than the love that you can keep drawing upon, for even when your own anger is aroused in response, or your own disruptive thoughts arise, you can bless them and be grateful for them, for these thoughts are the exhibition of energy seeking alignment, and you are in the position and the power of love to glorify that. So be it."

Jeshua knew that one of the matters concerning me was the event at the fig tree. Once when we had returned to Jerusalem after a time on the road, Jeshua saw a fig tree on the roadside and because we were hungry, we approached the tree intending to pick and eat its fruit. However, as we got closer, we could see that there was no fruit to be found on the tree. It was barren. The tree indeed seemed to be rejecting us by not bearing fruit to serve our hunger. Jeshua's response was to proclaim that this tree would never again bear fruit. Within a few minutes as we watched in awe, the tree withered right before our very eyes. We asked, "How did this happen and so quickly?"

Jeshua said, "With faith and the absence of doubt, not only are you able to instantly cause a tree to wither, but you can manifest even more profound things. You can, just by saying so, believing you have the power to do it, cause a mountain to crumble and fall into the sea. With your intent and faith in God, these things shall be done."

The incident at the fig tree troubled me. It brought to the fore all the concerns I had about the issue of rejection. I had so often felt rejected during our journeying by the many people who wanted no part of us and wouldn't offer us a place for the night or even a bite of bread.

Jeshua asked, "What is your concern about that day?"

I responded, "Well, the thing about it is that the rejection you received from that fig tree by its not bearing fruit was enough for you to put that tree into a state of dormancy. So what is considered a rejection? There are some issues that I observe which I consider rejection, but I am not certain. It is like when I ask for assistance from a person, perhaps for help choosing a special gift or about a place to stay and they choose not to cooperate. I know they could help, but they choose not to, even though I am convinced they could have done so. Please clear this up."

"I see," responded Jeshua. "It is not within the personality's power to punish or to retaliate for rejection, neither is it within their divine power to do so. But there is the law of 'cause and effect.' Within that natural law we can experience the consequences of rejection and envision that through rejection there is an expanded opportunity to grow.

"Now, while rejection can be real, sometimes what seems like rejection might, in fact, actually be choice. Someone may not be rejecting you at all but simply choosing something else for himself."

Jeshua continued, "Our interaction with the fig tree was a perfect example of what I am speaking about. You perceived that the fig tree rejected you, me and your other brothers. But what if I were to tell you that there was a larger divine plan? What if I were to say that God had divined that the fig tree would be barren and that I would cause it to wither in order to teach you a larger lesson about the true power that all of mankind has? And this may really surprise you: what if I were to say further that the fig tree had given its permission for all of this interaction? That would surprise you, would it not? Well, Mattai, I tell you, that is exactly what happened. You can then never judge the purpose and intent of another's actions."

He said, "Our personalities tend sometimes to act out disappointment or to act out anger or revenge when we perceive rejection. But we should never act in these ways, for to do so is playing the divine role in such a way as to assume that another's so-called karma, or so-called path, is within our vision. But it never is. All you can do is know that when there is an energy of rejection directed toward you, you can absorb that feeling and merge with it.

"When another in your world denies you, seemingly rejects you, because they are following their true heart song and their vision and you have not seen what that is, you simply have to trust. Whether their actions are of the highest good or denial of their highest good, you may command that the 'Lord God of their being' show them immediately their blessing multiplied or their self-curse multiplied.

"It is not up to you to decide which one it is, blessing or self-curse. It is just up to you to give them the blessing of the Law of God's energy. The law states 'what you give out, you get back tenfold.'"

And then He pointed out the difference between a blessing and a curse: "If your human personality made a decision that because 'you have rejected me, may you have tenfold rejection,' that would be a curse. If you say, 'because *you* have rejected *me*, I hope you suffer what you suffered me, I pray God to smite thee,' it would be a curse. And remember that a curse is born of fear. But it is a blessing to say 'your actions felt to me like denial, but I do not know your purpose or your reasons for so doing. Your actions may have seemed appropriate for you at that time. So, I bless you to experience this event fully.' This is a blessing because it has come from the heart of hearts. And the individual that has been fully blessed learns from his trials quickly and becomes clear of them. And all is multiplied in joy. But keep this in mind: a blessing would indeed be a curse if you were to decide how God's Light should be experienced in another soul."

Jeshua went on: "To be in the divine flow means accepting all situations that come to you, accepting them as they are without judgment, and making the best of these situations. When you do not and instead deny or curse another, you hurt yourself and you also hurt the other person, for it interrupts the energy that is designed to be played out. With this knowledge, the lesson for all concerned can be more quickly learned and integrated."

He then pointed to this: "In the context of all we have been discussing here about our human interactions, this one truth is key: it never serves us to expect someone else's behavior, which we may not like, to change. The only way to truly find peace is to accept their behavior, align our feelings and change our own response. We can truly only change ourselves, and that is what we must do.

"When you find yourself frustrated with the activity and behavior and choices of others around you, you should feel the frustration moving very quickly into acceptance and forgiveness. Then give yourself the intention and the gift of the proclamation:

> *I now forgive everyone for everything they do. I now forgive everyone for everything that I believe they do. I now forgive everyone for everything I think they do. I now forgive everyone for everything they say and everything they do. For everything they are is who I am.*

"Then, it is essential that you make these intentions, so that when you feel the human frustrations, when you feel the judgments, when you feel anxious, when you feel incompletely aligned or if someone else is not aligned with you, instead of indulging yourself and making excuses and reasons for all of the issues, instead simply breathe forgiveness about it. This is a practice that will quickly bring you into extraordinary unity with the divine. It is usually one of the simplest things that most humans tend to overlook. Even though they know it in theory, they refuse to practice it until after they have had their tantrums.

"Many humans walk around thinking that if everyone else would get their act together, then they would have it easy. For every moment they indulge in that thought, they keep themselves away from their unity with God. For every time a human panders to his judgments and suffers pain about daily experiences and supports that indulgence for more than a moment, that person acknowledges the illusion that something stands in separation from him or her. That acknowledgement should instead be expressing that: 'I love it completely and embrace my freedom of choice.' This would then be a process in forgiveness and an extraordinary expansion of how and where you will see the divine and how your memory will quicken to all that which has come before you and also all that you will experience in the future.

"Before I answer more of your questions, Mattai, I would like to share a story with you:

> *A Samaritan was walking down the road and was met by a member of the Jewish Sanhedrin. The Jewish priest spat upon the feet of the Samaritan as he passed him. Later, the Samaritan met a Nazarene who also spat upon his feet. As the Samaritan continued to walk down the road, he met a black man who came from Nubia. The Nubian bowed to the Samaritan in humility and asked if he might share his supper with him. They sat for a long while at the side of the road discussing their journeys, where each was heading. The Nubian explained that he had come to explore this country. It was never brought up between them the fact that each had experienced difficulty in their travels due to prejudice. But as they looked into each other's eyes and saw deep into the soul, each realized his similar challenging experience.*
>
> *When their long meal was completed and they both had brushed the crumbs from their lap, they stood and wished each other well. Then the Nubian said to the Samaritan, 'You are, my friend, on a journey that takes you deeper into God than it does anyone who has spat upon you.'*
>
> *The Samaritan replied, 'I am honored that you noticed.'*

"For in human life, the down-trodden, as some say, at times band together.

"The Nazarene led a much less spiritual life than the Samaritan, even though he felt that he was chosen because he practiced the Essene faith. But indeed, he was much less aligned to the grandness of God. The Nubian brought a perspective of challenge from his nation, and, by his color, said it was easy from his perspective to ignore the differences between people because he knew that they are all equal in God's eyes. Yet, he knew in the eyes of the Samaritan that others felt there was a difference.

"This story was told around Nazareth and beyond, and my Uncle Joseph told it to me when I was a child. So you, my friend Mattai, I tell you this story to remind you not to look at the down-trodden as less than you are and that there are in every human concerns and fears that may be unrecognized or unaccepted. But whether today you are in the body of a Samaritan, Nazarene, or a Nubian, you will always have the same God, and you always have the same path of pain.

"But pain was never God's intent. Pain comes from the belief that others are 'less than' and that if you were spit upon, you were less still.

"From time to time people in a culture speak out and say, 'We are equal but you others are not treating us as equals.' And while this is a good thing, we are to forgive ourselves all of our transgressions against others.

"Mattai, listen to me closely: that Nubian was *you* in a past life. The blessings that you have today are the result of our acceptance and decree of God and God's truth."

I reflected for a time, then marveled at this revelation. And then I moved on, asking Jeshua, "What is original sin?"

And Jeshua answered, "Our original sin was our choice to separate ourselves from God. While this could never happen completely, we are in our illusion of being separate.

"'I AM the Truth, I AM the Light, I AM the Way.' Mattai, you have heard me say this to you many times. The I AM is our inner being within our hearts that represents our connection with God. This is a sacred space.

"To clarify the I AM meaning, it is that flame residing within our hearts that represents the Father-Mother God, the God within, the God manifested in man. The I AM presence is the presence of God in the man, the Christ in you. Father is the initiator of creation. He is the director of intent. He represents inspiration, thought, or idea, the energy of love. The Mother is that which births the formation, the energy of will. The Son is that which is manifested, the manifested Christ. This is the result of the initiation of creation and the energy of will. This is form, even though it should not necessarily be interpreted as being dense. It is the actualization of these two energies. It is the I AM presence.

"I AM sounds very similar to the sound Om: this sound signifies that beingness of existence within us, that is 'God.' Remember the time that I spoke to you of my journeys to India? There the masters taught to use the mantra Om in their meditation when they are calling to God. You said, 'But teacher, if there are such great teachings and they are not Jewish, who will go to this kingdom of God?'

"And I said to you, 'All children on this earth are of God and I bring you the teaching as He who is One in God. There are others who are One in God in ways that I have not yet even known about.'"

I was amazed, "But how can that be? I have understood you to be the Messiah, the One."

And Jeshua said, "Do not tell others that I am the One. But I AM One. Do not let others know that they must convert into this religion, for it is the religion our fathers have given us. The Father, who is beyond our fathers, knows that all religions lead unto Him and unto His heart."

I continued along this vein, "Master, you told us all previously that your perspective about life and about God had expanded to encompass all religions and all beliefs. If that is so, how does your expansion correlate with the Torah teachings? Is the Torah no longer valid?"

Jeshua responded, "Indeed, Mattai, all teachings are valid, and all are joined by a thread of truth that leads to Father God. In the case of the Torah, it has been written for a more simplistic understanding for the general population."

Then I asked, "Well, then if that is so, Master, why must we follow this religion of our fathers? We could just as well follow the religion of Hinduism."

And Jeshua said, "As an example to those whom we teach, we do not have to shake away or deny the truth of our fathers, but instead we fulfill that truth and expand upon it in order to bring the greater truth forward. I encourage you to meditate and to pray, so that you can teach others to meditate and to pray. You show them by your example.

"Thank you, my friend. Thank you for listening and thank you for listening unto me as One and One we are, One I AM, One in the Father-Mother God as are you by your proclamation and by your desire."

I asked, "I have questions about the Buddha and your relationship with him as well. You always said that you learned so much from him. It seems to me that he is revered above others; even our sister Mary

Magdalene speaks words that came from the Buddha, and yet you say that you are the Son of God. Can you clarify for me your relationship with God? How does Buddha fit in? What is your relationship to him?"

Jeshua said, "I never spoke that I, in my humanness, was the true and only Son of God. That is misstated and misunderstood. The I AM is that I proclaim to express fully in me.

"I came after Buddha in the physical world. Buddha's presence here was for another time, another teaching and for another purpose. Buddha's treasure was to a world that knew bondage and a caste system. His gift to the world was of a new manner of relating to physical pain."

Jeshua went on: "I received Buddha's teachings as part of my education. And I allowed his teachings to be incorporated into my message of balance for individuals on their journey here on Earth. I have not come to Earth to become the messenger that will cause a new religion. That has nothing to do with my Christedness. My purpose is that in the region where I come to fulfill a law of Light and of love, I will touch others such as yourself who will then go about and teach still others this truth, because most do not have the opportunity of journeying to the land of Buddha, to the land of the Druids, to the land of the pyramids. So I encourage that you and your brothers go out and teach those who cannot reach elsewhere."

He added, "My teaching is the synthesis of all these things and of the Light and of the simplicity of God's truth. And I then speak that I AM the Way, the Truth, and the Light. Not Jeshua the man, but Jeshua, the I AM Presence. So when I speak to you, I tell you that the one true Son is not I, the Son, but that which I incorporate as unity with the Father. People say that I AM as Jeshua, the one true Son of God and that I came from God as His only begotten son. The true message is that I am not born to be the only Son of God, but the Son I AM is the Son that we all are. It is the part of me that is at One with the Father, the I AM."

Jeshua continued, "However, everyone who lives on Earth also dwells on Earth because they are the same. They just simply do not acknowledge it, feel it, or know it. They are not embracing the fact that they are born of the Father. People are strange in their thinking, for they will claim that they are children of God, yet they don't acknowledge that I, Jeshua, am their brother. Why do they not proclaim that they are One with God just as I AM? I carry every aspect of the Father within me and so do you, Mattai. And so does everyone. The Son I AM is that part of me that is the Father. It cannot be separate.

"While you understand that I have been born as the result of the direct impregnation of my Mother Mary by the Father in Heaven, I was not the only one, for throughout the history of humanity, this has occurred approximately 100 times. But it really doesn't matter even though this event appears to make me special, which is unfortunate because it implies that I was gifted in a way that no one could ever hope to achieve or to have that gift. And, of course, that conclusion runs counter to my teachings."

He said, "I have always told you, Mattai, that everyone has the same capacity. Of course, we all come into the world with unique and different gifts and talents. Nevertheless, those gifts can all lead us to the same place. The circumstance of my birth is not more than you because through the seed of your physical father contains the essence of the Father in Heaven. How is that not more miraculous, more extraordinary, that carried in the seed of a human is the code of the entirety of humanity and the entirety of the heavenly Father? For truly there is an extraordinary perfection in all of conception. You must see, Mattai, what an incredible demonstration of God's miracle is your physical form. This is no less miraculous than the virgin birth of myself."

And then Jeshua returned to the subject of Buddha: "Even Buddha did not see himself united with the Father, but living and dwelling in the bliss of the Father, as a shadow on earth that had to be reabsorbed. I have a different understanding and give the teaching in a different way, but that doesn't make the Buddha wrong in his way. And now, in the Light of Buddha, in its reabsorption into the Father-Mother God, he is now able to give others much of the teaching I have given. He still, though, teaches at a different point of heart and a difference of mind. I do not see myself separate from Buddha and I do not see myself as a better teacher than Buddha.

"Siddhartha Guatama, the last Buddha, was a man with a great many gifts given unto him in the physical world. And those gifts he let go. And in letting them go, he sought things through difficulty and denial. And so his greater teaching came out of the realization that God/Nevana did not dwell on the riches of man nor the poverty of man, but in the middle of all of life."

As to Jeshua's ultimate relationship with the Buddha: "I sit with

Buddha at the right hand of my Father. I sit with all who claim themselves to be in the glory of God. God does not literally have a right and a left hand, nor does He have a body or form as such, so in that expression let us not misunderstand the symbology. God is not a being which resembles humanity but a being which includes humanity in its own resemblance. Now, the consciousness of Lord Buddha is of an over soul. He oversees the Golden Ray, of which I am a part, in partnership."

Then Jeshua posed this question: "Is it possible for a teacher to be surpassed by a student? Only in the understanding that the student brings, not in the reality of who they are being. 'Greater things than these shall you do,' will not make you greater than who I am, because you, my brother, and so many others would be afraid to be greater than who I am. You would deny yourself the gifts that I have offered you that have come through the Holy Spirit.

"Mattai, I have never said you would be greater than or more important than I. But the things you should do and live through, the teachings you might offer, might resonate even greater than what I bring forward. I am not diminished in that, but I become greater in that. 'The teacher is honored as his student excels.' Join us then, my friend, at the right hand of the Father."

I acknowledged his words, "I accept this invitation. Thank you."

Jeshua said, "Be at peace. Today you will reap more golden rewards on the earth."

And then He continued, "People wish to see miracles, and instead of invoking their own power, they seek out someone else. An example here would be with faith healers. The faith healer invokes the power of the Holy Spirit and *Bam!* the seeker is shaking into a new kind of hell. Some of that so-called healing is real and some of it is not, and much of it is definitely not necessarily God's will. But some people through the experience are converted to a new faith. A new belief, new hope comes over them, as they see that a miracle could happen. But actually the conversion has not been real Light and real Love. It is still the false belief that someone else, someone outside themselves, perhaps me, even, is required to perform the miracle.

"If I could redo pieces of the experiences we've had thus far together, Mattai, there are those in my human understanding and from my divine perspective that I would redo right now. But these things are doing what they need to do on earth by calling people to love the Christ in themselves, and they are all blessed. Eventually, everyone will get it. So, you, Mattai, are not to preach but to share our story with details of their meanings, and then people might find themselves again more clearly. And so it is."

My next question dealt with a very sensitive issue: "Jeshua, tell me about your bringing Lazarus back from the dead."

Jeshua explained, "It is in our religious writings that God gave us the power to call forth the dry bones. Remember Ezekiel. Even dried-up bones that had no flesh could be called to life. It is a divine notion."

Before telling me about the circumstances with Lazarus, Jeshua explained why people die and the process of death.

"Many people are much confused about death and dying," He began. "People decide to leave this earth plane because often their present life journey is complete; they have experienced what they have set out for themselves. But another reason, quite common, is that one desires, however unconsciously, to escape the challenges, obligations and demands put upon them by family or community that seem to be overwhelming."

He continued, "When people decide to die, whatever the reason, they know they'll be leaving their families, friends, and colleagues, and many feel guilty because they believe that by going away they will be letting these people down. Consequently, they become very 'creative' in their choices about how to die. Some create diseases that eat at their insides. Others create a wearing out of the body: their circulation hardens and narrows so that the cells and organs begin to deteriorate from lack of nourishment and oxygen, and eventually all systems fail. They choose then what we might call socially acceptable ways to die. After all, if someone is struck by a devastating disease, how could anyone else criticize him? By choosing these methods to die, ways which seem obviously beyond our control, we escape the guilt at leaving our loved ones behind."

Then He returned to the subject of Lazarus: "Where Lazarus was concerned, the cause of his death was a certain abuse of his body. He did overindulge in food and drink. And he left quite extemporaneously: here I had a dear friend that I didn't get to say good-bye to, and his sisters were left to fend for themselves. It didn't seem fair, and it wasn't fair, but it was not just that: Lazarus still had some work to do here, and I had a purpose to fulfill.

"People are still debating this event of raising Lazarus from the dead. The doubters rationalize my actions by saying that perhaps Lazarus hadn't really been dead at all; he might simply have been in a coma. Of course, it has happened that people are thought to be dead, but they are not dead. Their breathing has become shallow or imperceptible, and because of that they do not respond to normal stimuli; their eyes are blank, their faces without expression. And so they are buried, buried alive. When they eventually awake from these states, they die anyway from the terror of being trapped in a dark closed tomb. Another scenario is that there can truly be a ceasing of all of a person's body responses, such as brain and heart activity for several minutes. They are presumed dead, the shroud is wrapped around them, and they are prepared for burial. Then suddenly, they open their eyes, speak and shock everyone around them. These are unfathomable mysteries to nearly everyone."

Jeshua pointed out that neither of these circumstances was the case with Lazarus. He said, "When I called Lazarus forth, he had been dead for more than just a few minutes. Remember? It was very stinky within that tomb. He was truly dead; his flesh had begun to rot. From a physical point of view, I had my work cut out for me to raise him up. But through the miracle of the Divine, there was nothing for me to do but to breathe life back into him and for his soul to choose to enter into the body again. It was his soul, which came back in.

"Lazarus had already been through a transformation of consciousness. He had already exited the physical form, and he knew and felt the freedom and purpose of life without form. He had already reviewed and examined his life's choices and had witnessed his own Karmic pattern. He had evolved into a higher beingness through this experience, so in a sense he came back into his body in a more whole state of consciousness to complete what needed to be done for his family and for me and my role on this earth."

Jeshua told me that Lazarus was the example that resurrection is possible. Then He added, "But is it a notion everyone should try? Perhaps not. It is not necessarily our purpose to go to a grave and call forth for someone to rise up or to stand in front of a crematorium and shout to the dead 'walk out of the flames.' It is not your job as a human to prove that your thoughts are aligned, therefore you can do whatever you choose. For what does that type of thinking reflect, but pride?"

Jeshua continued, "It is not even to call on the power of God to resurrect flesh and breathe life into it anew. It is rather to decide what is the simple meaning of all that? What is the everyday practicality of that? How does that knowledge and that truth serve you? But if we should ask God for resurrection, we must ask in faith and not demand that death be transmuted.

"The issue of resurrection is not only about raising the physically dead body. Can you resurrect the old life of your own memory and bring new love and life to it? Can you resurrect a thought or an emotion, or a story you once told about someone and why they are the way they are and then breathe new life into that dead story, to bring love present to it again so that it is no longer a tongue-wagging or a tongue-lashing about another's integrity, impeccability, or divinity? Also, a man may eat and drink appropriately and maintain his health but his thoughts may be poisonous. We try to kill off the old thoughts, the negativity, the poisonous beliefs. We try to bury them. Let us instead resurrect our thoughts, put them through the crucible of transmutation, because unless we do they become buried alive, never dead and buried."

I recalled that after Lazarus' resurrection, we had a party with lots of food. The neighbors had brought much of it, and then the runners went out to nearby regions and faraway people as well, and carried the message of this occurrence.

Jeshua said, "Now it is often requested that I bring others back from the dead. People ask me why, if I did it for my friend, I wouldn't also do it for them? I tell them that it does not come from me, but from my Father. It is not I who makes the choice but my Father who does so. And consequently, it is not for me to decide, for when it is in the Father's timing, all who need to be resurrected will be resurrected."

I addressed Jeshua, "You know, Rabboi, I have always wondered why, since you raised Lazarus from the dead, did you not do the same for your own beloved cousin, John the Baptist. But now, I think I see. It is not your decision but the Father's. But why would not God want to have His own messenger returned to the people?"

Jeshua said, "My cousin, John's, work here on earth was finished, his service to mankind complete by his final act, which was serving at my baptism. There was no need for John to be here any longer."

Still troubled about John, I forged on, "I also never did understand how the people could possibly execute someone who was a messenger of God. The prophet Elijah was written about in our holy text, and you proclaimed that John was Elijah's reincarnation. How could they not see the sign? How could it possibly be that they would let him die?"

"Remember, Mattai," answered Jeshua, "the priest asked John if he was not the reincarnation of the prophet Elijah, and he responded, "No, I am not."

And Jeshua, with tears apparent, said, "Sometimes people do not see the truth, even if it is right in front of them.

"John was so focused on his role given to him by God, that this was the only thing that mattered to him. He was totally focused in the here and now.

"You know, Mattai, it is the belief that the world as we know it will eventually come to an end. And when that happens God will awaken all of the dead. Some people fear that if their body is burned, cremated, or desecrated in any way, then God will not raise them up.

"God's plan is that even if your body is burnt to ashes and scattered all over the earth, it can still come together again in a flash of the Light and breath. In man's limited thinking he assumes that the present body is the one that will be resurrected, but, in fact, we have more than one life on earth, so which body would that be?

"Life is constantly renewed in the process of reincarnation; bodies are created anew. Which body would God choose? It really doesn't matter."

"Master," I asked, "we have spoken much now about the process of dying and the possibilities for resurrection and reincarnation, but what happens to a soul when it passes over?"

Jeshua gave me a long look and then responded, "You are shown all of your actions while on earth. You are not judged for these actions; rather, this can better be described as a 'correct viewing.' The soul, though, in witnessing the things it did or said that were harmful or which interfered with life or which did not follow its highest potential, can find judgment of itself. And then the soul can carry the burden of that judgment and feel shame and guilt, and they may feel the need for what you refer to as karmic payback. Some souls can view these events and can find loving forgiveness of them, and in that make clearer or more powerful choices in how they wish to serve. So in a sense, there is still the karmic activity, but instead of retribution it becomes contribution. You see?

"The laws of cause and effect are valid. But you can have the perspective that instead of punishment and retribution for your so-called sins, there can be realignment and contribution. What a distinction.

"So there is no outside judgment of your deeds, but rather observation. Any judgment you experience is simply self-imposed. If people thought in terms of discernment instead of judgment, the picture would become very clear. Judgment so often means a declaration of right or wrong rather than a choice."

Jeshua, apparently feeling that enough had been said on the subject of Lazarus, changed directions: "Mattai, your name is as sacred as the various names of God, whether I call you Mattai or Levi. We call forth who you are and bring the name of God within it. As I choose to call you Mattai, so God chose a peoples once; they have been referred to throughout time as 'the chosen.' Let me speak of them.

"The name 'the chosen' has shifted somewhat over time. It has never been perfectly understood since it was originally given. There is the belief among our Jewish people that they were 'chosen,' to be the leaders and to show the way for the people of the rest of the world to the Oneness of God. They were initiated, if you will, to be at the place where a new consciousness could be born. But the concept has been most distorted and twisted over time."

He said, "There has been manipulation by the priests to convince people that they are better than, beyond and also above everyone else. The priests also tell them that God will righteously favor them and bring them forward at the perfect time.

"God indeed will bring them forward in the perfect time, but not for the righteousness of wronging another. Beloved, let me say that being chosen does not mean being better. They were at that time chosen from among the nomadic people. There was quite a nomadic group of energy in the time of Abraham and for many generations that followed. So it was necessary that someone be asked and spoken for in order that they could be the spokesperson of God's will for the peoples of that time and of that prophecy. The 'chosen' people might have been Chinese or they might have been Mayan. Whoever the 'chosen' were did not matter. It happens that God chose Abraham and his tribe to carry out a mission. It also happens that Abraham and his tribe misinterpreted God's message, as any other tribe might have done, and here I am today carrying out my mission as a result. If Abraham had heard perfectly, if God's word had been brought forward in perfection, my presence would appear differently. My role would be different."

Jeshua added that the chosen people are the ones who choose: "They have chosen God, the Father, while people are chosen by God to be His messengers. By the nature of the God being or the nature of the gift for humanity by their very breath, they are chosen. So those who choose are in alignment with that.

"In a sense, all of you twelve disciples are aspects of me, Jeshua. Certainly, we are uniting. Your role is to unite all of the aspects of Mattai, as you know them to be, into the Oneness of who I, Jeshua, AM into the Oneness of who we are. While certainly not beyond your ability, that is a major task.

"I am supposing that all of you are considering that if I am going to fulfill my purpose, then I will need you and each one of your brothers to be proclaiming that you are each willing to fulfill your purpose and you are each very eager to know what is your purpose. What is it?

"For each of you, I cannot tell you what it is. But I can tell you that if you proclaim and do the will of God and you have faith that in any moment whatever life presents to you, you can choose according to that, then you will be fulfilling. You just need to be committed."

But I protested, "Rabboi Rabboi, I do not understand. When God wills me to do something and I cannot hear God speaking to me, how will I ever do the right thing?"

And Jeshua said to me, "Now you are sounding like Peter! Here is how it works. You pray daily the prayer that I taught you:

> *Our father which art in heaven hallowed be thy name. Thy kingdom come, thy will be done on earth as it is in heaven. Give us this day our*

daily bread, and forgive us our debts as we forgive our debtors. Lead us not into temptation, but deliver us from evil. For thine is the Kingdom and the power and the glory forever and ever. Amen.

"That yea, even as these words are spoken, you speak them from your heart, Thy will be done! And I state that asking that Thy will be done is a proclamation of your willingness to embody it. And so by making this statement, you are creating in yourself a vehicle, a vessel which cannot fail the plan. Even if you do not know whether to turn right or left, wherever you are, you are fulfilling the plan. That is the teaching now just as it has forever been.

"You need not worry about failing God. You can only know that if your desire and willingness is to serve the Divine, then however you are in your life, you are serving.

"You still are a little confounded and confused by this, correct? Your thinking is, *if only I knew what God wants of me, I will do it. Tell me what you want, God.* That has been your prayer, Mattai.

"God does not want to dictate a plan to you nor do I. I do not ever sit you all down and say, 'Now we are going to Jerusalem and this is what is going to happen. I need you to do this, and I need you to do that.' I do not do that with you. I do not say to you, 'Let's do Plan B. Let's skip Jerusalem for the Passover this year and let's have a small quiet family thing. Let's say prayers and we'll do our good mitzvahs.' I do not do that. I just say that we are following according to what is in front of us to do. So that is what everyone should do. I do not say so, so that you cannot or will not. I do not say these things so that they will be avoided. I say them because I know that even with the ability to do all the right things and then failing by the human standards and doing the wrong things instead, you will still be fulfilling the plan. You cannot fail God's plan if it is your intention to do His Will! It just requires commitment and a prayer that you are aligned to it and that is all there is to it."

And Jeshua said, "And now here is to God's will. Let us have a glass of wine."

And I said, "God wills us to drink wine and be drunkards?"

And Jeshua said, "God wills us to enjoy the fruits of the earth and to share our love with one another and that is it."

Jeshua's teachings were simple and constant. I was eternally questioning Him, always looking to get every drop of wisdom. Jeshua suggested that there would be a time He might need to go away, and I would panic. I would say, "But Rabboi, you cannot leave us. If you are going to go away, don't leave us before you tell us everything. Teach us everything. Make us masters."

And Jeshua said, "I ordained you for five functions: (1) to forgive the people's sins as the Father does; (2) to heal the sick; (3) to remove unclean spirits; (4) to feed the hungry, and (5) to minister to the poor and homeless.

"You, Mattai, may do all of this, for you were given the authority. You were given the authority to forgive. It is the Divine, which never holds anything against anyone but only opens more towards their highest potential. So to forgive someone of their sins, I say, 'I wash away the energy that is held.' Or 'I cut the strings', as Archangel Lord Michael proclaims. Another way to say this is that 'I free you of the bondage of your errors and transgressions. I hold nothing against you, for our God who is the Father in me holds nothing against you.'

"A sin is not breaking a rule per se. Sin is an error against your truth. It is a choice that is not in wholeness. It is not being in your wholeness, but rather being in separation. Sin is your transgression. It is your action of moving against the divine order. Every human does it consciously and unconsciously. So sin is not as those of religion have taught you. That is to be seen as evil. We do not judge it in that way. But, humans do make choices which are not of their highest because they move against the flow of the divine order."

Jeshua forgave through the Father, by becoming an instrument of intervention between the Father and the individual for their inappropriate actions. This then gave people the freedom to go forward and not look back at all their mistakes. This idea played out when Jeshua and we disciples came upon a scene in a town square where a prostitute was about to be stoned for her sins. Jeshua said to the crowd, "Those of you who have not sinned can cast the first stone." The townspeople, one by one, dropped their stones, turned and walked away. The prostitute then turned to Jeshua with thanks for saving her, to which Jeshua replied, "I forgive you of your sins, as the Father forgives. Repent, go and sin no more." The Father observes any actions where one repents and says, "I will do it no more."

While we were perfectly capable of performing miracles, that was not our primary function. We were to use miracles not only to assist people but to get their attention, then show them the truth behind the miracles and how they could create their own. We were to live and teach truth.

Jeshua counseled us time and time again that we were masters and that He would give us all the teachings. I would receive everything I could and Jeshua would say, "I am with you always."

I would always thank Him.

Jeshua would receive my thanks, saying "You're welcome, my friend. I give you the blessing. I kiss you upon your forehead and I ask that the Spirit of Light dance upon you and bring you the gifts that you pray are opened in you: the gift of sight, the gift of hearing, the gift of speaking, the gift of all knowing that which is our truth."

Jeshua said, "Continue to use your gifts to serve others. When doing acts of compassion and charity, do so anonymously, for if you boast of a generous act and are rewarded and placed on a pedestal of high position by your fellow man, your act has its own reward and is ended. However, when you act with humility and love in your heart for your fellow man instead of with pious feelings, you will gain much more on your path to enlightenment."

Jeshua said, "So it is when you pray. You must not be like hypocrites." Jeshua meant that an individual must not be one who prays loudly and openly in order to give the appearance that he is expressing his faith. It was common practice for certain priests and certain other people who wanted to be seen as devout to openly pray in order that they be recognized as practicing their religion. It was a method that people used to make themselves appear to be more spiritual or religious than they really were in their hearts. It certainly was hypocritical, for it wasn't true prayer. Some people, in order to appear pious, would pray openly on the street corners. Others went so far in their public display as to loudly preach their own moral attitudes.

Jeshua would tell us, "No one needs to hear your words or be involved, for this should be an internal conversation. It is your personal communication with your Father in Heaven. Remember too that repetition of prayer is not necessary and doesn't help your case, for your most private needs are already known by the Father, and repetition and memorization simply become mechanical, monotonous, redundant words."

On the subject of hypocrisy, Jeshua went on, "When you fast, you must not be like hypocrites and paint your faces." Jeshua was inferring that there are people, who by their interpretation of the Torah and by the letter of the law, publicly let it be known "Look at me. See, I am living the law of Moses."

Jeshua said, "The truth is that they were not living the law. They were just practicing it publicly. Make no mistake. I am not in judgment of the practices; I am only speaking to the heart of the matter. I am simply calling attention to the truth."

"Holy, Holy, Holy, Lord God of all Hosts is with you. Kodoish, Kodoish, Kodoish. Adonai, 'Tsebayoth[10]. Amen."

And then He told me a magical story.

Once in the land where the pyramids have existed forever, there was a man who walked with sandals, that barely protected his feet as sand-als should and now were weak and worn from the effects of the sands themselves. For he walked his journey by foot because he had no camel.

He had walked many miles and at one point of the journey, he came upon a small oasis. And at this oasis, there rested a camel. The camel showed signs of having been ridden and having been used by another human, but there was no other human in sight. The man reached down taking a sip from the deep well of water and rested there for just a moment while he looked at the camel.

Suddenly the camel began to speak to him. The camel said, "Master, I have been waiting for you, but you have circumvented this desert so long that you did not know that I was right here. Why did you wait until this moment to come to me?"

When the shock wore off of hearing the camel speak, the man said, "I have not been lost. I have been thinking. I have also been in deep prayer. I have finally come to this place because an answer to my prayer led me here."

The camel said, "And so we are here together. Now, get up on my back and the journey that is before you shall be easy on your feet

10 The symbol preceding the word 'Tsebayoth is called a dagesh. It is used to alert the reader that Ts is not pronounced as th but as ts. 'Tsebayoth means "host." The modern translation is "army."

and you will feel lightened in your heart."

Then the man mounted the camel and the camel rode off and went up over a hill. Beyond that hill the man saw things that he had never seen before. He said to himself, "This must be a mirage that I am seeing. It must only be the illusion of light reflecting on the sands." For what he saw were not the stone pyramids, but an extraordinary building that appeared to be of crystals and gems. And building upon building were in the shapes of gems themselves. One building was curved like a crystal dome and another curved in a pyramidal shape but much smaller than those pyramids that he knew of at Giza. There was another building in the shape that he did not know, but it had many sides to it. There were many other shapes of buildings as well. And as he approached these buildings, he realized that this was not an illusion, but this was presented to him as real.

And the camel loped up to the gateway of this city and he knelt down and allowed the man to climb off of him. The camel again spoke to the man and said, "Master, you have come to this city where now you are the King. Welcome home." With that, the camel turned and walked away and out of sight and the man saw the camel no more.

The man entered the kingdom and he wept. For there the angels did greet him. And there his own deep thoughts resided and his prayer welcomed him. For these thoughts, your prayers, and through your acknowledgements that you are worthy for all that you need, even the burning sand on your feet will not keep you from it. For it is there within you, expressing in the outer, more magnificently than your mind can conceive, and there the kingdom awaits you, in every breath, for you to be exalted in your inner journey and your outer world.

Jeshua continued, "How many lessons have the Father-Mother God given to us? Many, many. When you call forth to the Lord God of your being, you can speak to the fig tree and say, wither, and it withers, live and it lives. This has been given to you for eternity, long before the miracles that we see performed here and now.

"In the ancient books of our teachings we were given these words, 'What you speak occurs, what you bless is blessed, what is cursed is cursed.' Like Ezekiel, you may breathe life into dry bones. In his story, it was spoken that God said, 'Lay your hands on these dry bones and call flesh to grow on them. Call blood to come forth and flow.' Then in your power ask the Lord God to breathe life into them and they shall stand up and walk."

Jeshua said, "It is so, that you are powerful and yet you do not know it. So be healed and be whole by your words. Speak not, 'Oh, my feet are killing me!' Speak not condemnation or fear for your limbs, your feet, your hands or any other part of your body. Speak nothing but joyful celebration and confirm that wholeness is here in you now.

"Seek not that which will make the mind grow. But seek that which is the Seed of Light within you that grows infinitely.

"These words are important for they are not meant to shun education. We should exercise the act of thinking just as we would exercise the other muscles of the human body. But it is far better that we become open in spirit rather than to believe that with knowledge and information we become wise. Wisdom is not born of the knowledge of the mind, but of the knowing of the heart."

And Jeshua had a final word: "Mattai, I have said to you before: my message to you and to mankind is a message that is profound, yet simple. My message is that everyone holds the image of the Father within them. They are born of that being. And through the gift of the Mother God, they have form. And everyone who has God, who represents His love within them, has infinite power and is the master of all of their creations. By the deeds that you do and by the things you say, you will be known to the rest of the world and to the Son of God. Speak wisely, forgive, love one another even as I have loved you. These things are spoken to you my dear friend, Mattai, not because you do not understand them, but because you do not know what to do yet with all the other beliefs, all the other untruths that have been imprinted into your memory and into your body and onto the consciousness of thought of humans.

"I will now tell you what to do with these thoughts.

"Turn them into love. Turn every thought and every belief that you have been taught into love. And how, Mattai, do you do this? Through the alchemy that you have been taught. You don't get rid of these things. Rather, you turn them into love.

"Does the chemical alchemist get rid of lead and replace it with gold? No, there is nothing to be rid of. He simply turns lead into gold. We do not wish to empty your mind in the sense of ridding yourself of, or discarding, all other thoughts and experiences. But rather to place them within and fill them with love."

Jeshua and I then joined Peter, Judas, Thomas, James, John, Mary Magdalene and the others under the trees in the shade. I knew that we could all live our lives by these truths. I thought to myself, *keep the sand out of your sandals. Strap them well so you do not slip against the rocks. Walk safely so that you are one with the beauty that you walk upon.*

The next morning after thanking Jeshua's family for their grand and warm hospitality, we bade them good-bye.

Eighth Spiritual Law

Be worthy of love by being for another, Love. Where there has been transgression, forgive. Where there has been misunderstanding, allow. Where there has been misappropriation, give even more. There is in loving, more achieved to cause your heaven to manifest, than in any withholding. In the withholding of love, the blame, the judgment, the anger in these, there is hell. Do not cause your hell, for it is not the Father's will.

Explanation:

The cause of hell is the creation of withholding your love. Withholding love, blaming, cursing, anger, resentment, and judgment causes hell. Hell was not created by the Father, but by humans withholding their love of the Father and of one another in the Father.

As hell is self-created, if you curse another, your hell is living with that curse. You cannot go to hell based on another's curse, except if you believe yourself deserving of that curse, or if you are judgmental or become fearful because of the curse, or if you vibrate to the energy or frequency of the one who does the cursing.

Hell is the place of consciousness where there is denial of love and an emptiness of love. Hell is not eternal because nothing can be withheld from the Father for eternity. Only love is eternal. That hell is everlasting has been misconstrued in religious teachings.

When Mattai walked with Jeshua, there was a place outside Jerusalem where garbage burned continuously. That place was named hell, and it became in a way an allegory to show people that hell is one of the most painful and undesirable existences of consciousness. It truly seems to exist forever because there seems to be no hope or availability to reach out for help. And it may be for some as close to forever as is conceivable to the human mind.

But it is not God's will that it be forever, for God holds the Light available for all souls, even those in the darkest of their hell. But when they are in their darkness, they are feeling so unworthy and ashamed and so afraid of the Light that they cannot and will not reach for it.

There is no soul forever burning in their hell consciousness on earth, while embodied or even disembodied, that if they would simply cry unto God with all of their heart, "Forgive me, I am worthy of you, I love you," that God would completely redeem them from that hell.

CHAPTER 9

Jeshua: Private Thoughts, Great Challenges

Little did any of us know the complexity and depth of Jeshua's inner nature. Up to now He had held many unspoken views. He had also experienced much turmoil in His earlier years, just as we twelve continued to do. When for the first time He began to share His most private thoughts and also His emotional struggles, I listened intently and was to learn more about Jeshua than I could ever imagine.

He began by telling me that when He had been in a turbulent state, there were few in whom He could confide. He said that it was only by opening Himself completely through meditation and prayer to His Father God that He was able to get through many of the difficult times. He told me that He had received many blessings and great wisdom from the Father.

"You know something of these things, Mattai, you and the others," He said. "However, much of what I received I kept close to my heart and never told anyone. But through all of these experiences, I have learned that my will must be in complete alignment with His will. I must relinquish all challenges unto God's hands.

"One very human difficulty that has challenged me is that of frustration. And an example of a situation I found frustrating to the greatest degree concerned our laws of taxation. We have visited this issue often, and I have always told you that God's law is to render to God what is God's and to Caesar what is Caesar's. But man has superimposed his law over God's law and has made the system inequitable. There is greed within the higher governmental ranks.

"What I have found so confoundedly frustrating is that mankind does not realize the power it has to change this unjust system. And yet, by its very nature, the system itself is a gift from God, even with Caesar's symbol on it.

"If we cannot bless this absolute gift from the Divine, expressed through the laws of man, then we will always find ourselves at war within our own selves. We will always believe that we don't have enough.

"We must not fight our government with anger but must instead be reserved in our opinions. We must give appropriately when we are able, and we must trust that we are *always* given everything we need from the Father. When we have truly internalized this truth, then we can easily forgive our government. The rulers must be forgiven, for they know not what they do."

He went on: "I have also touched the face of anger. One of my greatest challenges has been with the priests. Just as I challenged them in the temple on that occasion when I was twelve, so now they defy me. As I become well known, they are threatened and denounce me.

"Mattai, you and many other people saw me get angry at what the moneychangers were doing. Interestingly, because they are taught and have come to see God as a vengeful God, the people weren't much disturbed by my outburst because they thought I had a perfect right to express myself in this way.

"But it was not that, as you know.

"Instead it was my ego's understanding of human degradation and my impatience with that human condition. Impatience is often acted out in anger.

"I have not acted out my ego-centered impatience too frequently, but occasionally I have and when this is so, I have prayed on it and blessed it, and in that it is aligned."

He then spoke of another type of impatience: "This is the divine impatience that does not act out in rage but instead acts out with a momentum to accomplish. In other words, in the divine understanding, if one were not impatient, one would never move. What would be the reason to move on something or make a new choice? Divine impatience, then, is that which says, 'I will move forward. I will make a new choice. I will make a new life. I will make a new universe.' This is not an energy born of boredom or anger, never; it can be perceived as an energy of opportunity, of growth."

Jeshua continued, "When I was demonstrating my anger at the

moneychangers, the anger was coming in part from my ego. But it was also in part driven divinely, because I was aware that by using my anger through the divine spirit, I could teach a valuable lesson.

"I pray that the lesson was not about teaching people that they had a right to deliberately go about showing anger to everyone in their path. But they have a right to feel anger. Then they have the opportunity to forgive the emotion."

He added, "In my humanity I had the right to be free of all the emotions, and I chose in this case to free myself by expressing through the anger, demonstrating it. You may have heard the word emotion expressed as 'energy in motion.' Well, that is what it is, actually acting out the emotion.

"And I gave it full force. I didn't just mutter under my breath something about 'why don't you get out of here?' I exploded, 'How dare you people!' And I called them vile names and I judged them. You saw me as I angrily threw a fit because they were in violation of the Law, the Jewish law, and they had really taken their violation to extremes. It was quite barbaric.

"It was not that I was justified in doing what I did. That wasn't the point. I had simply to give a lesson. The lesson was not that they were wrong, but ... it was that anger could be transmitted, healed, and transmuted."

Jeshua said His anger reached further still: "Beyond the issue of moneychangers, there were also the merchants selling doves for sacrifice. I was very annoyed about this custom as well.

"I had spoken to the crowds many times saying that these customs are no longer relevant. Our God requires no sacrifice. Remember the story of Abraham and Isaac. Well, to this day there remains a misunderstanding."

And He thought to clarify that: "It is true that discipline, or self-control, as it is known, such as fasting, forgiveness, or 'letting go' can seem like sacrifice, because these things are not easy for the human body, for the personality, or for the ego. But these things are not recommended so that humans feel forced to sacrifice. Rather, they are suggested so that the individual can create a shift out of old ways into new, expanded, God-driven ideas. So these rituals are not of a vibration of sacrifice but of new creation.

"Letting go is absolutely necessary in life. Even in the case of possession of a gift, a blessing of it and a release is important. The release doesn't have to be a destructive process or a painful letting go. But it becomes painful when one doesn't realize the importance of letting go, when one doesn't know inside themselves the wisdom of such an act."

He spoke of His own letting go: "I symbolically let go for forty days. I let go of my lusts for things. I forgave them. I blessed them through and through and beyond. I became transformed in that process.

"Sacrifices, letting go, the ritual of surrender — whatever the words are that describe this act — must come from a deep willingness, a deep faith, and a deep focus on transformation, and then we are served by being transformed. Without these, we maintain an energy of sacrifice and are served to perpetuate the holding on.

"For people to sacrifice in the name of their superstitious beliefs that these actions will appease a God separate from them, or prolong the inevitable or buy them a special dispensation, they are simply still holding very tightly to that very thing which they are sacrificing. And so it is."

Jeshua spoke next of pride: "I have suffered pride.

"I must tell you, Mattai, that bringing Lazarus back from the dead for me began as a prideful act.

"When Lazarus died, everyone was sad and even I cried my tears of sorrow. And I, the very human part of myself, had to go deep within to communicate with my Father and ask, 'Why? Why has this happened? Why must I suffer the pain of losing someone that I love so dearly? Why can I not be spared from all of this grief? What is my lesson in this sad event?'

"Then, my Father said to me, 'You are not the master of other people's flesh. You are the master of your own flesh.'

"Despite His words, I wanted Lazarus back. So the demons in me tempted me to call forth Lazarus. But I was careful to call upon and ask my Father for every bit of permission, and I proclaimed my unity along with incorporating every shred of my ego in order to call him forth.

"And so, I was not acting entirely from an expression of ego. If I had been, this miracle could not have worked. Truly, this act was the perfect blend of ego energy and divine energy, and that moment became a holy moment revealing the power of God. It was also filled with the magician that I knew I could be, and I make no judgment of that.

"I let you know this so that you may realize, Mattai, that my humanistic element was never lacking in any of these choices. My ego was always completely and fully involved. While it could not override the divine principle, I had to find a way to merge with it or the miracle could not have been accomplished.

"It took a great depth of prayer to align my self beyond my ego to the wisdom and willingness of the Father in order for the event to occur. But it wasn't the first time I had done this, you know. Long ago, the Holy Father said to me, 'Lay your hand upon these dry bones and cause them to rise.' And they rose. And the man who performed that miracle was the prophet, Ezekiel, and that was I, for I was known as Ezekiel in a lifetime long before I was born here as Jeshua ben Joseph.

"Now, let me go from revitalizing the old to nourishing the young."

Jeshua talked of children: "Another one of my concerns is the children. Often they are pushed aside and told to 'be seen, not heard.' You've heard that one, haven't you? But children have a need to express themselves. When I say to the children, 'Be quiet. Do not speak in foolishness,' I also say to them, 'Come unto me.' Then I say to the little ones, 'You must be heard.' I place them on my knee and ask them to give voice to all that is within them.

"Children must be allowed to voice their concerns and their opinions. By freely expressing these things, they are able to receive feedback from an elder and gain much wisdom. Through this interaction, they more quickly mature into responsible adults.

"So even to you, Mattai, and to all the others around you, those that appear to be fully-grown, I say, 'Come unto me. Speak to me from your heart. Do not silence yourself. Give what is your joy to give. Keep only silent when there is a need in you to be frivolous with the words and with the energies that are not giving or are not loving but are accusing or damning. In these ways, be silent and circulate that unto your own being until such a moment as you can find release of it in your prayers. Then, speak it forth and give it unto me for I am here for you.' All the children of my Father-Mother God should come unto me and let me celebrate with them who they are."

Jeshua then asked me, "Are you ready to make sacrifices for our teachings, even to the point of martyrdom?"

I answered, "Yes."

Jeshua said, "Indeed. Well, remember not to speak until you're shown, for the beingness that you are, the soul, has no reason to be martyred, no reason to feel that it is being impaled in the heart. This is not God's purpose for you.

"The Christedness that you are is seeking indeed its own manifestation here. And as I have had the privilege of being loved and being in love with all of my twelve and also all of the women who are in my circle of service, so I say to you, you must learn this love for everyone in your life."

He referred to one unique relationship in order to make His point: "A very poignant lesson for me in this has been my relationship with Mary Magdalene. Mary and I cannot share family life in the traditional ways, yet our love grows. Know that we fought about this, we argued vehemently. She has wanted and has pressured me to love her more deeply because she sees herself as special to me, and I have had to say, 'I cannot.' I fought with her angrily at times that she wanted so much from me. I fought with her because she was not able to see her perfect place in my life.

"Know this, my friend, that your love is growing as you call upon that I AM in you. And my love in you is ever, and forever we are one. As thou art the kingdom, the power, and glory forever and ever. And so it is."

He spoke of His views regarding humanity: "I feel at times very sad for the condition of mankind. I often remember the devastating burning of Sepphoris when I was a child. That event has stayed so vivid in my mind and heart, perhaps because I know that Jerusalem too will burn. The Romans will take this beloved city down. I weep for Jerusalem, but I know the walls must be torn down, because false walls cannot stand. And as the old temples fall, new temples will replace them. The temple that I refer to is you, for the body is the temple of the living soul and the God that you are is in this holy temple.

"I weep for the earth, which at a point in the future will break its crust open and form a new world. The people who form and shape the new temples will become the Light of Christ, and I will embrace these mighty Lights.

"You and I and your other brothers commune much in joy and laughter; we understand this important aspect of the human condition. But we also know that the human condition can be full of melodrama with unspeakable sadness that is contained within it. People feel that it is through strife that they consider they may grab hold of life and control it and control God. But constantly, as in a life journey, they are slipping on their moss-covered cobblestones. I continually divulge to them that there is no point in such strife. And they find that in the end in their day-to-day lives when the strife and struggle are over they look back and say, 'I really didn't have to make this such a hard job. I could have chosen another way. I could even have seen the humor in the situation.' Why I bring this up is to give levity to the consciousness of our brethren, because humor is part of who we are."

He said, "Even though an eternal life of bliss was promised, it is not guaranteed, because there is always choice in how to experience life. It is choice to live in bliss, peace, happiness, joy, and boundless love, the qualities of the divine. Eternal life is your gift from God; where you put your focus will determine how you will experience that eternal life.

"There is no pain here on earth except that you choose it and no pain that is eternal except by your belief that it is so, but through that belief you end up with the idea that you are going to spend an eternity in pain and suffering. That perceived pain, then, becomes an eternal damnation! And people will not let go. They pray and hope that God will make their pain disappear, but when they look over their shoulder, they see that it is still there. And then they fear it even more. Through that fear they draw even more pain to themselves, and that is often accompanied by drama and more chaos. They forget to simply let go and be in joy in this eternal life."

And then He asked, "Can you be in joy when you make mistakes? Can you forgive with those mistakes, even though the mistake might be serious, breaking a law of both man and the divine or consciously or deliberately hurting another.

"Can we look at that action and say, 'Humans let us forgive it, for they really don't know what they are doing? Forgive all of them, Father-Mother God, for they really do not understand any part of life now. They do not understand that everything they do comes back upon them. Nor do they understand that everything they say returns to them in this life and that their choices result in suffering rather than joy.'"

Continuing, "But this need not be so.

"So we must forgive them thus these choices, because they are like children who can't explain what they do, and we certainly do not expect children to have a reason for the things they do. We forgive because we know that they do not know.

"If we presume that someone knows better, that they know the law and the morality of life's expectations and they choose to break that, then they must be punished, condemned. In many countries condemnation means stoning or hanging — *death!* 'Forgive them for they know not what they do. For if they knew, they would not choose it.' It is that simple. If they really knew, they definitely would never choose it.

"Forgive yourself for choosing to suffer, for you do not know. But know now: you can choose bliss, joy, peace, and boundless love.

"Are you forgiving yourself, Mattai?"

"Yes," I said.

"Yes," Jeshua continued, "You must really forgive yourself, not just tolerate yourself or target your act by saying 'This shouldn't be happening.' That's not really forgiveness.

"I have seen many respond in this way: 'I'll just take a deep breath and pretend that this didn't really happen.' And all the while you're expressing fury over the choices that you have made and projecting blame and anguish and anger.

"Every one of you humans feels feelings, emotions, and patterns and then you must forgive them and truly bless them. And in that forgiveness allow a little bit of a chuckle at the ridiculousness of the continuation of these things and the choices which come from a part of you which does not know any better.

"It is like a child who has had a stomachache three times in a row from eating too many sweets but still goes back for more. The child says, 'Do you think that these sweets are related to the stomach ache? If so, so what? I really enjoy eating those sweets.' Humans choose to react just like that with one another. Knowing these things, they should behave differently. They say, 'I must have forgotten' or 'I may not have had it fully integrated, or obviously I did not learn it well. I could not have trusted what is truth, otherwise I would not have done this action or I would not have spoken these words. In that moment, this person would not know fully who they are. So how could I be blaming them for having this moment?'

"It is a Christ-like act to forgive 'for they know not what they do.' In your adult world, which is full of strife, when there is a transgression against you and you are big enough to forgive it, and you voice your forgiveness to the person with a laugh, you might be surprised that you are not so well received. The other person might say say, 'Who are you to forgive me? Who are you to laugh at me?' You say then, 'I am human and I am amused by my own choices. I mean no disrespect. I am just surrendering to the fact that I cannot control life.' So when your thoughts are behind your words, at least you know that this is a release of the control."

Jeshua went on: "Most laughter comes as a release and an integration of the realization that you are not in control. We laugh at the reflection of someone slipping on a wet floor, in part because his or her pain is our pain, and it helps us to integrate and be one with that. It helps us to acknowledge our unity in humanity. You can forgive that seeming insensitivity. It comes from a different part of the heart, but the laugh is still there as the recognition of 'look at what we do.'

"How often humans live in a world of illusion and they let themselves forget! Just as you are appalled at the child beating himself on the head with a stick just because it was there and crying out 'ouch, ouch, ouch' every time. You think *what silly choices that child makes.*

"Well, how is that so different from what adults do? You may laugh with pain and joy at a child who is learning this tough lesson. But really we forget to laugh when we do the same thing. It hurts, but that pain can be a release and a letting go. There can be forgiveness of it. The hurt doesn't have to be a sustained pain; you can let it go.

"When you feel a tightness in the body and then move the body, it hurts. When you keep yourself immobile or perfectly still, the pain is diminished, such as with an inflammation within a joint. In order to assist the healing process, you restrict movement. But for the pain in your emotional body, enlightenment often occurs because there has been movement of that energy. There is an opportunity with every movement for a release, for dissolving, for letting go.

"If you are sitting still, cross-legged, and are very comfortable, when suddenly you move your legs, you find that they are heavy, with pins and needles. It feels uncomfortable. It hurts because circulation and life are coming back into your body as a result of your movement. Pain shouldn't frighten you. It doesn't have to be interpreted as punishment. Rather, it is just an energy. And as soon as you are able to interpret whatever pain you have, whether it be physical or emotional, through a divine allowance and forgiveness, you draw that experience to you less frequently, less dramatically, and less potently.

"And so it is written that the Divine Love of the Father-Mother knows no bounds. God does not love only those who are remembering with every breath. God does not love only those who laugh. God loves you without conditions as to your choices. God always loves, always loves everyone and everything, with no conditions. God is only love."

He then said, "I am not really so different from you, Mattai. You simply perceive that it is so. In this lifetime part of my pathway is to integrate all of my selves, or incarnations, into One.

"During my transfiguration on Mt. Tabor, when Peter, John and James were present, it was a moment of full blessing from the Father-Mother God that caused the appearance of my body to almost be gone. I became visible as Light and only Light. There was far more Light there than Peter had reported. There were far more souls there than even Peter reported. Those who came to me were my beloved prophet friends with angelic support. Actually Melchizedek, Elijah, Josiah, and an aspect of myself, Ezekiel, appeared. However, they weren't so visible. Melchizedek offers to all of humanity the initiation into the Great White Brotherhood,[11] a group of masters committed to assisting mankind in its spiritual growth. I am privileged to be a part of that group.

"The transfiguration was not consciously done for the purpose of demonstrating anything. However, the experience was what it was. So it became a demonstration for that which I AM, the Way, the Truth, and the Light, for I AM the Light of the world. There was in that moment for me, in my experience, an acceleration that I thought would take me from the planet. I was transfigured not only to the eye in form, but also in the consciousness and mind such that I believed for that moment that I was complete, that there would be no more to come back to. My human flesh had

11 The word "white" in Great White Brotherhood refers to purity.

an experience with reality. It was a grand moment of blessing and unification, and in truth, I was shown and was told and reminded of the entire spiritual path that I was on. That was when I knew completely what my life would lead me to. Now to anyone else's vision of this experience, they could make it be anything they wanted to transpire in their minds. It simply was a prayerful moment of merging of my consciousness completely in its Light. You can do this too, Mattai."

Jeshua then spoke a personal message that I later realized was not only a promise but also a precursor to a very special request.

"I speak to you the word of peace, for peace I AM. Let me carry you through your difficulties. Let me be your sacred heart.

"I am not here to remove you from human choice but I can remove from you the veil and the pain of your illusions. I then continue to transmute the sins of the world. If you will give to me your pain and illusions, I will receive them unto the Father and return to you infinite love."

He continued, "Each of us is responsible for the entire world. This should not, however, be interpreted as a responsibility that if not fulfilled in exactly the way it is envisioned, one is not 'trying hard enough' and therefore must feel guilt or in some way diminished. In truth, this healing will occur not because one is putting out effort but because one is simply giving appropriately in all moments from a place of who he or she is, from the nature of his or her being.

"God you are, for there is in the Father-Mother God an essence that knows itself as you. You are not separate from the essence of God. You are participating in it. You are the creation of it.

"So, I thank you for this. I will uplift you and carry you if you need be. I will hold you dear. I will protect you in the peace that I am.

"How is it that I have carried peace and that I stand for it, and that no matter what else occurs, I am in peace? Humans think that it is only because I am Divine that somehow magically I am given this gift to find peace when you in your human bodies cannot. But my human body learned it and you believe yours cannot. So the peace I AM I give you! And I leave you with peace. I give you my kiss of assurance on your cheek that we are forever one!"

Jeshua said then, "I am the Truth, I am the Way, I am the Light, the

Life I AM. I AM. Mattai, choose to be that. Be the Light, be the Way, be the Truth."

And then He startled me somewhat when he added, "Be my scribe."

He went on to explain, "The words you speak and the words you write will be the words not just of my own speaking but they will be the voice of God.

"The words will come easily, and they will become precious and joyful. It will not matter if all the words get jumbled up, if your I AM being remains constant when you give them.

"Of course, it matters to the mind of man whether I walked on the water or by the water. But who I AM will never change. Of course, it matters to the mind of man whether I fed the multitude with two fish, ten fish, or three thousand fish. But who I AM will never change. You see, however the mind of man sees me, it does not alter who I AM. It is through how humans will reinvent and recreate the words and the stories of my time here that they may find me, that they may find the truth, and when they find themselves through me, then they will know their Father-Mother God.

"But their words might lead them away from the truth, and they might find themselves hunting for God and finding no God because their words have led their minds on a journey far away from what is truth. So you will have a mission to write the words that will echo the truth and lead them back to the truth. Your words will be of my memory, not just historically, but in the essence of who I AM, who we all are and what our purpose has been together. So be now my scribe."

I had already been keeping records of our travels and experiences for my own edification. But now, even more was being asked of me, and I felt so very moved by Jeshua's request. I was at once humbled and more than ever inspired by His assigning this cherished mission to me.

Jeshua went on: "Mattai, human experiences that are referred to as lifetimes, times of living physically on this earth, may be multiple through the oversoul of a being. But ultimately, no matter how many lifetimes you have, there is only one life. It is the life of the divine spark, and that life is God.

"Do not misconstrue. I never implied that Jeshua is my one and only incarnation of consciousness. I was in evolution along with the rest of humanity, and I chose every embodiment to experience and learn. At this particular time, through the grace of the Father-Mother God, I choose through Jeshua ben Joseph, to assimilate, receive, transmit and transmute the Divine in a larger way for my brothers and sisters. The life of the Father is what I give."

He added, "In this life experience, I have had a great longing to share with everyone the many wonders of the world, because just as do many other people who are consciously on the spiritual journey, I too would like just to have a normal life with normal conversations. But my spiritual guidance has prevented me from doing so. Though I often thought that while sitting around the campfire with friends it would be great to share more of these grand stories, I have actually said very little on the subject. I keep them secret and sacred unto myself. I do admit that with you twelve I have let my guard down at times and have shared some aspects of the stories intimately. I've also shared bits and pieces of my travels with a few of my closest friends, including Lazarus. But even at those times I have spoken very little about specific parts of these journeys. For the most part while I am open and friendly with all the people I meet, my travels and private thoughts represent a part of my life I feel that I cannot share. While I don't go out of my way to hide these things, I don't speak openly about them.

"If I were to open up completely, I would be putting myself in the role of a promoter and agent for these fantastic regions around the world, and I could stir up wanderlust among my people, who might think that they would be better off somewhere else."

Jeshua said that there were other reasons for witholding as well: "The other issue regarding these tales is that I do not wish to risk the possibility of distraction from the spiritual lessons that I am giving, because the travels in and of themselves are not relevant or important to my purpose.

"Sometimes, too, people are not ready for certain stories of the world. Like a child who is told a very exciting tale, the child gets caught up in it and may not understand that there could be danger in unfamiliar territory, in going beyond the safe world to actually act out some parts of the story. However, believing in his invincibility, he may be tempted.

"As astounding as my adventures have been, I have had no longing to go back and stay at these many places I visited; that was never part of my vision. It's true that I loved these far off lands for the unique experiences they revealed to me; however, of all the places I went, I loved my home the most.

"I have often weighed just what I should share with you twelve regarding my travels in preparing you for your future travels, for indeed I am preparing all of you to go out and to teach others, to heal others, and to share the message of our Oneness with all whom you encounter in many far-away places."

As I was ruminating about His intent in this statement, Jeshua opened my eyes to one aspect of how we twelve were to approach this mission. "When you find yourself in another location, wherever that is, you must be there with a willingness to love and honor that this place is a perfect home for you at this time. And as you arrive in a state of unconditional love and of welcoming, you must not attempt to make the people who abide there in any way wrong in their behavior. Rather, you must be non-judgmental and bring them only Love and Light. And when it comes time to leave, you must detach yourself and as I have said before, 'shake the dust from your sandals.'" Jeshua was implying that we must shake off the energy of the place.

And then Jeshua had a personal message for me, "I know that occasionally, Mattai, your own zealousness has stood in your way and you have tried to start a new religion. You have tried to convert people from their present thinking, because, in your opinion, they are wrong. But it is not your job to change the way they think; your role is simply to integrate love into their lives."

I could see now a faraway look in Jeshua's eyes and when I questioned Him about it, He said that He was reminiscing for a moment about His loving home. He reiterated that His home indeed was where His heart was many times, but He advised me that that didn't mean there was always smooth sailing there.

"I had an ongoing struggle with my mother," He said. "She would be pulling on my energies by asking me to participate more with the family. She wanted me to be more involved in teaching my brothers the religious traditions. She wanted me to be their rabbi and to sponsor them. My mother particularly wanted me to assume a prominent masculine role with my siblings.

"I would frequently tell my mother that although I was happy to teach them, I couldn't single them out and become their teacher. They would have to find their own designated teacher."

"Well," she would say crossly, "you are no longer available, your cousin John is no longer available, and your father is too busy. Who will teach them? It should be a family member who passes these teachings on."

And I would say to her, "But mother, we are all family of God.

"While she appeared to accept my response, I still felt a certain pressure, as if I was being encouraged to be more anchored in our family unit.

"This discourse was an ongoing theme of hers, which began when I was quite young. I was deeply saddened at repeatedly rejecting her requests. It was my desire to please my mother, but I felt that I was letting her down. My personal struggle with this was significant, yet knowing what my larger role was I could not accede to her request in the way she wanted.

"Yet I knew in my heart that I truly was accomplishing her goal. I was teaching my brothers, indeed, my entire family, very important things as a result of my frequent and prolonged absences from the family unit. Through my journeys I was an example to them of uniqueness and independence and how important it is to make a commitment to learning and developing oneself.

"Once, when I was about twenty-five, after having returned from a long journey with my Uncle Joseph, I was able at our Passover Seder dinner to bring to my entire family a brand new understanding, a refinement, if you will, of our celebration message and prayer. For that my mother was very appreciative and joyful. It was also a joy for me, for I felt that I had truly had an intimate exchange with them. I felt in a way like the family patriarch, even if for only a brief time. But I also recognized how joyful it was just to be home with my family and simply share with them, mindless of teaching them."

Jeshua then changed the subject to address an ongoing issue: "In our culture men have the power and the stature in the community. They are taught, and they are shown how to achieve. They have more opportunities.

Perhaps it is because I experience in my own household true equality that I wish for women to be brought into that status. I think it important for women to be like men in their abilities, to be on an equal footing with men. And so, I treat all the women I know with equality and share with them equally my teachings."

Jeshua said that there were those who did not always understand why He wanted to educate the women: "The men would ask, 'Why are you wasting your time on these women? Their job is simply to feed and take care of you.' Even in the temple the women are segregated. The attitude is that if they learn anything, so what. No, women have never really counted in the scheme of things; their importance has been considered inconsequential. I have had a lot of challenges on this subject.

"As I am a man, I was given unlimited possibilities in this world. Although we are expected to follow in our father's footsteps, and while we may be criticized if we step outside of that mold, still we are tolerated if we pursue another field of endeavor."

Jeshua then addressed His own path: "What did I set out to do? I was very focused and I could have excelled at a great number of things if I had chosen. I could have been the world's best carpenter or even the world's best miracle worker. However, these things were not my purpose. This is not what I set out to do. I simply set out to live my life and try to figure out from moment to moment what it was that God wanted of me. I do not always know the whole plan in every moment, you see. I do not always know everything, so I often ask, 'Now what?' And I am constantly in prayer asking, 'What is it you want of me, Father God? Do you want me to go and live with my mother and help her out with the family?' I would do it if I could. I ask, I receive, I am shown. Yes, I am shown in a prophetic manner. I am shown much which is ahead of me at any moment in the future. But I always recheck and always look and ask my Father. Certainly, not to doubt it but to be clear of the plan and certain that I have not for a moment stepped off the path and am still in line with what I was shown.

"It is said about me that I AM God in a physical body and I always know all things. I have access to all things as you do. But I live as a man. My body hungers and I feed it. My body thirsts and I drink. My body feels urges and I eliminate or do whatever it needs in order to satisfy those urges. Sometimes my body feels cold and I wrap a cloak around it. Do you understand, Mattai? I am living a life in fullness as a man, in my practice of meditation and of an at-one-ment with God. All those needs and concerns of a man evaporate into nothing. And not with every single breath I take into my body am I in that state of beingness.

"I am in the process of preparing myself with every step and every breath to be a God-Being who has fully manifested. I had not fully done so at the baptism. I have not fully done so in any other moment. During prayer and meditation I proclaim my intent to be fully manifested and I become that during these sacred moments, but I do not sustain that moment. But I will sustain my humanity through the end of my life span. Do you understand, Mattai? That is my blessing and my gift, to experience the suffering of humanity with humanity, not because it is a prescription that I or humanity needs, but because it is a circumstance of life and through that I demonstrate that the Father's will be done. Until such time that my Father calls me to Him, my transformation from the state of embodiment to Light and at-one-ment with Him will not be fully completed."

The day following these most intimate revelations, Peter, John and I had joined Jeshua for a walk, as the others lagged behind. Jeshua asked Peter, "Simon Peter, do you love me?" Jeshua sometimes referred to Peter as Simon or Simon Peter during personal moments.

Peter said, "Yes, Lord, you know I love you."

A little while later, Jeshua repeated, "Simon, do you love me?"

"Yes, Lord," Peter said again, "I love you."

Jeshua said, "Then feed my sheep. Feed my lambs." A little further down the road, Jeshua again asked, "Simon, do you love me?"

Peter, incredulous by now, beseeched Jeshua, "Lord, why do you ask me? You know all things about me. Why do you repeatedly ask me this question? I love you more than anything."

Then Jeshua said to Peter, "If you love me, care for my lambs."

It was now my turn to look disbelieving. I said to Jeshua in a perplexed tone, "Lord, you speak this to Simon Peter, 'You must feed my sheep and care for my lambs.' You are a good shepherd, but you have no sheep!"

And Jeshua said to me, "Mattai, those people who follow me are my sheep. The people who are yet to follow me are the lambs. I give unto you all the care taking of these people, for they are mine. If you love me, you will love mine." And with that statement, I backed away with an awe that filled my being.

Then Peter said, "Lord, whatever you ask, I shall do."

We then stopped to rest. Immediately and quite unexpectedly, an animated debate ensued about what Jeshua could possibly mean about putting us in charge of a mass of people. What was happening that He could not continue to lead and care for them? Was He going away? Giving up His job? Was He leaving us? What did it all mean? Why? A more ominous overtone crept into our discussion: was He going to die?

As we conversed together, the realization dawned that Jeshua was turning over responsibility, having us take charge, for He would not always be there as He had been, healing and teaching. There would be a day when He was no longer our rabbi.

We became anxiously apprehensive about this possible turn of events, and I thought to myself, *what enormous responsibility we could have*.

I felt in a way like a child that can no longer run out to play whenever he chooses but has instead to perform the chores that are assigned to him. I realized what a bittersweet moment that can be. The child thinks, *Well, I am now grownup, but I wish I weren't*. And as the nine-year-old looks around and sees a younger sibling playing freely while he has to do the chores, he might dream and remember what it was like to be carefree.

I then realized how precious these days were, days when we could simply follow along, listen and learn from our great friend. And then I wondered what in the world I and my brothers should do if called upon to do the leading.

The next day Jeshua called us all together and said, "We must go to Jerusalem soon." He told us that this voyage would be very important because God was summoning us to teach many there.

It would be a month before we made that fateful trip to Jerusalem, but we were nonetheless uneasy and apprehensive. As we walked through the olive grove, snacking on the ripened olives that had fallen to the ground, we considered the task before us. Thomas said, "Lord, why would any of us want to go into that big city when all we need do is skirt the outer edges and people will come? Why must we go where it feels so burdensome with injustice?"

And Jeshua replied, "Jerusalem, the holy city, was built upon my Father's word and there is the fulfillment of the law of all prophecy."

"But, Lord," pleaded John, "you tell us that God is full of grace and full of forgiveness. Would He not forgive us if we chose another city? It seems we are setting a trap for ourselves."

And Jeshua said, "Of course, our Father-Mother God would forgive us, but we must soon go to Jerusalem. The prophecy will not be fulfilled unless we go there."

We all looked up at Jeshua questioningly. Of course, we had the sense that something monumental would be happening in Jerusalem — we had heard enough about it — but we had no idea what it would be. Jeshua, seeing our bewildered stares, said, "I will tell you this much, my beloved brothers. As I am pledged to do my Father's will, His will is that certain events unfold in Jerusalem. Part of the prophecy is that as we make our presence known there, a stirring of the energies will take place. The priests will be disgruntled, and they will challenge me. It is my agreement with God that I will confront them and challenge them right back. I will Ascend to my Father and in three days time I will return and bring to you Light. So be it."

We all looked at each in confusion, because we did not understand what He had just said. Later, we would discuss these mysterious words and agree that Jeshua must mean that He would meditate and pray to the Father and then bring illumination to us.

But now, I spoke up, "Then, Lord, we shall go wherever you shall go. I shall come with you. Wherever you go, I am at your side."

And, Peter, sword in hand, not wanting to be left out, said, "I'll show these people that they have nothing on us. I'll show them, Lord, who is mightier."

Jeshua sighed, "Peter, control yourself. How many times have I needed to remind you of that? Remember, in spite of your impulsive behavior, I have chosen you to be the foundation for our group. So behave accordingly!"

As we continued to walk through the olive grove, we discussed the coming events. We talked over the logistics of where to go to prepare for our feast for Passover — our trip to Jerusalem would coincide with our Passover celebration — and how long to linger before heading into that great city.

And then Jeshua alluded to Mary Magdalene in a manner that defined our soon-to-be diverging pathway in a way that could not be denied. He told us, "Mary Magdalene will not be accompanying us to Jerusalem. She must be instructed to perform certain functions should anything happen to me. It was with a sense of alarm and foreboding that we heard these words. We looked anxiously at one another and I privately thought, *There is no doubt that this confrontation about which Jeshua speaks will have consequences.* And then I asked myself, *"What is going to happen in Jerusalem?"*

NINTH SPIRITUAL LAW

For every thought is a blessing or a curse. Where everything has been cursed, bring love onto it and it is healed. For the Father God is love and heals all things.

CHAPTER 10

The Crucifixion

The Jewish priests were plotting against us, but how that would play out we could not yet know. Because Jeshua was drawing such large crowds wherever He spoke, the priests were disturbed, fearing a threat to their power over the people and their position with Rome. Word had come to us of the rumblings within the hierarchy, and in that we had much concern about entering Jerusalem. When Jeshua said that we must go, we became alarmed. But we relaxed some when He quickly assured us that this trip would be fun. "Do not fear," He said.

Leaving Capernaum and traveling to Jerusalem, we neared the town of Bethphage, not far from Jerusalem. I recalled fondly the time when we taught her citizens the Blessings on that beautiful hillside. Rather than Jeshua going into town, He asked several of us to enter instead and find a donkey, which would be tied, along with her young colt, with a gamla (rope).

I, ever the practical moneyman, asked Jeshua, "Lord, what price shall we pay?"

Jeshua responded, "Nothing, for God placed the animals there for us."

Still concerned, I asked, "But Lord, what if we meet the owner and he requests coins, then what?"

Jeshua replied, "Mattai, do not be concerned. Just tell the owner we only wish to borrow his animals and that we will return them soon."

With Jeshua's reassurance, we headed into town and had not gotten far when I spotted a donkey and her colt tied up to a post, just as Jeshua had said. We untied them and led the animals back to where He and the others had been waiting. Jeshua mounted the donkey, and we started out for Jerusalem.

As we neared the city gates, we were met by a small crowd that had been told by travelers who passed us on the road that our arrival was imminent. Entering Jerusalem I spotted children high in the palms alongside the road. The adults awaiting our arrival had broken off branches of the palm trees and laid them on the ground as a show of respect for us. I heard their murmurs as we moved past: "Here is the king of Jews." I didn't know how the rest of my brothers felt, but I for a moment felt just like royalty; I sensed the esteem they held for what we represented.

We made our way through the welcoming crowd to the magnificent home of Jeshua's uncle, Joseph of Arimathea. Here in his richly decorated household we washed up and were hosted to a delectable meal, after which we joined in for songs and prayers. I was overwhelmed by the stylish furniture that adorned Joseph's home, so many different varieties, along with chiseled statuary and ornate treasures from all over the world.

Later in the evening Jeshua announced that this week would be a very special one, in which we would devote ourselves completely to teaching God's truth to all who would listen. He directed us to be ready at first light for a walk through the city, where we would make our way to the synagogues, through the temple square, then from marketplace to marketplace, in a quest to reach the greatest number of people.

We connected with many in this way for several days. My brothers and I were wholly involved gathering people together, organizing them for an efficient presentation and speaking to them in small groups, even individually, as they sometimes questioned Jeshua's meaning or spiritual interpretation. I personally performed many healings. And Jeshua had been right. This was a time of fun and also satisfaction.

On several evenings we traveled to Bethany for the night. Early the next morning we would return to Jerusalem to continue our work. Jeshua was at His all-out best during this week. He was exceptionally impassioned, shining with a particular glow. In His fervor, it seemed almost as if He knew something that we did not.

Jerusalem, of course, was the largest city in this area where we had been traveling, and we had largely avoided it because of the unrest produced by the priests' denunciation of Jeshua. The mood therefore was unstable; the people, having heard increasingly about Jeshua, were impatiently awaiting His arrival. They fervently sought His healings and avidly desired to hear the words that would improve their lives. They wanted simply to touch Him, to be by His side. They too sensed the winds of change and were desperate to get their turn. The feeling that ensued was one of restlessness and disgruntlement toward the priests. In this state they wrestled for position, and soon were pressing in on us, becoming sometimes unruly and boisterous, even demanding. The pandemonium disturbed me to a point that I repeatedly spoke to Jeshua about it. But He just brushed it off, saying, "The crowds want to experience us and receive our gifts now and they are just being a little rambunctious."

I felt that "rambunctious" was a gross understatement of the energy I was witnessing, but so it was for the entire week, with the crowds growing in size and becoming more difficult to handle. Sensing that a riot could erupt, I was reaching a breaking point, where I could no longer deal with the chaos, and then Jeshua announced that we would leave the city and return to Bethany for a while. He added that later we would return to Jerusalem. I breathed a sigh of relief.

How wonderful it was to leave this city of intensity and madness and return to the quiet, peaceful surroundings of Bethany with our friends Lazarus, Mary, and Martha. On the way there we made an out of the way detour to Bethphage to return the animals we had "borrowed."

I might have been prepared for a delicate situation in Lazarus' home between Mary and myself, because of how we had last parted, but that was not the case. While I could discern that Mary still held out hope for a deeper relationship with me, she did not press it and indeed was charming and gracious. I truly did love Mary and knew that she loved me. We fell into an easy, close alliance that was without pressure.

My brothers and I rested and recuperated at the house of Lazarus for a week. One might have thought that after all we had been through we would have been content to forget about the teachings and the crowds for a while, but that was not the case. During our time at Lazarus' home there was much discussion and a resulting dissension over preparations for our return to Jerusalem. Peter, ever feisty, asked, "What should we do? Shall we get swords and knives to defend ourselves?"

Then Thomas said, "Maybe we should employ an army to surround and protect us."

And Thaddeus asked, "Should we go at all?"

I, like my brothers, certainly had my inner doubts about returning to Jerusalem, but I had always been the ideal "number two" man, who carried out completely a superior's order, so at this juncture I stood, hands on hips, and pronounced emphatically, "Look, it is time to put our fears behind us and comply. We must do what our Lord says. He is not directing us to go and gather an army. I am sure that He is going to be just fine. Do you all think He doesn't know how to create a miracle if He had to, to save His own life?" Perhaps I was in a bit of denial, but I trusted completely that Jeshua knew the right thing to do.

Jeshua then reminded us, "There indeed will be a disturbance and an uprising when we enter Jerusalem again, but we must go because it is there that our Father's plan will unfold. No matter what occurs, I wish for you twelve to know that it is all in the fulfillment of our Father's plan."

This statement helped us to accept our upcoming trip, but we foresaw big problems ahead. We were all in fear, not just for Jeshua's safety but for our own as well.

Passover week was before us. Jeshua said, "The time has come. This day we must go to Jerusalem. Dress in your finest robes and sandals." With much trepidation we all prepared ourselves and began our uncertain journey.

Jeshua dressed in a clean, new seamless robe of the finest wool. He had been given the gift of a great medallion made of onyx and set in gold, which he wore on the girdle around His waist. On the medallion there was a likeness of a pyramid. Above the pyramid, the all-seeing eye of God. Similar images sometimes represented false gods, but this was no false god. Jeshua wore this magnificent piece as a decree of His unity with the Father and the perfection of His plan. He wore beautiful, rust-colored leather sandals that shined in the sunlight.

While heading for Jerusalem, we pleaded with Jeshua to turn back. "We do not want to return because, my Lord, the last time we were there we managed to rile up the temple priests. Now they are very angry and we feel they may be setting a trap."

He was steadfast, "We must continue our journey."

At last we were standing on the hillside outside the city gates looking down on Jerusalem. It was Thursday morning. Peter, Phillip and I approached Jeshua, and I said, "Teacher, I know you have said many times that this must be done, that we must go and participate in the greater celebration of this Passover and that we must do it within the walls of this great city of Jerusalem. Will God reveal His plan to us then? Will Rome be overturned? Will our load be lightened?"

And Jeshua said, "My friend, the load will not be lightened, except that you lighten your heart. Come then and let us be festive, come and let us be merry. Let us celebrate with enthusiasm and great joy the freedom of our people, the freedom of all people. The truth shall set you free. I AM the Way, the Truth, and the Light."

And I said with tears in my eyes, "Rabboi, Rabboi, I fear. I fear for our safety."

Jeshua looked at each of us. We were all expecting Him to well up with tears as we had and to be as deeply solemn as He had ever been. But instead, Jeshua made a silly face at me. He uttered a word that I had never heard Him say previously, "Bull!" Then He said, "This is not the time for tears, for they shall come later. Now is the time for rejoicing." And with that He sent me ahead to prepare the rooms that we would need for our feasting and for our stay in Jerusalem.

Proceeding on, Jeshua walked the streets of Jerusalem, and people gathered alongside Him, asking for His blessing. When they arrived at the house where we were to sup and celebrate Passover, I was waiting for them at the front door. We all freshened up, then sat down for a joyous visit with friends we had invited over, but it was not long before Jeshua bade them go. It was to be just us disciples who were to share this Passover supper.

We moved to the dining room and sat down around a large table. Our supper had been well prepared; it was an extraordinary meal of roasted meat and bitter herbs, served with unleavened bread. We had superb wine from the finest vineyards. We intoned the religious blessings of our traditional Passover prayers. During our repast we alternated between solemnity and joviality, but there was a continuous buzz, an undercurrent of interest and concern surrounding the events consuming our minds. The buzz became particularly heightened after a startling revelation from Jeshua.

He interrupted our festivities at one point to say, "You are all laughing now, but I will tell you that one among you will betray me." He went on, "You think that you all are supporting me, but someone here is not."

We all turned to each other and asked, "Will it be I?" And then we quickly answered our own question with the response, "Of course not, not I." To my right, I heard, "It couldn't be me. I love the Lord too much to ever betray Him."

Then John leaned over Jeshua's shoulder and asked Him directly, "Lord, it isn't I, is it?"

Jeshua responded, "He whom I will kiss is the one." Jeshua stood and circled the table while everyone held his breath. Then He bent down and kissed Judas.

Judas' face became a mask of conflicted emotions. He appeared shocked and angry, and also embarrassed to have been exposed. Feigning outrage, he nonetheless responded nervously in a muffled voice, "Lord, of course, you know it is not I. You could not possibly think that I would betray you." But soon after Judas abruptly arose and made an excuse to leave the room, saying, "I need to relieve myself."

We were most curious about where he was going and what he was up to. I recalled then a recent conversation that I had had with Judas and I shared it with the others. Judas had said to me, "Look, if the Master wants to carry on in the way He has been, ostensibly on a suicide course, who are we to stand in His way? Except I could not bear it if something happened to Him.

"And I said, 'Nor could any of us, Judas!'"

I explained to those at the table that Judas' comments were sparked by the Master's repeated words that "soon I will leave you." I told them that I certainly wondered what Jeshua meant by that comment and what we could do to protect Him? Could we possibly sway more people to our side?

I commented that I was sure Judas became frustrated at times because he was not doing more and being more effective in carrying out his own goals.

Judas never returned to our table that night, and when Phillip remarked on his absence, Jeshua said, "It is in the plan of the Divine. Let's just enjoy our meal."

At the completion of our supper Jeshua held up the unleavened bread and spoke, "*This is my body.*" He broke the bread and continued,

"*When you gather, do this in memory of me.*" We shared the unleavened bread, the Matzoth, as we called it.

Then Jeshua picked up a pitcher of wine, filled his chalice, held it high and said, "*This is my blood and in this is our eternal life.*" He took a sip from His cup and passed it so that each one of us could also sip from it.

When the cup came to me, I paused and for the first time examined it closely. This was an intricately carved silver cup that had been gifted to Joseph, Jeshua's father, who in turn had given it to his son. Jeshua always carried this cup with Him, even during His many travels and always spoke of it as sacred. Jeshua had taken this cup to a silversmith for engraving. Now it bore several Hebrew blessings, which included sacred letters, as well as some Druid symbols. I took a sip of the sweet wine and passed it to Phillip on my right.

Every one of us there had an intuitive understanding that the bread was a symbol of Jeshua's body and the wine of His life force and that breaking the bread symbolized His broken body and the wine represented the spilling of His blood. I had a vague premonition that this ritual might be setting the stage for a larger tradition.

We were on edge as to why Jeshua was declaring that we must remember Him and why this representation of His broken, bleeding body. While not certain, I certainly was perceiving my ever-escalating fears and growing suspicion. Then He again announced that He would ascend to His father and in three days time return to us bringing Light. He had made this assertion before, but I still was not clear about what it meant; however, this time I heard these words as a promise He would keep, and it made a lasting imprint on my consciousness.

The wine, however, was beginning to affect us all, and as the evening progressed, we became less concerned about possible future events. We all even forgot about our brother Judas and what he was up to.

We continued our celebration in much cajoling camaraderie and deep love. Finally, concluding, Jeshua said, "Let us walk in the Garden."

The garden He was referring to was the Garden of Gethsemane, a short walk away, where grew a grove of olive trees. When we got there, Jeshua said, "There is a place here with stones that resembles an altar. Mattai, will you come with me? And you, Peter, James and John, please, come and be with me. Stay close to me this night and pray with me." He also asked that we stay awake all night to keep watch for any goings on.

Peter, in an emotional outpouring, cried, "I will always support you, my Lord."

To Peter's dismay, Jeshua rejoined, "Peter, before the cock crows announcing the dawn, you will deny me three times."

Peter sputtered his objections, and then we kneeled to pray.

My brothers and I had been bolstering each other by silently rejecting that anything untoward or dangerous could happen. By refusing to talk about it, we convinced ourselves that we must be correct. I was, however, beginning to recognize the truth of our pretense: we were all in denial.

After a few short minutes of prayer, feeling the effects of this huge evening supper that overflowed with wine, I literally slumped over and fell asleep, as did the others, leaving Jeshua to pray all by Himself. When Jeshua looked up He saw us all stretched out on the ground, fast asleep.

A loud clanging in the distance startled me awake. Seeing Jeshua kneeling in prayer, I immediately realized that I had failed in His request to stay and pray with Him and to keep watch. I imagined that He had felt deeply hurt, abandoned by us. I felt very guilty and, aware of movement in the distance, was quick to apologize to Jeshua, who reassured me that I was forgiven.

Looking out, I saw lights. The sound of metal upon metal became louder and with that the voices of men approaching. As they came closer, carrying their lanterns, I could now make out the figures: they were temple guards accompanied by several priests. I glanced at Jeshua and inexplicably saw blood on His face.

By now everyone was awake and we gathered around Jeshua. When the intruders were before us, one man until now unseen stepped forward as if to greet us. To my amazement and shock I saw that it was Judas. I thought, *What is he doing with these priests and guards?* Before we could question him, he approached Jeshua and kissed him on the cheek. Jeshua returned his kiss and spoke softly in his ear. I didn't know what to make of it. Then immediately a priest pointed at Jeshua and said, "Arrest this man."

Suddenly, the guards rushed up, surrounded Jeshua and grabbed His arms. Peter quickly pulled his sword from its sheath and in a fury slashed one of the guards, severing his ear. Jeshua admonished Peter, who quickly withdrew.

Jeshua called out for us all to leave. He assured us that He would be all right. Frankly, I didn't know what to do. I didn't want to go but decided that for my own safety and that of the others, I would. We all scattered. I looked back once to see Jeshua being led away in the opposite direction by the guards. Peter, John, James and I had fled into the woods, and now we reassembled and circled back to follow Jeshua but at a distance. Lurking in the shadows so that we wouldn't be detected, we followed them all the way to the prison. When, after entering, they didn't come back out, we decided to disperse, because to be seen together in a group might arouse suspicion. Before we broke up, we agreed to meet at Lazarus' house if we lost contact, especially until things cooled off. For my own safety I felt that I must disguise myself in order to avoid being arrested. I stayed in Jerusalem but knew to keep away from the crowds for the time being.

I heard that Jeshua had been marched in chains from the jail to Caiaphas, the High Priest of our temple. I was alarmed because Caiaphas had condemned Jeshua and was the leader of those out to get Him. I felt certain that Jeshua would defend Himself and reveal to Caiaphas that He was the true Messiah and that seeing this, the High Priest would release Him. If all else failed, I felt certain that Jeshua would use His power to call upon the Father, and God would assist Him to simply walk out of prison.

When He arrived He was immediately placed before Caiaphas and questioned. Caiaphas then sent Jeshua to King Herod for further questioning. Herod in turn sent Him to Pontius Pilate, the Roman military governor of Judea. Pontius Pilate, not wanting to get involved in the internal conflicts between religion and politics, sent Jeshua right back to Caiaphas and the Sanhedrin, the Jewish supreme council and tribunal. There Jeshua was accused by His fellow priests, who did not understand or approve of His teachings and who sought to label Him as a heretic. But these rabbis could find no true heresy in Jeshua's word and could not find Him guilty. But they felt that they also could not let Him go.

Having no other recourse, the priests sent Jeshua back to Pontius Pilate, hoping to make His case a Roman issue, hoping He would be convicted of political heresy. Caiaphas fanned the flames by telling Pontius Pilate that Jeshua was preaching rebellion to overthrow Rome.

Reluctantly, Pontius Pilate assembled a trial and with the priests present again took up the questioning.

Pontius Pilate had hoped the entire situation would simply disappear. His dilemma was complicated. I'm sure that deep down he recognized Jeshua's greatness and certainly felt Him innocent, and while he did make a case to the priests at court that Jeshua had done no harm, he could take his argument only so far, because a conflict between the priests and the authorities could cause his Roman superiors to view him as weak, as having no control. This could result in a loss of his power from Rome. His attempt was to keep a semblance of peace and control in all situations. Pontius Pilate's power was so important to him, in fact, that he would give to the people almost any sacrifice so that he would be esteemed by them and deemed even more authoritative.

But now he was in a pinch and angry with everyone — King Herod, Caiaphas and the other priests — for putting him there. He lamented that this situation might so easily have been avoided. Had Jeshua simply admitted wrongdoing, confessed that He was not the Messiah, Caiaphas would have released Him, and Pontius Pilate would have been able to duck the entire issue of Jeshua's fate.

He did not want to make this decision because whatever he did would be controversial. Not only that, but he would be forced to look at why he had acted in a certain manner. Most men certainly did not want their motives questioned by others, but they also most especially did not want to be questioned by their own conscience. Introspection of this sort was uncomfortable and considered by most to be avoided at all costs. He searched for an idea that would get him off the hook.

After much quiet distress, Pontius Pilate hit upon a solution. He would offer up Jeshua to the people and let them make the decision. He felt much relief in this idea because he would be free of blame and the people would surely find Jeshua guiltless and would release Him.

I heard that Jeshua was being taken to the Roman palace on the temple square. This was the day of the Passover ceremony when it was decreed that one prisoner would be set free. I was certain that Jeshua would be the one, because of the number of people who loved Him. I saw Him as an innocent lamb. I obtained a robe with a hood to cover my head and moved cautiously to the square on the south side of the Roman palace, where I positioned myself in the far back of the crowds. I eagerly anticipated witnessing the end to the deception and craziness and welcoming my Master back.

The governor, Pontius Pilate, appeared at the balcony of his regional ruling palace, and a prisoner was brought forth to face him.

The crowds shouted, "Bar-Abbas, Bar-Abbas!" This was a man who had gained notoriety as a zealot. Even though he was a known murderer, he was considered in some quarters a folk hero because he had threatened to lead the Jews in a revolt against Rome.

Then suddenly, another appeared at the door of the balcony. It was Jeshua. I was shocked and devastated to see Him in chains. Despite my fears and unable to restrain myself, I shouted, "My Lord I am here. Come down." But the crowd was noisy, and no one paid me any attention.

My anxiety level was rising, but still I felt that surely the crowd would ask that Jeshua be released. I thought *He is a man of supreme purity, the Son of God. Bar-Abbas is nothing but a cold-blooded killer.*

Then I heard the buzz. "This Jeshua," they were saying, "He claims to be the true Son of God, our Messiah, and to know more than our priests. But He could not be; otherwise, He would rise up and smite our enemies. But this He has not done, so how could He be our Savior?"

Treachery surrounded me. I saw interlopers purposely stirring up the crowd against Jeshua, and I was sure that the traitorous priests had put them up to it.

By now I was in a fury. Why had we not organized ourselves so that we could speak to the crowd, tell them the truth and see Jeshua set free? We could have told of Jeshua's love and compassion for people, of the many miracles He had performed, of His purity and His innocence. I felt ashamed that instead we had all dispersed and scattered out of fear for our own lives.

The crucial moment had arrived. Would the tide be turned? Pontius Pilate shouted to the crowd, "Which of these two should I release today? Is it to be Bar-Abbas or Jeshua of Nazareth?"

The crowd's voice escalated to a crescendo: "Free Bar-Abbas!"

I could not believe what I was hearing. Had the people forgotten Him? Why, just last week, many of these same people were pleading for His help. No longer in fear of being recognized, I frantically called out,

"Free Jeshua, free Jeshua!" A few more voices chimed in, but alas, to no avail: we were drowned out.

A sinking feeling in my gut spiraled up and spread throughout my entire body. I was sick inside. There was obviously a conspiracy afoot, just as we had suspected, and by coming to Jerusalem, my brothers and I had fallen right into a well-laid trap. We just hadn't realized completely how much the priests feared Jeshua and with what venom they viewed Him. It had all happened so fast. I could see it all clearly now, though. It was indeed Caiaphas who had spearheaded this conspiracy.

The shouting continued, and I, though largely unheard beneath the larger roar of the crowd, was becoming hoarse. Then Pontius Pilate raised his hand asking for silence. The crowd settled, and Pontius Pilate pronounced, "Your vote is heard. Bar-Abbas will be freed." What I had feared most had occurred. Jeshua was going to be held and in His place, an evil man was to be set free.

But it was not yet over. Pontius Pilate solicited the crowd, "What shall I do with Jeshua ben Joseph?"

The crowd shouted back, "Let Him be crucified."

Pontius Pilate then asked of the crowd, "But what evil has He done?"

The crowd, ignoring the question, shouted, "Let Him be crucified."

Pontius Pilate, seemingly resigned to the crowd's plea, replied, "It shall be done."

After his decree, Pontius Pilate bowed his head and turned around to a water-filled bowl that stood behind him. He washed his hands and said despondently, "It shall be done, but I am innocent of this." It seemed as if he wished to cleanse his soul of the travesty. As he disappeared inside, the guards grabbed Jeshua and pushed Him back indoors as well.

Pontius Pilate in the end was not an evil man but simply one in fear, just like other men who feel they must adjust their belief system to the opinion of the masses. In all actuality, in another time and circumstance, he might have been a great friend to Jeshua.

Bar-Abbas was released into the crowd, and everyone began to clear out of the square. Just at that moment Roman soldiers appeared at a doorway to the street with Jeshua, still in chains. Where were they going with Jeshua now? I wondered.

This sudden appearance alerted me, and as the soldiers led Jeshua out onto the street and as a number of people followed, I fell in behind. Looking furtively around, I recognized several of my brothers, but still fearing that we would be exposed and arrested if we were all seen together, I chose to ignore them. They did the same.

Up ahead I could see the soldiers whipping Jeshua: His back was cut open and bleeding. We had arrived at the praetorian, the courtyard opening to the garrison that had been built near the northeast corner of the city. The procession halted. A small group milled around the courtyard keeping a distance from the soldiers, who were becoming more antagonistic and violent. My sobs, thus far held inward, threatened to burst forth in uncontrolled anguish, but somehow I held on to myself, perhaps still hoping that Jeshua would perform some miracle and save Himself.

But then additional soldiers marched out of the garrison. One held a crimson robe in his hands and moved forward to drape it around Jeshua. Another soldier had fashioned a branch of thorns into a loop; he approached Jeshua and roughly shoved it down on His head, sneering, "Here is your crown," and to the crowd, scornfully, "Here is your King of Jews."

How relentlessly cruel were these Roman soldiers. I couldn't help but for a moment think how I had cooperated with them. How could I have? How could I ever have shown respect for them? To me, now, they were evil incarnate.

The soldiers ripped off the crimson robe and began to mock Jeshua, to jeer Him; they even spat on Him. Then two soldiers dragged a large wooden crossbar out of the garrison and shoved it onto Jeshua's shoulder. Upright poles that held these crossbars were scattered all over the countryside. They were used over and over again because these days so many men were being crucified as criminals.

I was horrified, in a panic. Almost hysterical, I considered uniting with my brothers and attacking the soldiers, but their numbers were increasing, and one held an ominous whip. I thought better of the idea and decided to trail back behind, watching for an opening that I might take advantage of. But the opportunity never arose. Jeshua was being beaten now with the whip and pushed to walk up the steps that would take Him to the edge of town. He seemed exhausted and stumbled many times from the weight of the crossbar.

A tall, muscular man in the crowd then came forward and said to the soldier in charge, "I will carry the cross piece."

The soldier asked him, "And what is your name?"

"Simon of Cyrene," the man answered.

The soldier looked the man over, and, apparently, deciding that he had strength for the task, said, "Carry this cross."

It looked as if Jeshua was being taken to the outskirts of town, to Golgotha, where criminals were executed. The hill at Golgotha was at the edge of town where several stone quarries were located. These quarries were mined for rocks to pave the streets and build structures in Jerusalem. As we began to ascend the hill to Golgotha, we passed by the largest quarry, where a huge pit served as the city dump and also as a pauper's grave. The bodies of those who could not afford proper burial and also those who had died of contagious illnesses or who had been killed by robbers and left abandoned on the streets were dumped there. The stench coming from this huge pit filled our lungs.

The soldiers continued to whip Jeshua to make Him proceed faster, and He seemed to have pulled into Himself, acknowledging no one. It looked as if He was garnering every bit of strength to get to this destination. When we finally reached the top of the hill at Golgotha, Jeshua looked exhausted; I could feel His pain. I wished I could give Him a drink from my goatskin flask and pour healing oils on His wounds, but the soldiers prevented anyone from coming near.

I felt a wisp of air on my brow and then a strong breeze beginning to circulate. My first thoughts were of relief, that His body would be cooled and His pain eased. And then I looked up and saw that the sky was no longer a clear, azure blue but had darkened with large, black clouds rolling in. Those around me seemed oblivious to the changes in the air.

Peter, John, James and I had positioned ourselves at the very front of the crowd, no longer afraid of revealing our identities. We wanted to be as close as possible to Jeshua. At the sight of our beloved Lord suffering so greatly, we were determined to stand with Him in His profound resolve to see His role through. We knew too that standing openly beside Jeshua was not dangerous to us now that He was in custody. We realized that the soldiers and the priests truly feared only Jeshua and with Him in hand they figured the rest of us would flee in fright and present no threat. They obviously didn't know us very well.

I surveyed the scene, and saw that Jeshua's mother, Mary, was there, as were His brothers James and Joses and His sister Ruth. Joseph of Arimathea was there accompanied by a friend, Nicodemus. Mary's friend, Elizabeth, had come, and so had many family friends. The child, Hannah, was there, brought by Mother Mary. And, of course, Mary Magdalene. Always, Mary Magdalene.

There were also the ever-present priests, who continued to mock our Master, sticking around for the final outcome.

The rest of my brothers were scattered amongst the crowd, still disguised. Maintaining their positions in the background, they obviously were still afraid they might be hurt. I did not acknowledge them.

While I stood in front of that crowd, I was waiting to see what Jeshua would be directing us to do, even though I was continually reminding myself that we had already been given our directions. I knew that I must remember to live in the spirit of His life and teachings.

I reflected on Jeshua's promise, and even though I did not fully understand the entire meaning, I knew that He would keep that promise. Jeshua had left us with the certainty that all would not be over and that somehow I would see Him again and in some way find a fulfillment through all that had occurred and would yet occur. I put my deep faith in this. And even though I was witnessing Jeshua suffer physical pain and knew that I could face separation from Him, still I prayed to have faith and keep my focus on the truth of His promise. I steadfastly held that Jeshua would send His Holy Spirit to me. Unfortunately, in this moment, His promise did not make me smile.

My attention moved again to Jeshua. As I watched horrified, the soldiers laid Him down on the cross and began to drive nails into His wrists. They nailed a block of wood under His feet into which they drove nails through His ankles. At the first blow of the hammer, Jeshua flinched, but as the soldiers drove more nails through His flesh and into the wooden cross, He became still. His eyes were open, He seemed aware, yet He did not react to the assault. I was the one who cringed in pain with every single strike of the hammer.

With blood streaming from His forehead and down His face from the puncture wounds inflicted by His "crown of thorns," the soldiers secured the crossbar to the pole. Jeshua now hung on a cross on a hill high above Jerusalem overlooking a garbage pit filled with trash and decaying dead bodies.

I could not look at Him for long. The sight of my beloved Lord nailed to a cross and suffering so was too much for me. My eyes, blurred by tears, moved heavenward. The entire sky now was a ceiling of black, the mood foreboding; it mirrored my heart.

Suddenly Hannah, who must have been the youngest child there, ran up to a Roman soldier and angrily kicked him in the shins while shouting, "Get my Jeshua down from there. You don't know anything about God. Nobody should ever be treated this way."

As Hannah continued to cry and scream, I thought to myself, *what remarkable wisdom and bravery this small girl exhibits about how people ought to be treated and about how ignorant of God are the Romans.*

The atmosphere was unreal; I could not convince myself that what I was seeing was really happening. Surely, God would not allow His son to be treated in such a dastardly manner. I truly believed that at any moment Jeshua would fly off that cross and smite these vicious Roman soldiers and also the hateful priests.

The soldiers placed a crude sign above Jeshua's head, which read, "This is Jeshua, the King of Jews," and then they and the priests in a cacophony of laughter taunted Him.

But these acts seemed not to affect my Lord. He spoke up loudly, "I forgive you, even as my Father forgives you. I tell you this day, you will see Him in paradise."

My black mood was immediately broken, shifting into curiosity. I looked to see whom He was speaking to. Jeshua had turned His head to the left where another man hung on the cross. I had failed to even notice this man, but now I became aware of him and also of another man, to His right. The two, labeled as thieves, were nailed to a cross on either side of Jeshua.

As the thief asked forgiveness for his wrongdoings, Jeshua said, "You will be with my Father in the kingdom of Heaven soon."

Jeshua then looked down and fixed His attention on His family. He uttered, "Mother, come closer and bring John."

Mary, and our brother, John, moved slowly toward the cross. When they had established themselves directly underneath, they looked up, anguished. Jeshua said, "Mother, behold your son. And John, behold your mother."

I thought, *what does He mean? Our brother John is not Mary's real son.*

I once again permitted myself to glance up at Jeshua and heard Him say, "I am thirsty."

Then I saw a soldier push a stick with a wet rag tied to its end up to Jeshua's mouth. As it reached Him, instead of taking the moist cloth in His parched lips to moisten them, He flung His head away. And a voice in the crowd said, "They are giving Him vinegar."

My abject misery returned. *Oh*, I thought, *will this torture never stop? Is there no mercy for my Lord?* And a fiery rage engulfed me: it took aim at the soldiers and at the priests with their arrogance and false holiness.

Then from the corner of my eye, I saw a sudden, sharp movement. A Centurion on horseback charged toward Jeshua. He held a spear in his right hand. From the insignia on his epaulet, I recognized his rank: he was in charge of this travesty, and, it seemed, he had more mayhem to unleash. I could only assume that his weapon would be leveled at Jeshua.

My rage had consumed me now, and I reflexively charged the Centurion. I intended to grab his leg, pull him off his horse and pummel him. Just as I reached him, an unseen force, I know not what or from where, pressed against my shoulder and restrained me. At the same time I heard words I knew to be inaudible to those around me ring loudly in my head, "Thou shalt not harm."

I wasn't certain if one of my brothers had tried to stop me or whether some other force was interceding. I was never to know, because a moment later when I turned around, there was no one there.

Standing beside the Centurion's horse, I faced him as he glared down at me as if to say, "I could kill you right this minute for what you were about to do." I of all people knew the risk incurred by threatening a Roman army officer.

Jeshua then spoke clearly and poignantly from His position on the cross, "Father, forgive them for they know not what they do."

His words pierced deep into my mind and my soul, activating my memory of Him as He once before stood in front of me, saying, "Mattai, forgive them for they know not what they do." I knew that His was a personal message for me. I knew it was also a personal message for mankind.

Thunder clapped, and Centurion jerked his focus skyward. For the moment his attention was diverted from me. He paused, then slowly moved his horse to just beneath the cross where Jeshua hung. I continued to gaze upward and suddenly I saw a glorious sight, one that I will never, ever forget: the sky was filled with shining faces looking down at us. I knew that this was the host of angels sent from God to watch over His son and oversee this event.

I was awestruck by this spectacular scene, deeply moved. Then came from Jeshua's lips, "Ali, Ali, Lemana Shabakthani!" *My Lord, My Lord, why have you abandoned me?* It was then that I knew He would not descend the cross to stand at my side.

The next He spoke was, "I commend my Spirit into the hands of my Father."

The most profound sorrow settled over me, and I began to sob uncontrollably. Even in my grief I managed to look up and see the Centurion raise his right hand and fling the spear into my beloved Rabbi, piercing His sacred flesh and spilling out His blood. The Centurion's blow did not, as he had intended, strike Jeshua in the heart but hit below and on the right side of his ribcage, piercing His flesh. Jeshua bled profusely but did not die instantly. He was able to utter His final words, "It is finished."

His head slumped forward and His body went limp. A humble beginning, a humble end, for a man of the people.

Suddenly, the earth rumbled with a great roar, and the ground beneath my feet began a tumultuous movement shaking me off balance. I found myself on my knees where I began to moan and sob loudly. Nothing could console me; my loss was too great. I felt totally and completely alone now.

The rain began and quickly developed into a hard, cruel downpour. It was almost as if God was crying for His son. I heard the Centurion give his account, "I fear that we may have killed a holy man."

Joseph of Arimathea and Nicodemus, with grim expressions, climbed a ladder, removed the nails from Jeshua's feet, loosened the crossbar, and lowered Him down to remove the nails from His wrists.

The soldiers gathered around and bid for His belongings. They cast lots for His clothes, His belt and His medallion, and even for His rust-colored sandals. Then, with Jeshua's belongings in hand, they marched away.

Mother Mary and Mary Magdalene tenderly took Jeshua's tortured body in their arms, and rocking and keening their grief, lamented, "Why?" Finally, after what seemed an eternity, assisted by some of the other women, they wrapped Him with blankets, and Joseph of Arimathea and Nicodemus carried Him away.

I didn't know where to go or what to do, and at this point I didn't care. My Lord was dead and I felt my life over as well.

Finally, chilled to the bone by the cold, pouring rain, I got to my feet and, still sobbing, stumbled away, cursing this place and what had occurred. As darkness encompassed me, I walked further into it, my spirit low, my soul empty. Well into the night, I wandered still. At times I felt I might awaken from this terrible nightmare and find that nothing had changed, that I had only imagined the entire devastating event. But in the next moment the horror would descend over me, sending shivers to my limbs and a dull, cold lump to my belly.

The rain had lightened to a drizzle, but my clothes were soaked through. After a period of wandering I know not where, I became aware of my surroundings and found that I was in the wooded region of olive trees and in utter fatigue. I spotted a protected area tucked in beneath a small grove of trees, where I lay down to fall into a restless, but deep, sleep of blessed escape.

Tenth Spiritual Law

Thou shalt not suffer in the name of God. Thou shalt not bring suffering to others in the name of God. The suffering of human mind and heart, the suffering of flesh is the cause of separation, the sin, and fear of abandonment. Thou shalt not suffer. Thou shalt rejoice for thou has never been apart from God.

CHAPTER 11

The Aftermath: The Ministry Continues

When I awoke, the sun caught my eyes and the air smelled fresh from yesterday's rain. The birds greeted the morning with their songs.

For a moment I forgot the events of yesterday and looked around expecting to see Jeshua and my brothers. Then the awful realization hit, and a supreme desolation came over me. What would I do now? At first I couldn't think. I knew only that I was cold, wet, and hungry . . . and in abject misery. I forced my mind to the present, knowing that I must devise a plan of some kind. An idea formed: the house of Lazarus.

At Lazarus' home we were always welcomed. I would be comforted by the people I loved: Lazarus, Martha and my beloved Mary. *Yes,* I thought, *that is where I will go.* I got up and stretched my legs, taking in my surroundings. I got my bearings and moved off toward this house that I trusted would be a refuge for me.

I remembered that we had always agreed that if we had a problem in Jerusalem we would all meet in Bethany at the house of Lazarus. I imagined that my brothers might be there right now, and those hopeful thoughts steadied me and spurred me on.

After walking for a while I arrived and was met at the door by Mary, whose eyes were swollen with tears. We held each other for many silent, agonizing moments before she led me into the meeting room. I was not to be disappointed, for there they were, all of my brothers, save one, sitting in silent contemplation. I greeted them, spending several moments with each one, gazing deeply into their eyes. The tears began to flow again, and then anger surfaced. When our intense feelings subsided somewhat, we entered into a deep discussion of our situation.

As seemingly no progress was being made over what steps to take next, I suggested that we begin our prayers, that perhaps some clarity would result and we could come to agreement and a plan about what must be done.

Mary soon came in and announced that she and Martha would be serving a meal. I began to feel a little better already, hungry as I was. The thought of food made things seem almost normal again. But after dining everything again turned to chaos with grief, debates and disputes pouring forth.

Two new reports soon reached us. We received startling news that Judas had hanged himself. We learned, too, that Joseph of Arimathea and Nicodemus had taken Jeshua's body to a cave outside Jerusalem where he was entombed. His body had been laid on a ledge cut from the rock itself, prepared with the oil of frankincense, then wrapped in a shroud made of the finest linens. He had been given final blessings and was laid to rest. Joseph of Arimathea and his friend, Nicodemus, had jointly purchased this cave and had given it to Mary so that Jeshua's remains would have a secure and proper interment. We also heard that the priests were advocating that Jeshua's tomb be tightly guarded against grave robbers: specifically against us disciples, who might try to steal His body, then claim that He had risen from the dead.

It was at this juncture that I decided I must go to Jeshua's mother, Mary. I understood that she had remained in Jerusalem at the home of her uncle, Joseph of Arimathea. I knew she must be suffering terrible grief and thought that perhaps I could give her comfort.

I headed out alone. When I arrived Joseph's house was filled. There were many people present: Jeshua's entire family of brothers and sisters, Hannah, His uncles and their families, friends and neighbors, including Mary's confidant, Elizabeth, and, of course, Mary Magdalene.

I went right to Jeshua's mother and spoke to her, "I now know what you have carried within your heart since even before the birth of your Holy Son."

Mary smiled gently, and a tear fell from my eye. She said, "Yes, we all knew that this was part of a plan larger than any of us could conceive or control."

Mary acknowledged me for lovingly embracing "the promise," for living through the worst, which was a temptation to disbelieve. That temptation, which easily befell many of the others, raised the question that if

Jeshua were truly divine, why would this chain of events have had to happen. The logical conclusion for disbelievers was that a false god had let them down and there was no Messiah. Some of the other disciples and, surprisingly, Mary Magdalene, those who had so readily followed Jeshua, now fell into this trap of faithlessness. Not surprisingly, they all found themselves in an abyss of emptiness.

I did not linger. I saw that Mary had a support system and did not need for me to stay any longer. I excused myself and returned to Bethany and my brothers. When I arrived, the men had calmed down a bit. We began to seriously and rationally discuss the circumstances, which had brought us to this present, unfortunate state of affairs. What we had surmised indeed turned out to be fact.

Caiaphas had been out to get Jeshua. He was the one who had convinced King Herod to prod Pontius Pilate into doing away with Jeshua. He was the one to urge Herod to threaten Pilate, that if he wanted to keep his position he had better cater to Rome's wishes and Jerusalem's politics.

I saw firsthand Pilate's behavior and I felt in my heart that Pilate was a wise and compassionate man. But I also saw that he was in fear that the wrong word from Rome might cause him to lose his political post in Jerusalem. The region was political and the balance delicate. I was sure that Pilate knew Jeshua to be an innocent man without evil intentions and a devious plot to overthrow Rome. I perceived that he must truly have hoped and believed that by offering up Jeshua against the murderer Bar-Abbas that surely the people would choose to free Jeshua. This would relieve him of having to make a choice against Jeshua and, therefore, look bad in the eyes of Rome or in the people that he ruled. Naturally, he did not comprehend the bigger vision. Neither did he anticipate that the crowd, spurred on by Caiaphas' lackeys who were scattered amongst them, would have an unexpected change of heart and turn against Jeshua. Actually, only a handful of us had remained loyal to Jeshua.

I told my brothers that however devastating, this event was planned by God. We might have behaved differently: we could have organized a protest and spoken more loudly against what was happening, and in that we might have caused a delay in the proceedings, but in the end the outcome would have been the same, the inevitable would have happened, because God's plan was destined to be carried out, one way or another.

There were many passionate responses from my brothers, and the debate went on for hours. Finally I said, "This conversation could continue for days with no resolution. I suggest we put it aside for now and begin our prayers." Custom dictated that for seven days following a death we prayed. Everyone agreed.

The next morning, still in prayer, we heard a commotion at the front door. Shortly thereafter, Mary Magdalene burst in. She was out of breath and in a state of near hysteria, as she proclaimed, "Jeshua is alive! I have seen him! I met Him just outside His tomb."

There was great tumultuous bedlam as we all rose from our knees and, incredulous, started talking at once.

Finally, Peter's voice roared above the din, "What do you mean, woman? Explain yourself!"

Mary Magdalene was speaking so fast her words tumbled out in an incoherent babble. I took her aside, and calmed her down. She finally was able to make herself understood, although she remained breathless.

"Mary and I went to visit Jeshua's tomb this morning. When we arrived, there were no soldiers guarding it, and the stone had been removed from the opening. We went inside the tomb, but Jeshua wasn't there. The slab where we had laid Him was bare. My heart was beating so fast that I was weak. And then a Light began to fill the cave. And we could see an angel, and the Light emanating from the angel became so brilliant that I was at first blinded.

"But then the angel spoke to us saying that we need not fear. And the angel said, 'For I know you are here seeking the body of Jeshua, who was crucified. He is not here, for He is risen. Go quickly and inform His disciples that He is risen from the dead.'"

Mary Magdalene went on, "Mary seemed to understand some of what was happening, but I was simply overcome. She started to lead me away and said we should return home. But the only thing I could think about was hastening to find you all.

"And then along the path home we saw a figure approach, someone that at first I did not recognize. He spoke, 'Do not fear, for I have risen from the dead. Peace be with you. Do not touch me for I have yet fully ascended.'

"I could not imagine what He was talking about. And then he told me, 'Please, tell my disciples to go to upper Galilee and there I will meet them.'"

My heart leaped in almost disbelieving joy. But I also had a revelation. Remembering Jeshua's words just before our last trip to Jerusalem when he said that Mary Magdalene was to carry out a specific function if anything happened to Him, I realized that her task had been to discover His empty tomb and to be the first, along with His Mother, to see Him resurrected, then bring this miraculous news back to us. I realized too that Mother Mary and Mary Magdalene had been given this task together, so that they could act as support for each other.

Thomas refocused my attention by putting a damper on Mary's news, "I want to be sure that He is really alive. I won't believe this story until I can see and touch Him. Only then will we all know for certain." Thomas did not really doubt this turn of events so much as he was concerned about protecting us should the story prove untrue. He was afraid that our over-eagerness in wanting our master, Jeshua, with us might push us over the edge. While I am sure that there was some skepticism on his part, I am equally convinced that it was to a very small degree.

Ever the vigilant shepherd, forever herding my brothers back to the rules, I said, "I believe that we should continue our prayers, just in case. And besides, it can't hurt." And so saying, I dropped to my knees.

Then I thought to myself, *this is ludicrous. I've got to know, now! Get up, man! I'm going to find out whether or not what Mary Magdalene has said is true.*

I startled those who had complied with my orders to pray by jumping to my feet and saying, "I am going. Which of you will accompany me?" Everyone wanted to go, but we decided for security's sake that only three would venture out, for a large group could arouse suspicion. It was decided that John would go, and since there was no holding Peter back from this fact-finding mission, he would be the third. Peter, with sword in hand, insisted that he would be our protector. Mary Magdalene, while determined to go along, was finally convinced to stay behind with the rest of the disciples.

John, Peter and I set out. As we trekked toward the tomb, our spirits began to soar at the thought that we would find the place empty. Indeed, when we arrived, no one was in sight. We surmised that the soldiers guarding the tomb must have fled in fear that they would be blamed for the disappearance of Jeshua's body. On the other hand, they might have gone to Jerusalem to report the news to the priests that the tomb they were guarding was now empty.

Sure enough as we stood in front of Jeshua's tomb, we saw that the large rock that had sealed it had been moved. It was a huge rock; I estimated that it would have taken at least two strong men to push it aside. John shook his head at the sight.

While Peter stood guard outside, in case the guards returned, I cautiously ventured inside the opening; John followed ten steps behind. It felt damp inside, and I could detect the scent of frankincense and myrrh. At first we couldn't see much in the darkness, but once my eyes adjusted I began to make out the shapes of the interior of the tomb. A large rock was visible in the center, and a cavity was carved out of the stone next to the wall, where Jeshua's body had been placed. I reached over and touched the stone slab. It felt cold. I glanced up to the top of the rock and saw something there. As I took a sharper look, I could see that it was a piece of white cloth, neatly folded and perfectly placed. I recognized it as Jeshua's burial shroud. I gently picked it up and held it. I had an uneasy feeling as I did so, but as we left the tomb, I took it with me.

As we walked away from the tomb along a pathway, I saw something clinging to the bushes. I went over and picked it up. Curiously, it was another piece of the burial shroud. I knew it had to be because it still scented of frankincense. I picked up the shroud and neatly folded it like the other I held. "I will give this to His mother," I said to the others, and we hurried on to Joseph's home to find Mary.

When we got there, we found the atmosphere totally different from what it had been the day before. An air of excitement and joy now reigned. I sought out Mother Mary and presented her with the shroud. We then excused ourselves, explaining that Jeshua had summoned us to meet Him in the upper Galilee and we must go quickly.

We returned to Lazarus' house and animatedly related the facts of our discovery at the tomb. This time all of my brothers, along with Mary Magdalene, headed out toward Galilee. Arriving there, we trekked into an often visited spot and waited with great anticipation. Jeshua suddenly appeared in our midst. I fell to my knees, as did the others, all except for

Thomas, that is, who asked to see the wounds on His wrists, and at the beckoning of Jeshua slowly walked forward. Jeshua extended His hands. Thomas took them in his own and felt the wounds. He immediately fell to his knees weeping and pleading for forgiveness for having questioned Jeshua.

I looked up and intently studied Jeshua. He looked something like He always did, but at the same time He looked quite different. His body formed a sharper image, yet he was lucent and luminescent. This was an entirely unique quality, one that I had never seen before. And I'm sure neither had my brothers, judging from their disbelieving stares. We were curious about this new appearance, but we were joyous as well. Quite a mix of disparate reactions.

For me, Jeshua's appearance was confirmation that there was life beyond the physical form, for which I was extremely grateful. I rejoiced at this revelation and became tearful and overwhelmed by the realization. However, at the same time, I felt separate from Jeshua, and I was not alone in this feeling. While we felt joyful to have Him back, we were fearful that we could not sustain our relationship with Him. We recognized that Jeshua was no longer truly with us. He was beyond us in a way we felt we could not understand. Certainly, we could never expect to attain His level of consciousness, and unless we did, we could not sustain this physical relationship with Him for long.

But then He began to speak to us, not with words uttered from His lips but with thoughts that touched our hearts. We could feel His words, even if we could not physically hear them.

We were actually listening to His thoughts. Each of us received a personal message from Jeshua in this way. And each of us experienced a deeper communication with our Master than we had ever known. We felt within our hearts the echo of His love. He congratulated each one of us and acknowledged our individual efforts. We felt and heard His guidance as to what our next step was to be. When He spoke to all of us collectively, I still heard the message as if it had been coded just for me.

We were experiencing something truly extraordinary, expansive beyond what we had ever thought possible. Indeed, our body tissues and our minds were encompassing new thought forms: that one could be flesh — that we knew, and then non-flesh, in dying — that we knew too, but that one could actually be beyond flesh and communicate left me in wonder.

We were guided to know that when the I AM Jeshua was in our presence, He was no longer the man with whom we were accustomed to drinking our wine. He was a man no longer bound by earthly things. He was a deity reflecting divinity to us.

Jeshua said, "Brothers, I am One in the Father-Mother God as I am One with you. You are the Father-Mother God incarnate as I AM. I bless you to unfold and to know this as truth for all you are and for all you do! I have been Resurrected and have Ascended."

When we got over the initial impact of our encounter with the Ascended Jeshua and were attempting to integrate that experience, we wondered how He had come back to us. But all of our questions were neither asked nor answered immediately; rather, the pieces came together in the days that followed, for there was so much to integrate into our being.

Jeshua was not with us for every second of the day. He appeared and then disappeared, moving in and out of our presence constantly. We all yearned to know the details surrounding Jeshua's crucifixion, His Resurrection, and Ascension. And over time we got our answers in His words:

"My words as I neared the point of death of my body were to forgive those who tormented me by the nature of the divine right that they really didn't know what they were doing. It didn't mean that they didn't know that I AM the Son of God. *How foolish of them to be killing God!* No, that isn't exactly what I meant. I meant something much broader and simpler than that. I was asking my I AM in Father-Mother God to forgive all of humanity, for they do not know that they too are divine. And with that power of their divinity, they don't realize that they produce cause and effect situations that bring to them in a cycle everything that they create, whether good or evil. It eventually revisits them in a significant and predictable manner."

I humbly assimilated that statement and then asked, "My Lord, when you were on the cross, you said, 'My God, My God, why have you forsaken me?' I heard you say it."

Jeshua responded, "Well, there it was, the plan as it was shown me. Perhaps I had hoped that it would somehow be fulfilled before the end. I had a brief thought that at any moment God would transform the situation.

I knew that I needed the Father's say so before I could command things to change. You, Mattai, had witnessed me causing a fig tree to wither at my command. You had witnessed me multiplying the food. You heard that I had turned water into wine. You had witnessed me raising Lazarus from his grave. Was my crucifixion such a big deal for one who knew how to harness and command such power? But I had to wait for God's call before it was aligned and appropriate for me to do so, and that just wasn't coming. I thought that at any moment that call would come. In that moment when I said, 'God, why have you forsaken me?' I meant not only why have you abandoned me, but also why do I not understand this? 'Help me understand this.' That was my plea in that breath. And soon after that, I said, 'Into thy hands, I commend my Spirit.'"

Jeshua addressed me, "Mattai, I am grateful that you steadfastly held within your heart the promise I made."

Then Peter asked, "Lord, what about your Resurrection and Ascension? I don't understand this."

Jeshua replied, "At the crucifixion, I experienced a void in the place between life, death, and resurrection. Even that space between breathing and not breathing is a void. Between death and resurrection, you experience a representation of going down to your own hell. "Before my actual death, I was whipped and stabbed and I experienced pain. But that initial pain and shock to my body didn't last long, and afterward I felt no pain. I had learned to experience an altered state of consciousness, so that my body no longer felt this pain. I learned the principles of this process from the Hindus in the Indian States during my travels.

"After my death I went into that void, a complete emptiness. When you enter that emptiness you let yourself go and in that journey, you allow yourself to descend to hell. But what is hell? It is but a total and complete disconnection from God.

"That is part of our human duality, that as you descend into the void and complete that experience, you rise up again maintaining a frequency that elevates you to the state of readiness for Light work. You become a new being. You have a new life.

"You are then given the opportunity to choose a new identity to the world. If you choose that identity to be Christ and accept the 'I AM That Thou Art,' you have manifested ascension. You then release the ego.

"However, to be able to decide for the path of Christhood, your bodies must be cleansed and clear. Mankind has a number of distinct but connected bodies that serve to make up that divine you, your whole self. There is the physical, mental, emotional and psychic body. If all of these bodies have been cleared, then we are free to ascend. In other words we must be free of any attachments.

"For example, if in our minds we still judge people and are prejudiced, or hate anyone, we are not free. These thoughts bind us to this life. We are not operating in God's universe, which affirms an at-one-ness of all and commands us to love everyone and all things, which He has created, which includes everything.

"And how about our emotional body? Are we still addicted to habits and desires, such as alcohol, food, or perhaps sex? While some of these things are natural and healthy for our bodies, we are to experience them in moderation with recognition that they represent a portion of God's blessings. Can we give up the habituation if we are asked? Are we able to forgive perceived, real, or imagined transgressions against us? Are we able to forgive ourselves and release guilt that we have created? Remember, truly, God does not judge us, for He loves us unconditionally and, consequently, gives us free will to do as we please.

"Are you ready to release those material things that you have created in your life? Your luxuries, your fine clothes, your houses, your fine art work and even keepsakes that represent your family, friends, and your personal history? Or instead, do you wish to hold on to them? If you are truly willing to relinquish all these things and be completely free of all attachments, then you are ready, able, and free to make that decision of ascension.

"At that time my body vibrated at a higher frequency and all of my molecules and cells became the pure Divine Light of God.

"As you accept the process of ascension and your body is vibrating at a very high frequency, you will then create everything you need. During ascension, you not only take your body with you, but you also take on the appropriate body that you need at any given moment. You may also be at any place you wish, anytime you choose. You may even bi-locate and be at more than one place simultaneously.

"The myth that is believed is that the body itself resurrects from death, that the body itself moves from transformation from having let go completely to being filled up again with breath and life. The manifestation of that process is the appearance of a resurrection. The ascension is seen as new life given to you.

"What then are your choices? What will you do? Will you sustain the Light through it or will you carry the Light through density? Will you move Light towards and through all of your form and all of your being? Will you live in the Light? Living in the Light allows for there to be the appearance of density. But it is not really living in density. These things are so important because the full ascension cannot occur as long as a human is holding emotional patterns and blockages. There is no death for that emotional part. Ascension cannot occur when there is a holding of confusion or judgment by the mind, for then there is no letting go in the death of that.

"Many people believe that it all requires lofty spiritual ideas; however, it is really necessary that all of the bodies be resurrected for the ascension to be complete, not just the physical, but also the mental, the emotional and psychic. In the future some people will question that I was actually resurrected. But you all saw me resurrect others including Lazarus whom I brought back from death.

"Since that was true and it was believed that resurrection occurred through my saying it, why would there be any doubt that I was able to call my own body forth? I proclaim to all of you now that for my whole life, with every breath and action, I was preparing myself for my Ascension. And it was not until then, until the moment of my transformation from the density of flesh into the frequencies of Light that I fully realized the state of total and complete at-one-ment with God. It was in an ongoing resurrection, after physical death, and the process of ascension that the God — being I AM fully expressed and manifested. When Mary Magdalene saw me in the pathway outside my tomb, I was present in my resurrected body and had not fully ascended. A day later, I ascended."

I then asked, "How did you know to do all these things? Was this not difficult for you to know and do, to know clearly your path?"

Jeshua answered, "Before my 'coming out' party when I changed the water to wine, there wasn't as much pressure in my life because I wasn't surrounded by the thousands yet. There was at this time a building of energies. I was becoming used to the experience of being in the world as a teacher, as a rabbi. I had lived as a student for so many years. Then when I was to live among men, just as you, Mattai, thought to yourself after our first meeting, 'You're asking me to do what?', I would often ask my Father the same questions, 'You're asking me to do what? You want me to go where? How is it you want me to do this work?'

"Do you think that when I began my work, talking with my friends and you disciples that I clearly knew that this ministry would last a certain time and then I would be dead and lose my physical form? I didn't have all of that so clear at the beginning. What was clear is that there was to be a fulfillment of all things and there would be God's exquisite miracles of life upon life given. I suspected it would require a great sacrifice and transformation of form. However, like any other human, I hoped and prayed that the little inklings of truth were only my imaginings, and I did not let myself draw upon them. As we grew in our family and as we came less and less to play and have those kinds of intimate family gatherings at Capernaum, Cana, and elsewhere, it became more clear that these inklings were closer to the reality than my human self would have ever liked. By then it was almost too late, but of course, not really. It just required me to continue to surrender and believe in the words that I was speaking, walk my talk, if you will.

"But know this, my friends. My full God Christed joyful self is that which I had to call upon every day and every moment of the day. I could not assume that God was there in me taking over my body and my mind. It was necessary for me to constantly turn those things over to God, not have Him take over for me. Do you see the difference? And it wasn't always easy, it wasn't always fun. But it was always the only choice I had. This is why I could teach what I taught and live the way I lived. As I moved through those final days and those final hours and minutes, as I fully surrendered and said, 'Aha, I get it. Father, into your hands I commend my Spirit,' there was I able to move through the deepest initiation that I had yet to move through during all of those years in embodiment. And there was I able to work in the completion of transmutation that allowed Resurrection and then Ascension to be visible to all of you. But that did not occur while I was talking on the mount. That did not occur while I was performing miracles of healing. That did not occur when I was stilling the raging waters of the sea. That did not occur in any of those wondrous moments. Where I moved my whole life in Love, yes, there I was very Divine. But my absolute complete Ascension and Transformation did not occur until there was an absolute and complete surrender to my Father. It doesn't have to happen during human death. In fact, it seldom happens then. It can be at any time. But it has to happen, and with that, I give you the greater teaching.

"When was I Christed? Was it when I was baptized? Yes, I was Christed in every moment when I called upon my at-one-ment in the Father and the Ascension completed itself through the process of surrender. And I activated the completion that I could not even begin to witness within my human self. Human eyes could not have known what it would have looked like. I did not say, 'Oh, this is all going to work out okay. I am going to walk up the hill and allow the soldiers to nail me to the cross. When I let them do this, it will all work out.' No, did I do that self-talk such as 'I will now surrender and in three days, I am going to have a Light body?' No! Rather, I had to be in the moment. I could not let all of this be okay just because of the fact that I knew that in three days I would have a Light body. I had to be in the moment, surrendered in God, which is why for those who pray that they will be saved by me, they are in a state of great illusion. And what lies ahead for them is a surrender that will be far more than they imagine. So be it and so it is."

We decided to return to my house in Capernaum so that we could be more comfortable while continuing to learn from our Ascended Master. Here we felt it safe to bring up a concern that weighed heavily on all our minds.

John was finally the one who blurted out, "Jeshua, we have let you down! We betrayed your trust during that last night and day together."

"Yes," I chimed in. My eyes were locked on the floor in shame and guilt. I was sure the others felt just as John and I did.

"Well," Jeshua replied, "During that Last Supper we all were having fun and greatly enjoying each other's company. Then we all went to the Garden of Gethsemane, a place of great peace. For me, however, there was unrest: my brothers were snoring away on the ground, sleeping off the effects of the wine, while I was beseeching God to show me another way.

'Show me what I have missed,' I prayed, 'show me what I can do differently. Haven't I done enough? Why isn't it enough? Why can't I go and just retire into the blissful, peaceful seaside? Why do I need to go beyond this, to the rest of the way in this plan? Why am I not able to understand this?'

"My ego was in extraordinary pain. In knowing God's will, however, I recognized that these questions represented simply a ranting of fear and a panic of doubt. My higher self absolutely knew exactly what was being asked of me, but my ego felt that maybe I had manufactured this whole plan to act out some kind of glory and self-martyrdom. That's why there were all the questions to God: 'Did I mess this up? Maybe all this was not your plan, but instead my plan all along. So maybe now we are able to heal this and shift this. This doesn't seem like you, Father, to ask me to sacrifice my life. Even as you spared Isaac from the knife of his father at the altar, why am I to be sacrificed?' This was a deep lamentable prayer for me, and I beseeched God to show me. And my weeping and my mourning did not even waken you, my sleeping brothers!

"My ego suffered such extraordinary pain in the Garden on that night I was arrested. And then suddenly I had the realization, 'Oh my God in Heaven. This is true. This is really happening. This is not easy.'

"I knew it would not be easy, and I became bitter about it because I felt so alone. You all had fallen asleep and I was left to pray on my own. I had no one to witness and hold the energy of prayer with me. But all was in divine order; it was perfect, wasn't it? We all need to see the perfection in how things are. In the end these events were of my cup; they were my burden through my own choice.

"When I realized this, I let it all go and a peace came over me. I felt the word of my Father decree me as the One I AM. And with that I was able to rise up with a final breath of release.

"Then you all started to stir just in time to hear the clamoring and clattering of the guards who were about to set upon us. Now, it was easy for us at that point to be in the state of surrender. From a human description, you might say that I was in a state of disbelief. I say that because I didn't have an awareness or a comprehension from an external point of view. It was almost as if this event was occurring as a slow-motion replay for me.

"Meanwhile, a couple of you, my defenders, tried to fight off the guards, and I quickly stopped that. Then I let my brother, Judas, give me his kiss. I looked him in the eye and said, 'Now it is done!' I returned his kiss and said, 'Our Father forgives you.'

"Judas looked at me then, and in one vision, he recognized both my pain and my willingness. He saw his perfect part in this, and yet, in seeing my suffering, he himself suffered an agony and pain which took him into a deep, dark place that none of us could help him with. None of us was in a position to reassure him that he was loved.

"Most of you disciples did not see love in his act or feel love towards him anymore. You had only anger and resentment. But now you must forgive him, just as I have forgiven him. I have forgiven Peter as well, who in his fear, denied me three times that night before the cock crowed."

"But," James blurted out, "wasn't it Judas who betrayed you in the most dastardly way? He actually created your arrest, trial, and crucifixion. Why did he do this?"

Jeshua softly replied, "Judas had a plan that he never confided. It was a plan that differed from my plan, and he felt that the fewer who knew the specifics of it, the better. Judas was convinced, based on his deep inner thinking and sharing with us, that by creating a stir with the Romans, he would only be jailing me, thus temporarily protecting me. He figured that I would be safely tucked away and he would have time to get the crowds behind us. Remember how he would always say that things were coming to the point, coming to a head? Well, of course, ultimately they did. Judas had an ongoing emotional struggle with himself; he heard my teachings, but he also had his own strong opinions.

"One of the reasons Judas was so upset with me was that I would not play the game of being politically correct, nor would I take a stand to be so vocally politically incorrect that I would cause stirring and insurrection. Judas saw me not choosing clearly one side or the other. So from Judas' perspective, that was why his plan didn't work. It backfired according to his interpretation. His deepest hope was that I would shine the Light of God and break free of the shackles.

"It was a very sad day for me when we ate our dinner and spoke of the betrayals that were occurring. It was a very sad day when we discovered the obvious: that Judas could not bear the weight of his own shame, guilt, and anguish and that he took his own life. So we must all forgive him and send many blessings to our brother, for he is experiencing much anguish in his present state of being."

I asked Jeshua about the plot to kill Him. "How could it have been orchestrated by the high priest, Caiaphas, who was supposed to be a holy man of God? And how is it he had the power to persuade the crowd, however covert his plotting?"

Jeshua answered, "You must bless and forgive all our brothers and sisters, just as I have forgiven, not only you for any perceived wrongdoing but even the people in that crowd who asked that I be crucified.

"At any other time, I would have been bolder and stood up to Caiaphas. At another time I would have felt freer in giving Caiaphas the teachings and lessons he required, and I would have challenged his beliefs. I had done that before, which was part of the reason he was so determined to take me out of the picture.

"But after my arrest I went into an altered state. I became quieter and chose not to respond with my usual wit and wisdom and appropriate information. Rather, I responded with the energy and attitude of acceptance and love, as I continued to process and to go deeper within myself. I spoke very few words from the point of arrest forward. I was conserving my strength for the transmutation that was ahead of me.

"You ask why did I not do as I had always done in the past, to defend my truth and go after Caiaphas and the other priests by calling upon my knowledge of the Torah and the other teachings and pointing out that he was in error in his interpretation and understanding.

"Alas, there was no more to do. I had already given all of the teachings that he and the rest needed to have at that time. I had no more human impatience or anger with him. I simply had compassion for the continuation of our drama and God's plan. I inwardly composed my energy for transformation.

"I forgive all human decisions. You, Mattai, need to forgive yourself for them as well. I want you to know that there is no cause to fear your choice, whatever it may be, for if you would stand up to me and say, 'I don't understand' or 'I do not agree,' I would say, 'May you be blessed so that you always know who you are and what is in your heart.' And then when in your humility you ask, 'Is there something more I can learn?', then, I will give that to you. But I do not ever teach that you must suffer in order to follow me, or that you must in any way feel judged or intimidated to follow me. It is always your choice.

"And it isn't that I would ask you to follow me because I require followers. I ask simply that you stand in the truth that I know you are. If that feels comfortable, right, aligned, and blessed, then so be it. Part of me is in fullness with you.

"I never asked for thousands of people to follow me. I never asked for the masses and the throngs of people to hang onto every word. I never asked for that. I do not ask for temples to be built, for crosses to be hung up with my image of death on them. I ask only that you follow the Way I AM, the Truth I AM, the Light I AM, the Very Life I AM. And I ask only so that you, Mattai, and my other disciples know eternal peace and joy as Oneness with your Father-Mother God."

As the gift of the days with Jeshua continued, we were joined by Mother Mary and others. Jeshua would occasionally share a meal with us. All He really did was break bread and have a sip of wine. We asked Him how He managed to get along without eating? He replied that in His Ascended state He required no food. He said, "While eating doesn't defile my Ascended state, I do not process the food and drink through my alimentary canal as you do. I simply transmute the food. I am supping with you in order to share and to be sociable."

Jeshua left us at times in order to create an illusion of separation so that we could take time to contemplate and integrate His teachings.

As Jeshua seemed to just disappear, we were all curious about where He went when He wasn't with us. He explained, "I go to teach other people in other lands."

I asked challengingly, "Just where do you go?"

He replied, "I go west to a country across the great ocean, where the climate is tropical and where live a people with skin that is red, where long ago I traveled with my Uncle Joseph. From there I go north to a climate that is more temperate where also live the red-skinned ones. I return as well to the north where the Druids of the Isles of Britannia reside. I go south to Nubia and beyond to the black-skinned people who reside there." I also go east to islands in the Great Sea. I minister to and teach a brown-skinned group of people who reside there. I go further east to the Indian States to teach the Hindus whom Uncle Joseph and I also visited and then on to Tibet, China and Japan to teach the yellow-skinned people. I am not there to convert them, but I speak to them in terms they can understand about Love and the Divine Order. Whether they are Hindus, Buddhists, those more rooted to the earth and nature forms of worship of the Divine, even so-called pagans — whatever their beliefs — I speak to everyone according to their needs to understand the endless love that flows from the source of creation.

We asked Him, "How is this all possible?"

He replied, "Now that I am in Ascended form, I may travel in a vehicle called a Merkaba, which consists of a portion of my Light body. With that I am able to travel to other parts of the earth and beyond. What you do not comprehend is that when in this Light form, I have the ability to be in several places at once. It is called multi-location. This means I may project my body and consciousness to more than one place simultaneously and be fully in that place at any given time. This is true even though these locations are great distances apart spatially."

I was fascinated by this concept, even though I did not completely understand it, and neither did the rest, but He did leave us with a new concept to contemplate.

While we were integrating what Jeshua continued to teach us, sometimes we felt that we needed to be in a space of silent retreat. At other times we wanted a more vocal communion, and on these occasions we would break out in spontaneous laughter, particularly when we came to an understanding, in our inner being, of a particular piece of Jeshua's puzzle. The laughter was contagious and as one began, several others would start in, and soon we were all howling, except for those who had not understood: they sat in momentary judgment, frowning as though we were disturbing their sacred thoughts. While we were on this joyful high, it didn't take long to remember that it was Jeshua's laughter that had meant so much to us and that had provided so much healing. And even though Jeshua was often not physically present with us, we felt Him to be there.

Jeshua had more on His mind than simply explaining how He had come back to us, and the day came when He sat us down and made clear what our future roles were to be.

"You are to go to the far reaches of the world and teach God's truth, as I have taught you. Where you see that there is suffering, relieve it as best you can. When you are ignored and rejected, dust off your sandals and move on. But as you depart, bless those who rejected you, so that their souls may have a higher knowing of God's truth.

"Spread the word by telling my story. If you become concerned about whether you are doing God's will, you need not worry that you will fail me or my Father, if you have within your heart the desire, willingness, and intent to serve Him and do His will.

"There are many ways to spread the word. An example lies in the purpose of our newly arrived family member, Hannah:

"This brave and determined little one at my crucifixion challenged a Roman soldier. Hannah's role was to convert that Roman to know that there is a divinity larger than his Roman gods, and that divinity is Love and compassion. It took time for him to see the truth. Night after night he replayed that scene in his dreams: the agony of the little girl, kicking him and screaming at him to take me down from that cross. He could not release that memory or forget the expression in her eyes. And he began to pray for forgiveness and healing. And soon with his prayers he was given grace. His name was Antonios."

After Jeshua had been with us for forty days, He told us that His teachings with us were over. Although we had anticipated this eventuality, His announcement left us numb and grief-stricken. He promised that before He left He would give each of us a personal message and blessing. Our spirits rose again because at least we had something from Him to look forward to.

I awaited my turn and when it came I was overcome with emotion. Jeshua took my hands, looked deeply into my eyes, and projected into my mind, "Know that I am always with you. I bring you peace. I AM the Peace of Life. I AM the Peace of all God. I am standing with all who will ask me to be present with peace. I offer healing of body, mind, and spirit, for even if the body makes a movement to be aligned with the dust from whence it came, it goes there healed, not broken. Know this: that no body that one of Light consciousness loves dearly will be disintegrated into the earth as a broken body but will be whole, celebrating the earth as a face of the *Goddess* and another face of the great Mother-Father God. So as it is in all things, we say to you, my peace be with you always in this day.

"You, Mattai, as a healer may not be meant to make those who are dead rise up and walk. That was not what you came for. It is not you who will make those sores disappear from their faces and from their bodies. But you will make the sores of separation be whole again, be healed, and you will bring the knowledge that all things are but temporary in this form, and the eternal God dwells forever in every cell, physical and non-physical, and in every particle in every breath.

"So my friend, remember this: you are not a healer who has not figured how to do it yet. You are a healer who does what is in God's plan, not in yours. As always when I would say to another 'I am One in the Father,' I know that it is my alignment with that soul to make someone arise and walk.

"And you have the same power. It is not for you to judge when it is occurring though. It is for you to trust that as you call forth the Divine to be entering every particle of the cells of life, there is mystery and it is God's alone. Remember this when you write the teachings.

"Mattai, because at times you pretend you do not know, I will give you this prayer.

> *I always know what to do and I always follow through with that doing. I always know who I am, and I always give that to the world. I always know all there is to know, and I do my part in the world. I know what to do and I know how to do it, for I am One in the mind of God and so it is. We are merging into the heart of God as one. I am the teacher of peace. I am the pattern.*

"Mattai, you and I are part of the original group, sharing the message of love. Now, go forth to the peoples of the world, to my sheep, my lambs, and tell our story. Teach God's truth. Shalom!"

After speaking to all of us, Jeshua said, "I go now to complete my ministry with my peoples of the world and beyond. When I have completed this mission, I will return to my Father in Heaven and sit at His right hand, from where He rules His kingdom. But know that some day I will return to you." With that He vanished in a burst of brilliant Light.

Alarmed about His departure but with His words ringing within us, including the promise of His return, we knew now that we must accept His absence and begin our missions. It was indeed time to shake the dust from our sandals and move on.

Jeshua had requested that rather than going out as a group, we split up and travel in pairs. In this way we could spread ourselves out and reach more people. We did agree to keep in communication with each other, and we scheduled periodic reunions. I teamed up alternately with Thomas, James and John, and for a very brief time with Phillip.

We chose to reunite at the home of Lazarus. As Lazarus and his sisters were Jeshua's best friends, so too were they now ours. Their house was large and their hospitality had no equal, which certainly worked to advantage when we planned large gatherings for our many friends. Retreating to Lazarus' home also gave me an extra gift: the opportunity once again to be with Mary. We continued to have deep feelings for each other. As time passed I came to understand and appreciate Mary of Bethany even more. I saw her in relationship to our Master, with her family, and ultimately I understood her great love for me. My love for her grew ever deeper. Although our moments together were fleeting, because I was traveling far and reaching the masses now, our relationship never faltered.

We disciples felt a total dedication to our proselytizing. Those who were married saw their relationships transformed because the women were no longer brought along. Our motto was "leave your family at home." We incorrectly felt that Jeshua would have wanted that. The family members felt quite abandoned, and most moved to Capernaum where they reconstructed a sense of community among themselves in order to claim a support system.

One of the most adversely affected was Peter's family. His wife, Beatrix's, unhappiness knew no bounds, and she insisted that Peter build a new house in Capernaum across from the temple and marketplace. Peter's mother-in-law had recently died and left a small inheritance. He combined that with his own funds and was able to build the home his wife wished. But once he had moved his brood from the tiny house into their grand new quarters, he washed his hands of Beatrix. Peter proclaimed, "That's it for me." We understood his putting an end to the years of browbeating, but what Peter did next would sorely test the love and respect we had for him. He announced, "I am going to Rome, and I am going alone!"

We couldn't believe our ears, and a stir of resentment circulated among us. We felt that Peter was abandoning us. He clearly was letting us down. His own blood brother, Andrew, confronted him, "How do you have the gall to go off on your own when it is our obligation to work as a team? Jeshua has said, 'Go ye, two-by-two, and teach.'"

Peter responded, "I am no longer Simon; I am Peter. I am transformed, and the Lord has given me a purpose."

While we were confused and disappointed by Peter's pronouncement, even more we were worried about him. We were afraid he was doomed without the presence of our protection, particularly since Peter had never gained control of his quick and virulent temper.

Peter had a specific focus and a definite, practical plan as he entered Rome. Determined to carry Jeshua's message forward, he planned to tap into the Roman blueprint to establish a new religion of worship. But first he would have to convert the Romans. That turned out to be not as daunting as it might have seemed.

The strong arm of the Roman Empire had been invading and conquering other nations time and time again and in many cases adopting foreign religions and philosophies as their own. Peter had astutely surmised that he would be able to sway Rome toward the new Christianity, then tap into their political machine and military muscle to spread the Word far and wide.

In one sense Peter's plan was nothing short of brilliant: to take advantage of a successful structure, rather than to reinvent the wheel, made for smart efficiency. However, I was convinced that Jeshua would not have approved: He knew that to organize His work would simply be establishing a new way of worshipping, and that had previously proved a failure. Jeshua had always said that organizing anything took the true message out of its doing.

Peter felt very much alone in his endeavors and was terribly lonely because he did not have his brothers' support and allegiance. But he had been the one to want to go it alone, and the other disciples had their focus where they believed it belonged: teaching in the field.

Peter also became bitter because he perceived himself to be the self-appointed magistrate to spread this new teaching to the world, and this he truly did not want. Rather, he really desired only to be one of the guys again. He didn't want his new job but he thought that this was what Jeshua had asked of him.

Eventually several of Jeshua's students joined Peter in Rome. They found him preaching Jeshua's words and converting a considerable number of people to his belief. These students stayed with Peter and assisted him in his ministry. Among the poor his words were spreading most rapidly.

I got word that Peter's wife had died, and that he had permanently reunited with his children, who were now living with him in Rome.

After Peter had been in Rome for a number of years, the Roman Senate became threatened by the rebelliousness of the converts. While they did not number greatly, they were fanatically promoting monotheism, rather than polytheism.

Sometimes I wished I had gone with Peter. I was tempted because his mission seemed an adventure to me. After all, I was familiar with Rome and its ways, and I wanted to share this experience with Peter. But he chose to go alone, partly because he believed that the world needed as many disciples as possible spreading the Word. He also felt that he was important enough and big enough to handle it himself. Peter's ego didn't want the inevitable confusion and indecisiveness that would have been caused by having another person involved. Later he saw things differently and ultimately regretted this decision.

I couldn't help but observe that there seems sometimes to be a gap between the one who creates a message and the ones attempting to convey the message. There can be many different understandings and approaches to carrying out the original thought. With Peter, it was as if he was not totally in touch with the fullness of Jeshua's message and he went off track in carrying it out.

In my own life now, I needed to carve out a path that would honor Jeshua's desires yet fulfill my own needs. I loved family and always desired to have a closer relationship with my own. But that was not possible, so I adopted Jeshua's family and also Mary of Bethany's family as my true kin.

I assisted Mother Mary and her children and grandchildren every chance I had. When I visited them I taught them their numbers and how to budget not only their money but also their time. This family came to think of me as a brother. After all, I was about the same age as Joses.

Mary's family continued to seek education and spiritual support from their local Essene temple, but the whole of the Essene community began to disintegrate. People withdrew from their faith because of so much turmoil after the crucifixion. There was a reason for this: the religious atmosphere shifted; rumors circulated and threats were made against those who would dare entertain any teachings outside the standards set by the high priests of Jerusalem. The priests indeed became even more brazen in their quest to eliminate anyone whom they felt was a threat to their power. The Essene influence, therefore, significantly diminished to the point where it became an underground activity. Meetings had to be held in homes behind closed doors. One could not speak openly of his faith.

Another threat caused the Jews to retreat into silence as well. The Romans were becoming more tyrannical than ever. Even Bar-Abbas, the zealot, had been re-arrested and finally crucified.

The uncertainty and chaos had escalated into such a point that three years after Jeshua Ascended, our brother John, whom Jeshua from the cross had appointed to take care of Mary, went to her and said, "There is so much turmoil in Nazareth now that it is no longer safe for you here." John urged Mary to sell her house and leave Nazareth. Mary promptly complied.

John took Mary to a lovely hill overlooking Ephesus in Asia Minor, a place Jeshua had often spoken about. While this place emanated peace and beauty and Mary loved it, unfortunately at first, she would be somewhat lonely, as the family did not join her. Everyone had dispersed, each going his or her own way.

After Mother Mary's move her beloved uncle, Joseph of Arimathea, died. After Jeshua's death, considering Joseph's age and the circumstances surrounding the political climate, he stopped traveling and worked tirelessly to bring harmony to the disparate factions in his community. His devotion to Mary's family and to his own had never wavered and during his final years, he was more than ever in their company.

While we were teaching and performing miracles for many people in many lands, keeping the movement of Light and Love alive, we had largely ignored Judea. Neither did we venture very far into Jerusalem, but we did continue to do some teaching around the region of Galilee, particularly at the Essene communities. However, in spite of this, as the Essenes continued to withdraw from public, there were fewer and fewer students. The teachings became more hidden. The priests in the temples in Jerusalem, indeed, the entire Sanhedrin, opposed all outside sects.

And then a great edict went out: *Let there be a unification of the teachings of the Torah.* Under this edict many more of the true spiritual Kabalistic teachings went deep underground, and some even disappeared.

About this time we heard a surprising story from good sources about a Gentile named Paul, who was going around speaking about our Lord as if he knew Him personally. According to what was told to me, this man, Paul, experienced a manifestation before his very eyes. He was traveling on horseback in a remote region on the road to Damascus — that very same Via Maris, where I had collected the taxes for Rome so long ago — when suddenly Jeshua appeared before him in a blaze of light. Paul was so startled that he was literally jolted from his horse by this experience.

The significance of this event that occurred about five years after Jeshua's Ascension, was that it served as a unification for Paul with the essence of Jeshua, and it resulted in what Paul called his conversion. He was awakened to a different belief and philosophy, the one that Jeshua taught, and it changed his life.

Paul began to speak publicly and teach what he knew of Jeshua's message; however, he never attempted to contact us disciples. While I felt that in general what Paul was teaching was accurate, I had some concerns about some of the specifics and was definitely unhappy about some of the claims he was making. Our paths would cross at a later time.

Four years after Mother Mary moved to Ephesus I visited her for what would prove to be the last time. When I arrived, she appeared happy and peaceful. I asked her how she was doing there away from her family. She replied that she enjoyed her days there. She often went down into the city where she was always treated with great love and respect.

She said, "While I do not integrate into the community there, I always enjoy communicating and hearing the gossip of the women and getting caught up on the city's activities. This is always a good getaway. Most of the time, though, I spend here at my retreat in contemplation and prayer. From time to time I welcome visitors, and there have been many. Mary Magdalene has come, as has my friend, Elizabeth, who stayed for four months. All my children come to see me. My daughter, Elizabeth, and I have become closer, and Ruth comes often to visit. I love to see her."

While I was there I planted a rose garden for her. Mary loved roses and I knew that she would spend many joyful hours around those beautiful blooms.

Before I left her Mary held my head in her hands and said, "My dear Son, you are a good man and I am happy to share with you. Even though you have felt close to me, I know that you wanted to be even closer, yet I seemed to have many others vying for my attention. But you are indeed special. In the future whenever you smell roses, think of me."

Coming down the mountain and approaching the city of Ephesus, where I planned to take a ship north, I remembered Jeshua telling us that His mother would like this beautiful retreat. I reflected about how John was put in charge of caring for Mary after Jeshua was gone. I had heard that John was on the island of Patos, not far from where I was. Entering Ephesus, I stopped at one of our safe houses — we had four of these — and greeted the hosts. They had not seen any of us disciples for quite awhile.

We continued to meet when we could. Along with our reunion sites in Bethany and Capernaum, we had meeting locations in Asia Minor and Greece, which we could reach by boat. Because we were many times scattered about at great distances from each other, not everyone always turned up for our meetings together, but we did the best we could.

Later I received word that Mother Mary had died. I felt a great personal loss. She was a grand lady. I always wished I could have had a mother like her. In fact, in many ways I did consider her my own mother. Mother Mary had so many great qualities, but one of the most unusual was that as many times as I was with her, she always had a kind word for everyone and seemed forever happy and at peace. I missed her enormously. I was grateful that I was able to offer her the gift of the roses, which I knew she had enjoyed for the last several years of her life.

Mary Magdalene married in later life to a dear friend who had lost his wife. The two were raising a child together. Mary nurtured and taught the child well, and she was most content now and at peace in her companionable relationships. But she always held Jeshua in her heart, at the seat of her sacred temple.

Mary continued her studies, learning more deeply the teachings Jeshua had given about the mysteries of life and spirit. She journeyed to Rome once and was exposed to many unique sights there. She was then safely escorted back from Rome around the Mediterranean to Ephesus where she visited with Mother Mary near the end of Mary's life.

Mary Magdalene led a very full life of peace, but it was without the wide travels and the teaching that we all embarked upon. Because she was a woman, it was not her place. Her efforts needed to be more limited; otherwise, she would have risked being publicly chastised and perhaps even stoned to death. There was no place for a Rabbiest, female Rabbi.

However, she wrote of her experience and knowledge and did much teaching in other ways, such as in the women's sewing circles in private homes and even in conversations around the campfires and other places. Mary once told me that she had a beautiful life with her husband and the child and also with her memories of our life together with Jeshua. She shared these memories every chance she had, meeting with the women at the wells to tell the tales of her life and times with our great Master Jeshua. Occasionally, the men would gather around and listen, fascinated by her colorful, amazing stories. But mostly, she taught the women. And as women in our time were given no power to become teachers, she taught them appropriately how to heal and how to carry out their spirituality. She regularly visited sick children in their homes and healed them. I had seen Mary Magdalene in such trials in her life that I felt happy and gratified that she now was in a place of peace.

On the other hand, I was displeased with the ministry of others. As time went on and Paul's fame grew, I became more and more disturbed about what he chose to do with Jeshua's teachings. It was about ten years after his conversion that we heard that Paul was preaching in Greece. Thomas and I were presently traveling together, and we decided to go to Greece and confront Paul. When we finally met him, the atmosphere was tense.

Thomas and I summarily chastised Paul for his inflexibility in refusing to consider an expanded version of what he thought Jeshua's teachings were and also for the promises he was making to the people. Paul continued to defend himself, believing that our truth did not apply to him. On one particular point where Paul's views were skewed, we were firm: that women were in every way, save physically and biologically, equal to men.

In addition, some of the rewards he was promising people who would convert to Jeshua's teaching were exaggerated. After a light slap on the wrist from Thomas and me, we departed, even though in my heart, I didn't feel that he would significantly alter his teachings, even after our attempts to clarify some of Jeshua's teachings.

Age slowly crept into my body. During my ministry I had traveled to many countries: Sryia, Lebanon, Asia Minor, Greece, Africa, and Georgia, in the Caucasus region between the Black and Caspian seas. I spent much time in Egypt, in Galilee, and also in parts of Judea where many Essene priests and the small groups that held to the Essene doctrine were forced to hide. I felt that I had worked my mission with excellence.

One day I sent a message to Phillip, advising him that I would like to meet. Phillip and I got together at the safe house along the Sea of Galilee. Except for Peter, whom we had not seen in a number of years, we were the last two disciples still alive. At first, we had gone out two-by-two, but one-by-one my brothers had died or been killed, and now Phillip and I were alone. We commiserated.

Some of the disciples, in the end and after all that Jeshua had taught us, still had misunderstood and tried to start new religions. Peter certainly did, though his methods were different, trying as he did to use the Roman political structure to accomplish it.

Our teachings had had an effect; there is no doubt of that. As we had gone to the people, teaching Jeshua's words, the converts to this new spiritualism were growing. While not numbering enough to make a majority, still the movement was enough to serve as a catalyst for unrest and conflict among the religious hierarchy, and the priests began to take sides in their own dispute. Soon a full-scale philosophical battle raged among them.

I was sixty-three and still ambitious. I felt that I must make a journey to Nubia, even though my age would make traveling such a distance arduous. I had been to this land before and here I experienced a much greater receptivity to the word I was bringing. I gave what I considered a most impassioned, glorious talk, perhaps my best ever, then retired to the house where I was staying.

It was dusk, barely light, when I heard a noise behind me. Before I could turn around a man reached around in front of my neck and slit my throat.

I died quickly, for that was my time to go. I was martyred as I had expected to be, at some time, in some place. It was my belief that in order to see God, I should follow Jeshua's path and accept martyrdom as a certainty.

My delusion was that I had to martyr myself, as Jeshua was martyred in order to be at God's right hand.

Throughout the African countries at this time, spontaneous violence reigned. Killing was an ordinary daily occurrence. Perhaps knowing that deep within my soul is why I chose to make my last stand in this country.

What an end to a glorious life, a life that I was so privileged to share and to be a major player in. A life in which the most remarkable man who ever set foot on Earth performed His role as His Father in Heaven asked of Him, and did it with absolute perfection. A role that was to change the consciousness of mankind. And I, Mattai, was chosen as a scribe to record the miracles, the events, the whole glorious story. I will forever be so thankful to my Father for that opportunity.

Eleventh Spiritual Law

All serve, all must be served.

Expanation:

So it is through this idea that we come to forgive, for expecting that service is given according to our whim or convenience, we must forgive ourselves for holding these expectations. When we pray, my will to do Thy will, we may become shaken to our very core of existence, for ultimately in that we let loose of free will. As we let go, manifestation of many things begins to occur. We have experienced this, and sometimes when we do we feel uncomfortable with the particular circumstance that impacts us. In fact, we may not like it at all. And we wonder whether we really mean "my will is Thy will." When challenged by the universe you may affirm that you are really ready to face whatever outcome occurs and that you are sufficiently strong for it. Your response should be that "I am not here to prove anything but to serve."

Chapter 12

Then and Now

In undertaking the writing of this book twenty-one points emerged that I saw as foundational, that I hoped would be the obvious underpinnings to which readers might take heart:

1. *That no one religion is right or wrong; that no one religion is better or worse than another. Instead of finding fault with a religion, which may differ, it is to encompass all of God's ways, be correct in what God wants and seek the highest good.*
2. *It is not necessary to start a new religion when new views and ideas come forth. Jesus said, "You may choose to follow your father's religion. He never renounced Judaism, nor did He say that all must convert to Christianity. He simply weaved the advanced thought into what had gone before.*
3. *Christ was not a Christian, Mohammed was not a Muslim, Buddha was not a Buddhist, and Krishna was not a Hindu. These great spiritual teachers were not bound by religious rules; the rules came later from the men who dogmatized their teachings.*
4. *Jesus came not to save the world but to serve it.*
5. *Each of us is here to reflect God's Light to all.*
6. *Our mission is only to give and receive Love.*
7. *We need to forgive ourselves and others for events that happen that we perceive are wrong.*
8. *Everyone holds the image of the Father within themselves.*
9. *You are not the master of other people's flesh, you are the master of your own flesh.*
10. *Everyone who has God, who represents His love within them, has infinite power and is a master of all of their creations.*
11. *God wishes us to have abundance.*

12. *We may manifest what we need by visualizing it, knowing it can occur, proclaiming it to be done, setting intention of it, believing it and lastly thanking God for it.*
13. *Healing is accomplished when we visualize the one to be healed as being perfect and whole.*
14. *By the deeds that you do and by the things that you say you will be known to the rest of the world and to the Son of God.*
15. *Turn every thought and every belief that you have been taught into Love.*
16. *Love God with all of your heart and all of humanity as yourself.*
17. *You do not need to produce results to prove worthiness. The greatest and only requirement is Love.*
18. *The Kingdom of God is within. It is that you are aligned with that which is the hosts of all living God.*
19. *Everyone who has God, who represents His love within them, has infinite power and is the master of all their creations.*
20. *Jesus said, "But know that some day I will return."*
21. *And finally, in realizing the truth of these points, people might be empowered in freedom.*

I traveled to Israel amidst the final stages of writing this text. It was my first trip to the Middle East, and it came about not quite by accident or coincidence, for I believe in neither of those two phenomena. Rather, the event visited me synchronistically, which I experience often enough that I am no longer surprised by it.

On the evening of Good Friday, I had been watching a CBS special on the life of Jesus. At the end of the program viewers were advised that they could contact an expert with their questions about Him. This expert taught Sacred Studies at the University of Southern Florida; not only could he read ancient languages but he was also involved in an archaeological excavation of the city in the region where Jesus grew up. That man was none other than James Strange, Ph.D., with whom I was acquainted, indeed, whom I had befriended and collaborated with in the early 1980s.

I immediately called my erstwhile colleague and renewed our friendship. He told me about his upcoming trip to Israel where he would index the artifacts he had uncovered during his excavations. He asked for me to join him. I agreed and promptly made travel arrangements for my wife, Jean-Marie, and myself.

What an opportunity! I felt that there would be much to uncover for me personally and much knowledge to gain in order to solidify my book. Now I would be able to observe and experience first-hand all the places I was writing about. I desired to bring the stories to life and bridge them to the present time.

I also had for some time felt a churning within me of some unresolved emotional turmoil stemming from that region. I believed that by setting foot on the soil and viewing the sights there I would be able to open my heart in a deeper, more complete way and find forgiveness for whatever indiscretions I perceived had been perpetrated there. There had been many involved: the Romans, the Jews, all the people, even the land itself. I would be able to revisit, then hopefully release the ancestral Jewish and Christian faith-based dogma. As I saw it my trip would certainly cover much territory, both geographically and spiritually.

Also, since I had written about Matthew and his experiences in that region, I wanted to know if I could understand first-hand his trials, what he had learned and how he had evolved as a result of the events in his life.

I was in joy and great anticipation as Jean-Marie and I set out on our journey. But it didn't take long for the mood to change once we got there. We arrived in Tel Aviv, but Jean-Marie's luggage didn't. Our guide, whom we were to meet upon arrival, was nowhere in sight. He had misunderstood the schedule and didn't catch up to us until the next morning. I was beginning to sense the conflict and chaos of the region and was getting edgy.

We retired to our hotel and in the morning we set out. Our guide, who finally appeared, escorted us to the upper Galilee. Originally, there were to be seven in our tour group, but because of the continuing conflict between the Jews and the Palestinians and the inherent danger around us, seven shrank to just two — Jean-Marie and me. That turned to our advantage, for then we could control the itinerary to our liking.

We took a thoroughly enjoyable tour of Galilee and sailed its sea. We visited Cana, Capernaum, and the Valley of Armageddon. And then we went on to Sepphoris to meet Professor Strange. After a tour around his excavation site and a review of the artifacts that had been uncovered, he took us on to Nazareth and a small village within the city. Dr. Strange proudly related to us that this village represented an example of his discoveries and findings from over twenty-five years of excavation. The village, constructed in the center of town, is a re-creation of Nazareth as it was two thousand years ago. Full-size replicas of several houses and a temple have been constructed there, and scenes of the daily life of that ancient time are played out each day by local people in period costume. While in this re-created Nazarene village, we were served food that was traditionally eaten in Matthew's and Jesus' time. This meal consisted of a mixture of olive oil, hyssop, and sesame seed that was called zatar, the same term that was used two thousand years ago; an unleavened bread that was used to dip into the zatar, and also yogurt made from goat's milk. All of this was not only authentic but also quite tasty.

Our ncxt excursion was to the city of Jerusalem. Along the way we stopped to take a dip in the river Jordan. Once in Jerusalem we noticed that hostility was palpable and distrust rampant. During our first day there, a suicide terrorist bombed a shopping mall. He had strapped dynamite to his body and detonated it as he stood at the center's entrance, killing not only himself but several others as well.

Our second day was in old Jerusalem. We came upon a building, which is said to contain the tomb of King David. In a room next door I encountered a rabbi using the Old Testament in an attempt to prove that Jesus was not the Messiah. I asked the man if he felt that peace would never return to Israel until "his" Messiah appeared to smite all Jewish enemies. He looked at the ground and said hesitantly, "Yes, that is my belief."

Much has happened in the two thousand years since Jesus and Matthew taught together in Galilee. If Jesus were to walk today into Jerusalem, He might exhibit a certain level of disillusionment that in two thousand years mankind has learned virtually nothing about His teachings. He would say, "As the Israelis are not bound by the Palestinians, neither are the Palestinians bound by anyone. Neither is another's enemy." He would have added, "This land is blessed by God and, therefore, must be considered sacred. Our heavenly Father, known by some as Lord Jehovah, known by others as the Lord Allah, known, indeed, by many names, wants acceptance of this concept and peace in the region."

Jesus would also have said, "Do not possess the land that was given to you by God, but rather be blessed in this land which was given to you, for is this not given to all of you? Is God not giving to all of the people of earth?"

So I ask now for everyone who is Jewish, Palestinian, Arabic, Muslim, Christian, Buddhist, Taoist, Hindu, pagan, or whatever of the many names on earth that is given to you, to follow your heart and the spirit of God in realizing that the earth belongs to all. We are the stewards of this land. We must forgive and bless that all may have that understanding.

In the beatitudes, we learn that the meek shall inherit the earth. In other words, be humble and you will have everything given to you. Also be the meekest, be the lowliest of slaves, the most timid, shy, and retiring of all people, and you will get your reward. Will it be taken away from everyone else, which is the way it is occasionally interpreted? I say it is the humblest of heart, the most trusting of heart that recognizes the truth, which is that everything here is already everyone's.

God does not give unto one more than He gives to another, just as nothing is given by a mother that is greater one child to another. So, in God, all needs are fulfilled with all children.

Today many people are still resistant to hearing Jesus' message; some are even arrogant, thinking how dare you bring this message, because they believe that *He is not the Messiah.*

When Moses and his people looked back and reviewed religious history, they felt that they didn't measure up to Abraham, the Father of the chosen people. And then Jesus came and their interpretation of Jesus' words and also the disciples' words was that Jesus was the chosen one. And again they felt they could not measure up. This placed them in confusion. On the one hand many believed that they were the "chosen" people; on the other hand, they felt "less than" and were convinced that they could never attain the level of wisdom reached by Abraham and Jesus. When Jesus continued to reveal what it truly meant to be "chosen" and said to them, "You can do what I do," it was simply a source of conflict for them, for they believed themselves so inadequate that they could not even speak the name of God for fear of offending Him.

Also, many felt that they had been persecuted for many centuries. Because of their belief that they were victims, they saw the Messiah as one who would annihilate their enemies and rescue them.

But when Jesus came and instead proclaimed, "Love your enemies," they could not accept that He was anything but a fool. Indeed, He probably looked the fool sometimes, for He was willing to perform according to the greater spiritual law, no matter how it looked, no matter how it sounded, no matter how it seemed to others.

This was their pattern because they put responsibility for their lives outside themselves. They believed that their rescue would elevate them and established their special position in their relationship with God. They did not see themselves as One, even though the teachings of the Torah said that they were One.

It was often understood that they, the Jewish people, were One, and everyone else outside was not part of the "Oneness." The "others" then were not chosen by God, not accepted, but rather simply tolerated. I should point out that this is merely one interpretation, a possibility of the direction this might take.

Matthew had his own interpretation of this land and these people. Initially, he was a segregationist. Because of this consciousness, he viewed the Essenes and the Pharisees and the Sadducees, even though they were all Jews, as completely separate. Actually, there was sometimes great separation in their views. And it was just that with which Matthew became impatient. Matthew had served the single-minded Romans; he had also served the open-minded Jesus, and he was impatient with all of the mishegoss among the Jews. He became impatient with all of the fighting among the Jewish people. His impatience became fuel for him and, unfortunately, it affected his teaching. Because his ego had not completely aligned and healed, his message of love was misread and taken out of context.

Matthew's judgments about the separation of the various Jewish sects caused him internal conflict, particularly when he saw any one sect claiming to be of the true lineage, the true heritage, the "chosen." Matthew felt that this petty jockeying for position was not only ridiculous but it also held many away from the message being taught.

Except for his segregationist views, I largely agree with Matthew's opinion. I have empathy for the people there today. I truly feel the sacred history of this region. For so many thousands of years, so many of God's faithful children have struggled here in order to gain and keep a foothold in this land and make it theirs.

I empathize with the people, both Palestinians and Jews, for their longstanding patience, in their expectation that God will show up and finally remove their enemies and manifest peace.

Jesus did live there, and He brought much to the people, though the written records are scarce. The Romans took little note, and the Jewish priests suppressed His impact in order that the stories disappear and become, they hoped, "out of sight, out of mind." Their ploy obviously did not work, because Jesus' message of love and peace still stands today.

Remember, Jesus did not come to His people only to put salve on their wounds. He did not wish to proclaim that they were victims. Anything but that! Instead, Jesus came to say love everyone, including your enemy. Lift yourself up. Pray quietly, go within and find your God, for there is within not persecution but a welcoming. Love those who persecute you, so that they might be healed and there may be wholeness in all of life on earth. His message could have been misinterpreted in so many ways and, indeed, it has been, then and now.

For all intents and purposes, Jesus was sacrificed because he was perceived as a traitor with an agenda to overthrow the Roman government and take over. But it was not Rome that murdered Jesus. It was His own people. The true reason was never stated, but the people would never have wanted someone to be killed merely for loving them enough to present to them freedom from the Roman grip. Obviously then, it was the priests' desire to silence the truth for fear that their power would be taken from them, for fear that Rome would come down harder and harder upon those who wanted to continue to live in the lap of their priestly luxury.

Rome gave a lot to the priests. It gave them many freedoms: the freedom to take, or, actually, to steal, money from people; the freedom to assert their power and control not only over their people but in the courts as well. The priests built themselves up to believe that they were very, very important. In truth they were not elevated in status in the minds of the Romans; they were only tolerated. Nonetheless, they sucked out the lifeblood of the very people whom they claimed they were there to serve.

Jerusalem is big and crowded. In the city itself, there is a holiness, but that holiness is an undercurrent of life, largely hidden. People do not clearly recall the history of the sacredness that is contained in the stones, the earth and in the artifacts that reflect the blessings as well as the anger and bloodshed of the past. Still, many feel an emotional attachment to this place, and they want a piece of it; they want to belong. This feeling, then, is the generating point for much of the war that happens in this region.

I ask who is most angry? Is it the Jewish people? Or the Palestinians? Nobody is blamed in any way over others, but the Jews, in their persecution that has occurred for so many centuries, experience more repeated anger than others.

When the twelve tribes fled over the period of so many years and moved away from Israel all those years ago to other distant lands, scattering to all parts of the world, they abandoned their holy city and when they left, they cursed the city, and that curse remained.

Jesus had said to His disciples, "As I stand on this hill, looking at Jerusalem, I weep because I know that the people themselves are causing negative things to occur again and again. I weep that my beautiful temple in Jerusalem will be destroyed. I weep because I remember the vision of the Romans burning the city of Sepphoris, and I see the same thing for Jerusalem. I weep for my human and divine self that there will be no other way to respond to these events, for I cannot change them: they will have to play out."

Jesus' vision had been of the events during the year 70 AD, when Christianity was established, the priests maintained control, and the Romans were on a rampage to stamp out all that they perceived was a threat. It was at this time that order and rule over the people broke down. Rome stepped in, sending their soldiers in force and destroying the temple in Jerusalem. Many of the Jews fled Israel as they were in fear. Today in Jerusalem people are still lamenting at the Wailing Wall the destruction of the temple by the Romans.

Jesus wept for Jerusalem because He knew that it would be broken down as it completes its phase of service as an anchoring of the faith. He wept for His ego. He wept for those who were holding onto the city.

This may be a most propitious moment to speak of an irony existing today that was born of that time. In the year 640 AD the Muslims arrived to take over this region. The Jews that remained had up to this time been subject to so many takeovers from those who had tried to annihilate their religion, but this time was different: the Muslims, instead of insisting that the Jews flee, encouraged them to stay, to integrate into the new society and to keep their sovereignty as Jews. Today, it is the Jews who would displace the Muslims.

The focus today has been brought to the United States of America with horrendous acts of hatred and intolerance being perpetrated. It has caused many, many people to suffer. I hear the words ring out, "we are at war."

When innocent people are sacrificed and soldiers fight and die on the battlefield, there is much healing to be done, and the place where they died must be blessed with a consciousness that shows the mightiness of our Oneness with God. There is no doubt that we need angelic support in these healing efforts, and we are blessed by the presence of the archangel Michael, whose role is to battle the forces of evil. As we ask Lord Michael to walk before us to prepare the battlefield, not for a battle that we are going into but for one that still exists and where many lives have been lost, we are comforted and supported.

We must clear and ease the anguish of these souls who are lost. Their personal demons are often cast out from their embodiment through rage and the sword. The remnants of their anguish remain to affect those who follow. Today we must remember to bless these places where lives were lost, where zealots turned a great energy of anger and war against themselves.

I carry the tools of blessing, so that I know of my righteousness, not that I am right over wrong, but that I am righteous in my faith that there is now an opportunity for Light to absorb all of this anger and anguish and heal all that has laid itself there on the battlefield.

Today humans have a great guilt and shame at their deepest levels about being persecuted and victimized in the name of God. What is so unfortunate is that there is no real understanding that the persecutions have come not at the hand of God but out of our belief that we are not worthy of God's love. It also comes because of our false righteousness and the blame and condemnation we have of others for their God.

Persecution comes not only to the Jewish people but to all who have ever walked the line of Jewish love of our God. For all of mankind, the guilt can be cleared, the shame can be cleared. When we clear, we find ourselves more easily willing to rejoin God in love and equality, for Jesus' teaching was love and no other thing.

My willingness to do this clearing has often been expressed outwardly with action, which is important because we can't do it quietly all of the time. Some forms of action result in marching. The Light is no less expressed whether walking in a parade to a drumbeat, which symbolizes the losses in battle, or in silence. There is a fierce and mighty power in marching.

Despite rampant anger and hatred among so many, the world has gone on. It has endured over these many two thousand years. In spite of holy wars, in spite of inquisitions, in spite of crosses burning, in spite of bombings and annihilations, all of these things that humans have done in the name of their Lord God, the world lives on. So in spite of however those who came after Jesus handled the leading of the sheep, the human race has survived. And many have thrived and evolved. Some claimed to have survived their religious education and their indoctrinations. And in some cases, it certainly is survival, because at the root of all of it is one single and profound truth: all of us on this planet are brothers and sisters, and we all deeply desire one thing: to be One with God, for in Him all is Love.

War never resolved anything, ever, whether it was a matter of fighting for a principle of religion or a principle of a lineage. I urge: Pray for Peace! There is a great gift for every soul that sees the inhumanity of war. They have the opportunity to look deep within themselves and forgive, bless and align the war they find there: the conflict between personality and inner child, between personality and the God-self. They can also look at how they are when they are at war with their spouses or their children or when they are at war with the grocer, the driver on the road or the terrorist. In aligning these conflicts there is greater peace. The greatest truth in this is that if these things are not brought into wholeness within the inner being, there will always be wars, because what is not aligned inwardly is always expressed outwardly.

I believe that we must love those persons we consider to be despots and murderers. Even though we may not agree with their behavior and decisions, we must love their souls. We must be grateful for their contributions to the world, even though we may not understand them, for everything that occurs is part of the divine plan.

My gift during my trip was that I was able to forgive and heal within myself all of my attitudes and judgments that had come before. This healing did not come without effort, and it was at great personal cost. While there, I witnessed the current incredible politics and the many religious scams, and I forgave them. Because of the profound sacredness that this land represents, it would have been easy to be angry at this profanity and condemn it. After all, Jesus had responded with anger as He overturned the merchants' tables on the steps of the temple. But I know now that these existing behaviors require complete blessings and forgiveness rather than the full physical expression that Jesus exhibited. And so, it was not just the past, but also the present with which I blended that I was able to forgive and heal. It was important that I experience the healing and see it through the span of time, through space and matter.

Many of the buildings there are said to be sacred sites. While they might hold a bit of the sacred energy, they are not in themselves sacred. I didn't stand at each of the sites where sacred events supposedly took place. That was not important. I just needed to bless these sites as the symbolic structures they are, for while these structures were much misused in the name of monetary profit, so also were they centers of vision and teaching and great guidance. My reverence for these never wanes.

We pray for Jerusalem, for there is a tearing down of things that are old and making ready for the new, the new Jerusalem. That which would be called peace as a presence and possibility here is very shaken because of the expression of fear and the intention of ownership. We bless this place and we bless all who live in their fear there. I would not have that place desecrated, yet I will say that if man's behavior brought flood or the fires of purification, then so be it. We do not have to hold onto the past for fear of losing it. We trust that it dwells within us, and the new Jerusalem is created in the heavens. Just as we pray for peace and healing in the city of Jerusalem and surrounding areas, and as we do the same for the United States, I do not wish for anyone to hold and control with prayer that it remain as it has in the past. It cannot. It must follow its path of consciousness in its shifting. It must follow its path of purification. It must lose its old body in order to be born anew. We must trust in the perfect alignment that all those things will occur for those who have need of it, both there and elsewhere on this earth.

God blesses this place and all other places and all the journeys that will come in the future. Weep for the human loss and needless suffering, then move through that weeping into gratitude and transform it into joy.

Can we feel human pain and still be grateful? Can we feel the suffering of the human mind and emotions and still have gratitude? I pray that this human lesson will be learned well, for with gratitude, suffering is transformed into Light. That is the Law.

We pray that there be a perfect alignment within ourselves and within all that serves to reflect to us. Where there cannot be, we surrender those issues that will play out according to divine will.

The divine will is not meant for destruction or suffering but for human alignment and understanding. It is often misunderstood, because of the examples in the Old Testament, about God's intention for the flood or God's destruction of Sodom and Gomorrah. It is not God's anger or vengeance that was laid upon earth, but God's recognition of human evolution that they caused amongst themselves a need for cleansing and purification. They were so caught up in their own anger, fear, and negativity that they created for themselves a magnet for destruction. They prayed for destruction, but, at the same time, they feared it. And today it is common for humans to pray for anything and everything to happen in order to change the pain they experience in their reality.

God allowed for that evolution through the cosmic laws to become manifest and so it will be for Jerusalem and the world. These things are prophecy, not because God is a being who smites the humans but because God as a loving consciousness allows for the evolution to manifest its destiny. We need not fear or blame God in these matters nor the human thought and emotion that drive God's energy here on earth. We cannot blame it, but rather we must love it. That is the lesson here: to love all of it.

The I AM America the New Jerusalem, is being born and this is reflected in new material and prophecies that bridge these thousands of years.

When my trip to Israel was completed and I was flying home, I thought to myself, *in spite of Jesus' teachings, there are still many who do not like their neighbors because they perceive them as being different.* This is true whether that neighbor is next door, across town, or in another country. The truth is, and I know this in my heart, that the real power in the United States lies in the differences among all the races and religions of the people. The true power then is in the unification of the differences.

I experienced emotional stress from my travels to Israel. I had gone there in joy and enthusiasm. But I recognized the anguish that went back so many years; I felt a personal grief and sadness for those years, and not only for the past but also for what was happening currently. I did my best to bless and let go these events, but I carried the patterning in my physical body, and it would have its effects on me.

Upon returning, I began to work on healing my own separation to create reunification in my personal life. This is necessary when this sense of separation is perceived in any partnership. We all have moments when we feel that life is so easy and fun. Then there are those moments when we look into the mirror and ask *why am I doing this? Why am I here?* This occurs for me, particularly, when I choose to tell someone the truth, as I see it, and am rejected. I ask myself, *why is this not easier and smoother and why am I having so much resentment? There appears to be a war with everyone.*

This condition exhibits most profoundly when one goes into places where anger is expressed through war, and separation is enforced, because these stimulate one's own memory of his own personal wars. How it manifested with me is that I suffered chest pains, which accelerated to a point that required me to be evacuated by helicopter to the Central Hospital in Denver for an emergency heart procedure. Fortunately, I am generally in good health and do the correct things that adequately strengthen and balance my body; consequently, I remained in the hospital only overnight and was discharged the following day.

Healing into wellness is an ongoing process, and I continue to nurture myself and mend all of my bodies: physical, mental, emotional, and spiritual. Greater spiritual alignment can then be brought about, thereby allowing the healthy space for life to exist within me. My strength emanates from my faith in God and support from my family.

In the simple villages where Matthew, Jesus, and most of the rest grew up and played as children and later walked together as a team, these places today still hold some of that energy of fun and excitement. Many of the towns are just rubble, however. Professor Strange and others have spent a lifetime digging out these places to see what clues they hold of the past, yet we know that it isn't critical that anything be found. It isn't important that a map of the life of a man they called Jesus be rediscovered.

It isn't imperative to trace Christianity, for that isn't important for the evolution of spiritual life on this planet. These things already exist in their perfection. It isn't that certain events cannot be healed or will not be healed or will not transform. Rather, there is a pattern of Christianity that will continue to move forward. In time further evidence of Jesus' presence may be discovered, such as more information about His life, the location of the Essene school He attended; the medallion He wore on His last trip to Jerusalem may be found in England, and information may come forth about His shroud that Matthew found. When these things are presented to the world, the world may be awakened, and, unfortunately, more war could result. Hopefully though, the world may find great surrender and more healing instead. All of the possibilities are there.

The excavation has no purpose except to satisfy the human need to find out if Jesus existed. But I know that for some, no proof exists that will be enough. This proof will not cause reunification. What will cause reunification for the world is the love and the ongoing truth that is spoken about God through me, this book and through many others who know.

This truth, which must be spoken, is not that Jesus was alive and that He is our Savior. No, that is not what needs to be said now by me. Why? Because religions have already said that and do so now. In their saying that, what has happened is that there has been a distortion of the truth: people are led to feel helpless and weak and to view that they will always be submissive to Jesus, and that only through Jesus will they ever have any hope of being anything. The truth is much more expansive than those religious teachings.

The truth is that only through what Jesus represents — the I AM consciousness — can you receive the Father, not through the man Jesus, not even through the God/Jesus as some believe, but through the personal I AM. Through the name and power of Jesus Christ, you might find in your surrender your own I AM. I would hope that would occur. But, you see, it has still been poured out, outside of self, based on interpretation of what Jesus asked of you.

Because of the conflict that is being played there, it will be a long time before I go back to those lands, those holy lands of Israel.

I have traced Jesus' footsteps not only in Israel but also, over the past several years, in many other parts of the world and have found evidence of His presence. What I found was a common theme which was proclaimed by Jesus, which is "I shall return some day."

I visited the sites in Mexico where He had worked His miracles, counseled the people on herbal healing and showed them God's truth. The museums in this region document His presence. I found that He was called *Quetzalcoatl,* which means the feathered serpent, referring to a brilliantly plumaged golden-green and scarlet bird found in the tropical Americas and also to the serpent, which was a symbol of wisdom for the ancients.

Today, the jungle has overgrown many of the temples and hidden them from searching eyes, but even so, artifacts left by the great white God, Quetzalcoatl, are found, and His teachings still are practiced by the natives. Their religion is centered in the temples and around the pyramids and includes a ceremony called the *Thirteen Steps to the Fire*, which represent rules for daily living. It is considered a privilege to walk up these steps, as each step higher represents an achievement:

Step 1: *Commit no petty act and treat your fellow man as you would be treated.*

Step 2: *Seek the spirit of truth. Then build the foundation of your life and your thoughts on this truth.*

Step 3: *The work that is before you, you must strive to do and take personal responsibility for it instead of giving it to others.*

Steps 4-10: *These are essentially the Ten Commandments: three of them are condensed into one of the seven.*

Steps 11-13: *The last three are deemed so sacred that they are not given to the public. The only words that are heard about these steps are these: many hear the call but few are chosen.*

While He was called by other names, Quetzalcoatl was the most recognized. Quetzalcoatl ministered to the people from the Yucatan to Guatemala, through all the cities of the Mayans who are the predecessors of today's Mexican natives. Shrines in His honor were built in the magnificent temples in that region including Coba, Palenque, Kabah, and Uxmal. To all of these shrines, there were long boulevards from four directions that intersected, marking great crosses upon the land.

When Jesus departed this land, He promised the natives that He would return one day. So when the tall, white-skinned Hernando Cortez arrived from Spain by boat in the 1550s and made his way to the great center of Aztec civilization — which today is Mexico City — it is not surprising that their ruler, Montezuma, welcomed him with friendly open arms, for the Aztecs believed that this was their God returned. The tribe even allowed Cortez to take at will gold and jewels from their treasury.

One day, inevitably, a disagreement broke out between Cortez' soldiers and the Aztecs; the argument escalated, and fighting ensued. Cortez, as the leader, became involved and was injured and bled. At that point it was all over for the Spaniard, because the Aztecs knew that Jesus could not bleed. When He had visited the native civilizations fifteen hundred years prior, He was in His Ascended state, in His Light Body.

A similar story plays out in Hawaii. I have been there a number of times and have heard lore from the native people that are similar to the events in Mexico, that Jesus went to these Pacific Islands after His Ascension. I had wanted to investigate.

Captain James Cook, born in 1728 in England, was a famous explorer of the Pacific Islands, Australia, New Zealand, and Antarctica. He spent much time on the islands of Tahiti and Hawaii. He loved Hawaii so that he decided to retire there.

The legend retained in the culture of native Hawaiians tells of a tall white god that appeared to their people: this god taught, ministered to, and healed them. Then as abruptly as he had materialized, he disappeared, but not before promising them that some day he would return.

Captain Cook, because he was a white man, was thought by the Hawaiians to be their returning god. Soon after James Cook retired on the Big Island of Hawaii, an argument broke out and the Captain was injured. After the natives saw his blood being spilled, they realized that they had been deceived. Captain Cook experienced an untimely death by clubbing at the hands of the natives.

Following in Jesus' footsteps took me to Glastonbury in England, where I was shown a tree bordered by a protective fence and told that it is an off-shoot of the original tree planted by Jesus and Joseph of Arimathea when they visited this place. This evidence of His presence there with his uncle helped to confirm my belief in the stories I have uncovered.

I also visited a sacred city in northern India called Rishikesh. Running through the center of this city is the holy river Ganges, where the pilgrims bathe themselves for purification. There I was told by the holy men that legend has it that Jesus visited at this place long ago.

I traveled to Ephesus and walked its ancient cobblestone streets and entered the old library structure, just as Jesus had. I went to the top of the mountain above this excavated city to the peaceful location where Mother Mary lived the last years of her life. The site is blessed by the presence of a small chapel, which is said to represent the location of her original residence. In the surrounding regions, one can still find an ancient well and garden.

In North America, now the United States, where He worked with the natives, the tribes honored His presence symbolically with the white buffalo, a high spiritual icon.

The white buffalo is symbolic of purity; it is interesting that it reflected Jesus skin color as well. While the mystical tales handed down from the Native Americans, both in hieroglyphics and by word-of-mouth, does not constitute irrefutable scientific proof of Jesus presence, for me it certainly provides comfortable confirmation for my inspirational writings.

The shroud of Turin remains a gift to the world. It is important to me because Matthew had found this shroud near Jesus tomb and given it to Mary. He folded it and kept it not so much as a sacred relic but as a memento of Jesus. At first Matthew wondered, where did He go? What did this all mean? After Mary s death, it was passed around.

The shroud of Turin was the same material that Jeshua was wrapped with after His crucifixion. It emanated an atomic radiation that came from His fire within.

Padre Pio, a Capuchin priest from San Giovanni Rotondo, Italy, who was born in 1887 and died in 1968, and whose canonization has been approved by the Vatican, first reported the image of Jesus on the shroud. Before this, church authorities did not fully recognize His image. They had confirmed only type AB blood stains on the cloth, which, according to Jesus, matches His blood type. The patterns of the crown of thorns lies at the head of the shroud. Jesus claims that in the future we will see evidence that the particles of flowers growing in that day still appear in the weave of the cloth. The essence of the oil of frankincense used for His burial preparation will also be found in the shroud. Frankincense, a common oil used in that time, is even today considered holy.

A face cloth exists today that few know about. It is presently in the hands of monks in Spain. This was the cloth that was first put over Jesus' face after He was taken down from the cross.

I reveal this to my readers because it demonstrates that this is one of the many wondrous signs that the Father-Mother God is presently manifesting. These items have been preserved in form for years, not simply to make us believers in Jesus the Christ, or to prove His existence as a man, but rather that people come to know the power of the Light of God.

Is it not a miracle that not only do these images appear on the cloth, but that the shroud itself has survived throughout all this time? It has survived not only the elements of nature but through feuds and wars, through religious unrest and spiritual chaos, which has devastated so much else. Through all of these it has survived. Up to now faith alone has been the vehicle for belief in whom this shroud belonged to. But soon science will add a new dimension and bring others closer to the faith.

And what has happened to the medallion that Jesus wore on His belt when He entered Jerusalem for the last time on the day before Good Friday? Where is that medallion today? Jesus says that it is in the refined world and will manifest in the physical world again. It will be seen as an ancient, somewhat worn, but remarkable, preserved piece from two thousand years ago. This gem-encrusted medallion will be found in a place nowhere near Jerusalem. It will be found in a treasury in England. Don't forget that the Roman roads and shipping routes to England were frequently traveled. Jesus journeyed to these places with His uncle.

Jesus' role was to fulfill the prophecies. In order to do so, He chose to integrate the teachings of past prophets, such as Buddha.

While Buddhism has spread throughout the world reaching millions in many countries who practice its path, it is Christianity, as distorted as some of it has come to be, that has spread the farthest and fastest of any religious teachings. Jesus had a purpose in that, and now our role is to help unravel some of the distortions and bring Christianity back to its simplicity and powerful truth.

The way of the Buddhist teachings, which wended their way throughout the cultures of India, Tibet, Nepal, and even into the Orient, and which were so well understood in these regions, were not so different from the Christian teachings. But the Buddhist teachings moved more quietly and more slowly, primarily because the Buddhist monks shut out the world, shunning common daily life. They did not travel out of their region, and so people on a spiritual quest would need to seek them out; they would have to go to the monks.

Jesus, then, changed this pattern. He went to the people. His style was to bring a message in a way that it could be heard far and wide. And later, Jesus sent His disciples forth to teach, and the word spread still more widely and quickly. Jesus' philosophy was that the enlightened should not hide their Light and their Message "under a bushel." In His words, "A city built on a hill can not be hidden."

Prophets and holy men have come and gone, some without much notice. But Jesus stays in the mind and heart of mankind still. What has made Him so different is that after His martyred crucifixion, He came back. If He could be resurrected, would that not prove that all things are possible? And further, He continued to teach here on earth after His Ascension into Light Body form.

The misfortune of the disciples was that when they saw the brutal crucifixion, they saw what they deemed to be their own future laid before them. They assumed that they would have to follow in Jesus' footsteps and complete their own journeys by being martyred. They so feared this outcome that they created exactly that. It was not that the Romans immediately came after them — after all, it wasn't until the year forty-two AD that the Romans felt so threatened by Christian ideology that they ousted the Christians from Rome — and they considered them so much a threat that they acted swiftly and strongly, no matter where they were. It was that the disciples spent a lifetime looking over their shoulders, in fear, and they manifested their own brutal deaths.

Jesus did not martyr Himself for the sake of spirit, for, indeed, the concept of spirit in His eyes was no greater than any man's life. He allowed His martyrdom to occur so that humanity could witness it, so that He could fulfill the prophecy and in that fulfillment give rise to a people finding freedom from oppression, the oppression they found within their very beings. Through fulfillment of the prophecy people would find freedom by recognizing God as a loving deity. Sadly, many throughout history have distorted the meaning of Jesus' sacrifice and purpose.

Jesus in His memory of His life recognized that the greatest misunderstanding was that people used His example of martyrdom as a model for their own lives and for their salvation. They have affirmed for themselves that pain and suffering are the doorway to heaven.

Jesus did say, "Lest a man lay down his life, he cannot enter the Kingdom." He did not mean that man had to sell his soul to the devil to reach the Kingdom of Heaven. But in many ways that is just what humanity has done. Humans have taken on suffering for the greater glory of God rather than to realize that God does not require suffering. Rather, suffering is an attitude. Suffering is not put upon one to torture that someone. It is put upon one by one's own thought and emotion. It is a curse brought about by oneself. Jesus would sanction us to know that we are empowered in the Divine to love ourselves enough to lift this curse.

We can certainly understand how the message may have been misinterpreted: the way human dramas play out seems to validate our erroneous beliefs. We must go deeper into the esoteric understanding of Jesus' choices and our own choices. Our choices now are that we let ourselves be glorified in who we are — the I AM — and to recognize the angelic realm and its connection with the Divine, which sends blessings to humanity directly from the highest angelic beings, which are called the Elohim. For those of us willing to claim that holy connection, it does not put us in a state of glory beyond other humans, but it allows us to accomplish all that our spirit intends to give to this earth. When anyone I come in contact with says, "Who do you think you are? You don't act like God. You don't act like an angel," I will say, "Forgive me. Thank you for reminding me." That's all I have to say. I don't have to prove anything.

People are going to find it difficult to realize their own glory when they place Jesus and the Father beyond their own reach, where their own belief says to them, "You only reach us when you die." That gives them a very big motivation to die, doesn't it? *We must be joyful and be in Heaven on earth at all times.*

Matthew wanted to be obedient to Jesus' word at all times, but he interpreted Jesus' journey as a need to preach and to convert, a need to correct humanity. However, Jesus was only encouraging His disciples to be active in the Word He spoke, so that they would all know that Love is the only law and teach this to others. But rather than teach that Love is the only law, sometimes, instead, they taught that Jesus was the law. They made a religion of Jesus; they made Him a Deity, and they created themselves in His image, duplicating His methods and miracles, while at the same time believing that it was impossible to attain His level of consciousness, His wisdom.

That interpretation was not His intention. Rather, Matthew and the others should have touched people and allowed them to be empowered by that which He came to teach, which was Love. And though they gave much of that essence and much of it was received, there have been centuries of distortions of the Word, in the name of religious power. Church teachings have created Jesus to be an example of something that is beyond reach of the common man.

What Matthew and the others wrote two thousand years ago had more to do with the times than it had to do with the entirety of the message. Indeed, nothing in this present book is a new message from what Jeshua shared two thousand years ago; it is simply a restatement, presented in a new language and made available in a new way, where people may be more attuned to the meaning of His words. Where in the culture of two thousand years ago only a limited number of people understood and supported the expanded spiritual concepts of love, compassion and forgiveness, now there is a large group of supporting people who are desiring to read and hear these words.

As Jesus' message was repeated through the centuries, while there is no blame involved, some of the original meanings were altered. The alterations resulted from the disciples' strong driving desire to share Jesus, the man, and the relationship they had with Him, rather than to be the example of what He taught and live it completely. Matthew and others inaugurated the distortion, which has lasted and grown over two thousand years.

Even though Jesus always told the disciples that it was "not their purpose to start a church," Peter did just that. He is credited with starting the first Catholic Church.

When Jesus renamed Simon the fisherman Peter and blessed him as Peter of the Rock, it was seen that on this rock Jesus would build his church. In his misinterpretation of Jesus' directive, Peter felt pressured and went forth with his own ideas.

Jesus had no intention ever in the whole of His consciousness to begin a new religion, to begin a new faith outside His Judaism and the religion of His people. But He had a full intention to create within this faith a place, an identity for a belief in love to thrive. For just as the Essene faction, as it was called, or element of Judaism, was a big part of His life in boyhood, just as that differed from other sects within Judaism, so Jesus believed that He would bring the balance of love into all the teachings that He had learned and keep that within the sacredness of the teachings of His ancestors and the ancestors of their people.

So Jesus did not imply to Peter that he form a new religion but simply to be available as an anchor, that when all the disciples went out two-by-two into the world to share love they would be able to return, to be supported, to receive encouragement and attain a regrouping of their energy. Jesus knew it could not be in Jerusalem, so He enlisted Peter to seek out where would be a good site for the disciples to establish their gathering place that would be safe and secure.

A church is created to worship God. However, how that is done maybe different among peoples, cultures and religions. The site at which this worship occurs is also seen differently by these diverse groups. Jesus' teachings as to how this might look is that the church is a place for people to gather in celebration of their faith, and in that, to worship, to pray together, to praise together, to play together and to sing, to be unified. Jesus never meant that there needed to be a large religious edifice, simply a "center" for teaching and learning and praying.

In the religion of that time many important teachings, in my opinion, were minimized. One important issue was that of reincarnation. In the inner sanctums of the elite temples, these things were taught, but the disciples did not teach reincarnation to the masses because the people were not open to that level of learning.

I must say that reincarnation to me is a reality, but whether one believes in it is not important, for here and now should be our main focus.

Throughout my medical practice, I have observed that many of my patients have connected with the events and experiences of other lifetimes. It isn't a need of mine to prove the reality of past lives, to anyone, either my own or another's. Nevertheless, I have had past life remembrance. If you choose to call that reincarnation, you may. Or if you choose to call that a cellular memory, you may. Either way, there is an emotional connection with experiences of the past.

The Roman church has always been judged for withholding information from the people. It has seemed, then and now, that the purpose of withholding was to control the people and maintain their power, but it was not that, at least not originally. Rather, it was seen that the people were not ready to understand very sophisticated information; in this sense the subject of reincarnation has been buried.

In the Essene teachings and some of the other factions of Judaism, the reincarnation consciousness was somewhat alive. Jesus learned about it in His Essene studies, and He explored the concept much more deeply through His travels.

The principles of reincarnation are not a necessary component to spiritual beliefs because on another level, we would teach that reincarnation is a myth. Just as it holds a truth, and the freedom of consciousness to understand it is encouraged, it is a myth because in reality, in the larger universal sense, there is no time. Everyone moves from embodiment to embodiment. One does not follow the line of his history. It is that at any one moment one can become merged with God and then gain a spark of awareness that to serve his or her growth and the growth of others, a new embodiment is required, and you choose that.

For those who embrace the concept of reincarnation and know of certain past lives of, perhaps, prominence and great wisdom, this lifetime provides a test of sorts. They wish to know *how could I be so forgetful now of who I AM and all that I have done? If I performed great works and mastered great feats, how could I not have that capacity so fully developed now?* Everyone will have the task to bring those experiences into balance in this life experience, and also to bring this life experience to bear as a great gift to that other lifetime as well.

It sometimes could appear that one lifetime is of greater importance than another, but that is not so. No one lifetime is a greater or lesser experience. All lifetimes are necessary and contribute to the whole.

In writing now about the life of Matthew I can bring a freshness that is more meaningful to the culture now and to the evolution of consciousness. Writing today I can bring about knowledge outside the political framework and dogmas that were present two thousand years ago.

People see religious systems quite differently today, some two thousand years after the time of Jesus and Matthew. Today, many people look at the organized religions of the world with disdain, with doubt, with anger and also a sense of mistrust because of the misalignment of power.

We can't blame Peter for the problem because if he hadn't done what he did, someone else would have. The disciples must not be blamed for "doing things all wrong." While each of them followed Jesus' request to go out into the world, each of them went without clearly believing they were as He was.

What it might look like today if they had gone out with the belief in their I AM clearly entrenched and revealing that to the world would be people awakening to their own mystical experience with God. They would know new ways to pray and to meditate, thus making their connection with God and knowing divine truth. Groups would still form, in order for people support one another. New religious sects might form, as new possibilities for direct communion with God were explored. And in that the role of priests would shift. There still might be the same degree of martyrdom, perhaps even more than in the past, but people would have wept more silently about certain religious practices. They might not have felt obligated to stand up and become martyrs. Rather, instead of openly disagreeing with those whose religions were different, they could have stood with them, prayed with them, accepted them, while at the same time knowing that their outer expression of worship did not reflect their inner wisdom and growth. They would have been able to join in their expression rather than fight. There would be something so unique in these people that they would be envied, and others would desire to have what they exhibited. They would be encouraged then to seek it for themselves and, in so doing, let go of their fear and pain and their separation.

This is occurring now, in perfect time. Throughout the world many like-minded people are gathering to share ideas and beliefs. This phenomenon is created as spiritual families are finding each other. It is almost as if each has an invisible internal magnet which draws them together. They are all being awakened to a new realization of how to be, within themselves and how to be relating to one another. For me, this link seems to follow from our former past lives together.

In that ancient time the disciples were a bit like chickens pecking at the dirt, looking for food. They were attempting to make themselves understood, trying to create a new message that would be reasonably worthwhile for people to hear. And the new word did spread like wildfire, but it had to be filtered and watered down, changed and re-arranged, in order to be accepted.

What is occurring now is that there is such a magnificent rising of consciousness among people, that now the reality of Jesus' word can be lived more fully and can be more easily expressed. More truth can be told to more people than ever before in history. This is true even though many factions exist which would dictate their own distorted interpretation of the Bible. Pain and fear result at times over this because these particular individuals seem, falsely so, to have more power than the rest of the world.

The new awakening for our time in history promises more expression and a fulfillment of even more joy as individuals grasp the truth that they need not pound into some that they are doing it wrong and pray for others to wake up, for nobody has it wrong. Nobody has ever done it wrong. All the events that happened were destined to happen. It is possible that the pathway to those events might have been different, if Jesus' message had been presented in another way, but the outcome would have been the same. Ultimately, the goal was for us to know that we have the power to directly connect with God, who, in the end is the last word, who is all there is.

Some say Jeshua came to earth to save everyone! If that had been Jeshua's goal, He would have been a failure. But He was no failure, for His goal was not to save the world, but to serve it.

We need to keep a vision of this because in our humanness, there are times when we are distracted by our possibilities. Then it is easy for the focus to become what is possible, instead of what is necessary. Sometimes we feel that somehow we are a cause of all that happens around us and we wonder whether we have done the right thing. Humanity's ego needs to be kept in check and in balance.

Jesus, until the end of His physical life, honored the religion of His Fathers. He was born of the seed of Abraham in that lifetime. Therefore, in that embodiment, He gave blessing and homage through all of the

Jewish teachings. He did, however, distill and clarify them, creating seeds of truth. He did argue, if you will, with the priests. But He argued only within intellectual realms, engaging in discussions and discourses in order to present possible new interpretations. He never said, "I will no longer be a Jew." He never said, "I will no longer honor the religion of my Father." He did not come here to destroy but to build.

In the two thousand years since Jesus lived, most individuals have not lived His law of Love. Most people have not turned the other cheek. We have not practiced allowance, acceptance or perseverance. Instead we view and judge others as evil, as bad seeds that God could not possibly accept. And so, the holy wars, many of which are fought, ironically, in Jesus' name, keep raging. There is, especially now, a need for great compassion for those who misunderstand and fear.

My intent in writing this book has been to further my own process of forgiveness and also to set the record straight. We know that each person is responsible for his or her choices and actions and also for his or her own soul's growth. We all have the need to see our responsibility, do that responsibility, actually be the responsibility. When we do take that responsibility for all of our actions, we do so not only for our own soul's growth but for all souls' growth as well.

As is often said, "No one can do it for you." Yet when it is said that Jesus "died for their sins," there is also truth in that. All through Jesus' life, in His teachings, in His being, and in the whole of His expression, His accomplishment was that new life might manifest for everyone. While He did not take away free will, He truly took on the karma of many souls, lightening their load, so to speak, so that they might encounter the Light more easily. That is the way a Christ works; it is the purpose and mission of a Christ, or Messiah, to give in a such a way that He receives the dross of others, lifting energetic veils and preparing for a new freedom through which others are able to make a clear choice. Jesus, as one with the Father-Mother God, was empowered to cause such a blessing that that blessing shed Light through and lifted the density from others.

How did Jesus take on the sins of others? As He cleared away His own sins and errors of judgment, He achieved a higher frequency of His soul's mission and in that magnification of His Light, He could then place Light upon the error of others, not for judgment's sake, but for the sake of illumination. Where there is illumination, there is a willingness by people to acknowledge that they also are Jesus, the I AM. Their communion with Jesus allows Him to transmute their limitations and judgments. As one becomes more unified with others, then in that unification, Jesus takes on still more for transmutation. Their problems then become His problems, as they become part of Him. This doesn't mean that He takes on more burdens. It means only that He is more capable through the love vibration that He extends Himself into of healing and aligning. Everyone still holds his or her own conscious responsibility for accepting and stepping into that possibility.

In a way, we can say it has already been done through Jesus. He has already transmuted all. Most people do not accept that idea, however, and so the more masters there are doing the work that He chose to do, the more likely it will be that others will find it easier to step into that grace. You see that grace as an energy just completely uplifts, and all of the error completely dissolves.

Consider this: exorcisms are often performed to remove demons from humans who are possessed. The Light is shined, and the demon is dispelled. I have personal knowledge of this. Jeshua himself lifted a great deal of the demonic influence from humanity. But, you know, many times the demons return. I also have knowledge and experience of this. Many people reclaim their demons and other contaminations. They did so in Jesus' time, and there was absolutely no way He was able to keep this from ever being available to humanity, because humans, as they think and with their habits and free will, would again claim their own evil once again.

I saw this in my own practice of exorcism. I would cleanse a person of some of their demons, only to discover to my dismay that when they returned for a recheck, they were back to their previous conditions with new demons again polluting their body, mind, and spirit. I have a saying that "You can take the demon away from the man, but not necessarily the man away from the demon."

Be cautious, my friends. Be cautious of those in your world who would tell you that it is important to stir up fear. Be cautious of those who would tell you that the pathway to God is assured by identifying evil and evil ones, for it is not. And I bring this to you because all is in readiness for this thinking to take place in our world. There will be many who will warn of the antichrist, who will point out the demons around every corner, both here on earth and from other realities and other universes. There will be so many who speak these words that you will feel that in order to be safe you have to identify every evil.

"Know your enemy." You've heard that one. When that phrase was initially spoken, it was never meant to be a consideration of battle with another. It was simply a plea that one needs to know with whom he is dealing within himself. If you know yourself well, you know why your enemy exists. That's all there is and you can love yourself and love your enemy, even as God loves you.

The purpose of my listening within for the stories of Jesus and Matthew and their phenomenal life together and for the sharing of them with all who will hear is not so crucial that it becomes a new Bible. What matters to me is only that this message comes from my heart, for you are all forever my brothers, my sisters.

We are entering a revolution at this time on the earth. This revolution is political, but it is also spiritual, and it is audacious and bold. It does not hold back in stating God's Truth and declaring that now is the time to hear it.

Remember Jesus said, "Those who have ears, let them hear." Not everyone has the ear for it. There will always be some who cannot hear. Meanwhile, more individuals will hear, feel, and see the truth. Some like a tidal wave, others like a trickling of water that flows over them bit by bit. The more souls that can receive the truth and expand into it, the easier it will be for the next wave and even the wave after that to receive and know the truth, and a great fire can be ignited. The only way in which this fire can be put out appropriately is for those who are ignited to surrender and allow the Holy Spirit to wash over and fill them. And many who will read this book, even if they are able to read only a few words, could be moved. Others, who read more of it, if they fight and resist it, can find themselves receiving a gift of more Light so that their pain is transformed into the joy of knowing the truth.

Share with others how they might join together again in consciousness and prayer. This is a wise gift to give. There is a profound and wondrous love that comes from our Father-Mother God.

The circle of friendship and divine devotion of Jesus' day is a continuation from a previous time that leads straight to today. The perfection of what occurred then is seen as part of the tapestry of what was begun eons before. That fulfilled prophecy was born out of another time and circumstance. The life and times of the man we call Jesus does not stand alone as an isolated event. Rather, it stands as part of the tapestry, which we are now again weaving in new colors and new patterns. It is important that we all look to see friendship and brotherhood, healing and forgiveness with all who are on the planet now and all who have walked the planet in the past, for we are One and certainly in the eyes of the Father-Mother God, this is so. Amen!

TWELFTH SPIRITUAL LAW

Seek ye the God you are and know that I AM here.

A

B

C

D

E

H

I

J

K,L

M

N

O

P

Q,R

S

T

U,V

W